Collisions and their Causes

by
Captain Richard A. Cahill

*"A superior seaman uses his superior judgment to keep
out of situations requiring his superior skills."*

Fairplay Publications

Published and distributed by
FAIRPLAY PUBLICATIONS LTD
52/54 Southwark Street, London SE1 1UJ
Telephone 403 3164
Telex 884595 FPLAY G

ISBN 0-905045-46-7
Copyright © 1983 by Fairplay Publications Ltd

Printed by Page Bros (Norwich) Ltd,
Mile Cross Lane, Norwich, Norfolk NR6 6SA

Contents

The Author

Richard A. Cahill, who most recently has been in command of large American flag container-ships, graduated from the U.S. Merchant Marine Academy, Kings Point, in 1943. He has served afloat as a licensed deck officer since that time, being promoted to Master in 1961. A Fellow of the Royal Institute of Navigation, he is a past Member of its Technical Committee and currently a Member of Council. He is also a Fellow of the Nautical Institute. He holds a Master's Degree in Business Administration from New York University and has served as a Visiting Professor in Nautical Science at the U.S. Merchant Marine Academy. He lives in London.

Foreword

Accounts of shipping casualties have always been of particular interest to mariners but have previously only become available in either official reports, which make dull reading, or in books written by persons with little or no sea experience. Richard Cahill is uniquely qualified to write about collisions at sea as his career has spanned four decades, over half of which has been in command, during which time he has taken a special interest in collision prevention, contributing several papers to nautical journals on this topic.

This is, I believe, the most comprehensive selection of accounts of collisions ever published. Separate consideration has been given to collisions associated with different types of encounter situations in both clear and restricted visibility and in open seas or confined waters. The author has found it possible to cover such a wide range without including descriptions of accidents of earlier years which are unlikely to be relevant to present day circumstances.

In addition to giving detailed accounts of many collisions Captain Cahill has added his own comments relating to the causes of particular casualties and on general aspects of collision avoidance. Readers may not agree with all that is said but the comments should lead to a greater insight as to why collisions at sea continue to occur so frequently.

Few mariners become involved in a major shipping casualty and there is a general attitude that accidents happen to *other* ships. This book is likely to increase awareness of the circumstances in which collisions occur and may therefore make an effective contribution to safety at sea.

A. N. COCKCROFT
M.Phil.Extra Master, FRIN, FNI

Preface and Acknowledgements

Disasters at sea seldom fail to rivet the attention of the general public. They are often replete with all the elements that make a great news story: drama, mystery, acts of heroism and cowardice, superhuman efforts and appalling ineptness, and most recently, the possibility and danger of catostrophic pollution. The *Torrey Canyon* gave us the first glimpse of this polluted future, and it was most recently brought home by the fouling of the beaches of Brittany by *Amoco Cadiz*.

Until fairly recently the man on the street, or in this context we should perhaps say, man on the beaches, could view these maritime accidents with dispassion and sympathy for those involved. The appearance of the super-tanker and now the VLCC and ULCC have put paid to those past attitudes. The effects of casualties on the scale of *Amoco Cadiz* are so widespread that they are felt directly by most if not all of the citizens of the Western world, if not the whole world.

The immediate costs deriving from the loss of the vessel and its cargo, and the attendant claim from those directly affected by the pollution, are reflected to a slight but not negligible degree in the price of fuel. Those whose livelihood comes from the creatures of the sea, at least in the affected area, suffer a diminution in their incomes, and the price of sea-food shows a direct and almost immediate effect. That in turn works a hardship on those for whom fish is a staple of their diet and those involved in its supply. Vacationers may only be inconvenienced, but those who cater to them are hit directly in the pocketbook. And so on *ad infinitum*.

One of the less immediate, but by no means negligible, effects is the impact of the disaster on those who earn their living on the sea. Until quite recently the consequences were often beneficial in that they gave an impetus to long overdue reforms or corrective measures that were badly needed. The loss of *Titanic* was a classic example.

The *Andrea Doria/Stockholm* collision led to eventual adoption of the law requiring VHF radios on vessels of 300 gross tons and over navigating in U.S. waters, so bringing this invaluable anti-collision aid onto the international scene. It also helped bring about needed amendment to the Collision Avoidance Rules.

But not all such disasters have such beneficial side-effects. The *Amoco Cadiz* stranding resulted in hastily adopted regulations and traffic schemes that have at least some questionable aspects, and another catastrophe of that magnitude could well generate pressures that would bring about "solutions" that all mariners might deplore. While strandings are capable of the most spectacular effects, collision usually holds the potential for the most horrendous consequences since it could involve two of the very largest vessels, as indeed it did not long ago in the case of *Aegean Captain/Atlantic Empress,* and it is to the causes of collisions that we will direct our attention here. In a subsequent volume we will consider the causes of strandings.

Freedom of the seas, like freedom everywhere in recent years, has seen much abuse. The indispensable corollary of freedom is responsibility, as philosophers down the ages have pointed out. Without it we have license, and much of what attempts to shelter behind emotional appeals to uphold the freedom of the seas is in fact pure license.

The problem of coming to grips with the causes of maritime disaster is almost wholly a professional one. The sea is a very tolerant mistress in many respects in that she seems to have an *almost* infinite tolerance for those who trust to luck. Many ships sailing the world's oceans are manned and commanded by those who should confine their sailing to the bathtub, but luck and the underwriters enable them to ply their "trade" in blissful ignorance of the rudiments of the mariner's profession.

Ironically many if not most of the seamen involved in the collisions recounted in this book were considerably above average ability, if we consider a world-wide average. Some were men with a solid record of competent service behind them, but the conjunction of an uncharacteristic lapse of judgment or simple mistake at the time fate chose to frown rather than smile led them into disaster. Others had perhaps less skill, and some were victims of pressure from employers, associates and other less identifiable sources that may have upset their judgment or calculations at the critical juncture.

The accounts in the pages that follow are filled with instances where basic principles and practice of seamen were flouted and ignored, more often than not by seamen who knew, or should have known better. There are lessons to be learned in these few moments in which careers were wrecked. This book is directed mostly towards the young men embarking upon a career at sea. Yet there are lessons, or warnings, enough for everyone here, from the new apprentice or cadet to the veteran shipmaster with several decades of command under his belt.

While every attempt has been made to achieve accuracy and follow the facts insofar as they are available the objective is to present a logical reconstruction for means of illustrating particular points and aspects of the Rules and their infraction. The fact that certain particulars may differ somewhat from the accepted "facts" as given in legal documents and accounts (if they do) should be immaterial as respects the conclusions drawn and opinions offered. Completely fictitious cases would have served the purpose as well but would not have had the impact (no pun intended), or the benefit of court decisions, of accounts of actual collisions. Nonetheless, there has been no conscious effort to manipulate the facts in order to produce a particular result or effect. Every effort has been made to let the facts speak for themselves.

In a few instances we have differed with the conclusions reached by the courts, and where that was the case we have tried to show why and how we came to differ. The bulk of the cases were drawn from the *Lloyd's Law Reports* and to a somewhat lesser extent the *American Maritime Cases*. Reports of Liberian Boards of Investigation have been used in a few instances as well as private sources that are acknowledged elsewhere.

While the Collision Rules as written are, or should be, unambiguous so that all vessels encountering one another should be in no doubt as to what Rule governs and hence how they should conduct themselves in a particular situation the reality is somewhat different, as the cases in this book so amply demonstrate. In so many cases a collision occurs not because one vessel wilfully disregarded the applicable Rule but because the mariner at the con suffered from a misconception as to what Rule governed.

Some of this was due to a faulty understanding of the Rules, but in many cases it was due to the inability of one or both vessels to define with precision just what their relationship was in respect to the other. Such misconceptions are most common in converging/overtaking situations and starboard bow reciprocal meeting cases, but they are not confined to them. Where such misconceptions operate it can lead to both vessels assuming they are in a stand-on position, and while that will not inevitably lead to collision, it will often draw them into close quarters which is the inevitable prelude to collision.

While the study of the Rules and a clear understanding of them may prevent a mariner from becoming a victim of misconception that will obviously not protect him from the folly and foibles of others. It can therefore be instructive to study cases where a misconception of a Rule or a faulty appreciation of a situation led mariners into collision.

Since the objective of such an exposition is to instruct some of the observations made and judgments offered here may seem somewhat harsh. It is not our intent to condemn — though in a few cases the facts would seem to lead one in that direction — but by adopting a critical posture to expose all faults of commission and omission that might have contributed to the casualty. By so doing a more complete understanding of how the collision came about may be gained.

It is very hard not to have sympathy for some of the men involved here and the predicaments that force of circumstances and the faults of others enmeshed them in. In some of these cases the faults of others were so gross that it would seem to be a rank miscarriage of justice to involve them in any portion of the blame. Nonetheless, in some cases the court did so hold, the view being that no matter how complete the mismanagement and ineptness of the one, the other's conduct must be reasonably flawless for him to escape blame.

* * * * * * * *

This book grew out of a series of lectures I gave at the U.S. Merchant Marine Academy at Kings Point, N.Y. in the fall of 1981 on ship casualties. I would first of all like to thank Rear Admiral Thomas A. King the Superintendent and Capt. Paul Krinsky the Dean for providing me with that opportunity which also allowed me to do some of the initial research. I would also like to acknowledge the courtesy and help of Capt. William T. McMullen, Head of the Department of Nautical Science. Lastly, I want to thank Miss Elizabeth Fuseler the Librarian and particularly Mr. George Billy, the Assistant Librarian, and their staff for their kindness and assistance in conducting my research activities.

Dr. John Kemp, Head of the School of Navigation of the London Polytechnic, offered me the use of the facilities of that institution which were invaluable in carrying out the bulk of the research, and Miss Joyce Calvert the Under Librarian and here assistants Elizabeth Lampard and Ron Poyser were unfailingly courteous and most helpful in providing me with whatever assistance I asked for.

Capt. A. N. Cockcroft, Senior Lecturer at the Polytechnic and co-author of *A Guide to the Collision Avoidance Rules,* read most of the chapters as I wrote them and offered much useful advice and help out of his vast fund of knowledge of collisions during the post radar decades. He also generously provided me with material from his private files and directed me to other sources of invaluable information. His criticisms and comments were of the greatest help.

Mr. Michael Richey, Director of the Royal Institute of Navigation until his retirement at the end of 1982, kindly granted permission to reproduce two articles that appeared in the *Journal* under the titles: "The Avoidance of Close Quarters in Clear Weather" (January 1982); and "The Hazards of Close Overtaking" (May 1982), the latter in a much abbreviated form.

Before venturing to offer my views and opinions on this potentially controversial subject I thought it no more than prudent to seek the opinion of a number of my peers — other serving shipmasters — before they appeared in print. Jerome Benyo, Owen Clancy Jr., Eugene Olson, Howland V. Rowe and Frank Seitz have all read the manuscript and offered much helpful comment and criticism.

Finally R. P. Holubowicz, of Marine Ventures Ltd., London, gave encouragement, editorial criticism and friendly advice. My brother Dan P. Cahill offered his trenchant criticism.

I would like to thank the editors of the *Lloyd's Law Reports* and the *American Maritime Cases* for permission to quote extensively from those journals and the editor of Stanford Maritime Ltd. to quote from Cockcroft and Lameijer's *A Guide to the Collision Avoidance Rules.*

The efforts of Michael Grey, the editor of *Fairplay International Shipping Weekly* in helping me to put the manuscript in its final form warrants my sincere appreciation and gratitude. His knowledge of the craft of editing wedded to his experience as a master mariner made his help invaluable.

While those mentioned above by-and-large have in general concurred with the views expressed herein I must emphasise that I alone must bear the burden for the opinions offered and the responsibility for whatever flaws and errors remain.

I am indebted to Captain Jack Michelle, Vice-President of the Associated Branch Pilots of the Port of New Orleans for the quote on the title page. It was found by him on a brass plaque in a nautical supply store in New Orleans without attribution.

Author's Note

Though the terms and abbreviations used in the text should be familiar to all mariners the occasional non-seafarer who may refer to this work might find some confusing. The phrase: "green to green" is the equivalent of starboard to starboard, as "red to red" is the equivalent of port to port. CPA and miss-distance refer to the closest point of approach when two vessels are passing. GM is a designation of stability and of a vessel's ability to right herself when inclined. All courses and bearings are true unless otherwise noted.

The terms "Elder Brethren" and "Assessor," or "Nautical Assessor," are frequently used in reference to accounts published in the *Lloyd's Law Reports,* on which the author has heavily relied. These terms are largely interchangeable since Assessors are also sometimes Elder Brethren and vice-versa. An appointment to the ranks of Elder Brethren is a distinction awarded to a mariner in recognition of his achievements and service. A period of command of either merchant or naval vessels is a prerequisite. Once placed on the list of Elder Brethren one is eligible to serve in the role of nautical assessor advising admiralty courts in casualty cases.

Nautical Assessors are appointed by the Board of Trade (now Department of Trade) and must have amongst other requirements at least five years of service in command. Appointments are for three years and are reviewed triennially. The length of time that has elapsed between the appointment and last sea service should not normally be more than five years.* Members of the Elder Brethren are called in to give assistance and advice when the case is originally heard. If it goes to appeal then Nautical Assessors perform that function.

Most of the cases used here have been taken from the *Lloyd's Law Reports* and *American Maritime Cases* where an award for damages is given. While the division of damages will ordinarily be a reflection of the degree of blame that the court decided should be attached to the actions of each vessel it is not always an accurate assessment of the degree of fault of the mariners involved, though generally there will be a close correspondence. An example of an exception is the *Transhawaii/Republica de Columbia* case where the failure of the owner's representatives to properly repair the steering gear played a decisive role in the award of damages.

In a few of the cases no division of damages is given. These cases were based upon accounts of official investigations made for the purpose of ascertaining the degree of culpability of the individuals involved. Hence no award of damages.

We have used the convention here of referring to quotes from Marsden as being made by that author whereas the actual author being quoted may be one of the several later revisors of that volume ordinarily referred to by the original author's name.

For ease of presentation I have ignored the fact that women are appearing in increasing numbers on the bridges of ships. Where I have used the masculine pronoun women readers are invited to add the feminine.

---

* See "Formal Investigations and 471 Inquiries," Captain John Arthur, *Seaways,* January 1982.

Chapter One

A Fresh Look at the *Andrea Doria/Stockholm* Collision

The collision between *Andrea Doria* and *Stockholm* as the former vessel emerged from a fog bank off Nantucket lightvessel in the summer of 1956 was one of the great maritime disasters of modern times. There was much dispute and debate in the press at that time over who was at fault, but it was clear from the very beginning to those with the experience to judge that both vessels were to blame. Where sea room is available a prudent mariner does not let another approach so close that some sudden and unanticipated move does not allow time to take effective evasive action. But though the event was high in drama because it involved two passenger ships, one of which subsequently sank with loss of life, the events leading up to it differed little in any significant respect from many other collisions either before or since.

Andrea Doria was bound for New York with a full complement of passengers and encountered fog during mid-afternoon when still some 150 miles or so to the east of Nantucket lightship. The master, Captain Piero Calamai, spent most of the next eight hours on the bridge until the disaster at 2310.

The fog lifted briefly around 1600 and then set in thick again and remained that way until moments before the tragedy. The course was 267°, which was designed to take the vessel about a mile south of the lightship. The sea speed of just over 23 knots was allegedly reduced by a little over a knot when the fog was encountered bringing it down to about 21.8 knots. That really had no material result except for the ironic fact that if *Andrea Doria* had been proceeding at a higher speed the collision would almost certainly not have happened. The meeting would have taken place earlier in clear weather to the west of the fog bank and the vessels would have met on almost reciprocal courses and effected a routine passing. But the ships did meet and collide, and it is the story of that event that attracts our attention.

As the Italian liner approached Nantucket there were three very experienced officers on the bridge in addition to the master: a senior and junior watch officer and the staff captain. All held master's licenses. About 2130 the lightship was picked up on the radar 17 miles off. A Loran fix and an RDF bearing all agreed to help confirm that the target on the scope was indeed the lightship, and at 2220 *Andrea Doria* passed one mile to the south of the lightvessel, still in thick fog. The staff captain offered to relieve the master for a spell at this time but Captain Calamai declined and his second-in-command went below.

Course was now set for 268° directly for Ambrose lightship, which marks the entrance to the port of New York. According to the testimony after the event, at 2245 the 2nd officer detected an echo on the radar screen bearing 4° on the starboard bow, at 272°, at a distance of 17 miles. It was also stated that it soon became apparent from the swiftness of the rate of closing that the pip represented an eastbound vessel rather than one travelling in the same direction. That caused some disquiet since the track for eastbound vessels was 20 miles to the south.

In spite of the fact that a Marconi Locator Graph (a radar plotting device) was in the plotting table next to the radar no effort was made to use it. That was the first and crucial mistake since even a relative motion plot would have given early warning of the close approach of the other vessel and its speed. Yet in spite of the fact that the 2nd officer made no plot he was, according to later testimony, remarkably if not suspiciously accurate in his initial estimate of the CPA (Closest Point of Approach). In response to the master's query as to how far off the approaching vessel would pass he replied, "About one mile to starboard."[1] A reconstruction of the respective positions and courses made good of the two vessels at that time shows that if *Stockholm* was 17 miles off bearing 272° at 2245 she would in fact have passed almost exactly 1 mile due south of the Italian liner if both kept their courses. When the Swedish vessel was 3½ miles off, bearing, according to the testimony, 15° to starboard or 283° at about 2305, a plot would have shown the vessels passing at eight-tenths of a mile.

Aboard *Stockholm*, when Captain Harry Nordensen left the bridge in charge of his young 3rd officer Johan-Ernst Carstens he had ordered a course of 087° to be steered, which was supposed to take his ship 1 mile south of Nantucket, the exact spot for which *Andrea Doria* was aiming. That was about 2140. At 2230 the 3rd officer changed to 089° to compensate for a northerly set, and that was the course she was steering when she was reportedly first picked up on the Italian vessel's radar at 2245. At approximately 2250 Carstens altered 2° more to starboard to 091°, which was when he first discovered *Andrea Doria* about 12 miles off slightly to port, or so he later maintained.

Carstens began to plot the echo on his radar using a "Bial Plotter", a plastic disc that fitted over the face of the scope allowing a plot to be made on it with a grease pencil. He claimed that his first bearing plotted at 10 miles showed *Doria* 2° on the port bow and at 6 miles the bearing had opened to 4°. Such a plot would give a CPA of less than six-tenths of a mile to port though he concluded that the miss-distance would be approximately three-quarters of a mile.

At first it seemed a routine approach but as the vessels closed Carstens began to become concerned about his inability to see this fast moving vessel which was now well within the range of visibility prescribed for mast lights and approaching that (2 miles at the time) of sidelights. According to all accounts, just as *Doria* passed inside the 2 mile range ring on the radar scope the lookout on the bridge wing sang out, "lights to port".* Carstens joined him on the bridge wing and saw the first dim glow of her lights on his port bow and called out to the quartermaster to starboard his helm. After the ship had swung almost 20° to the right Carstens gave the order to steady on that heading. The telephone then rang; it was the lookout in the crow's nest reporting *Doria*'s lights. After that distraction Carstens checked the radar before returning to the port bridge wing to look again at the approaching ship. It had been almost two minutes since her first sighting and he had not looked at her again since entering the wheelhouse to give the order for the course alteration. As he turned his binoculars on her he was stunned to see her mast lights now open to the right as well as her green sidelight and the blaze of her rows of port and deck lights. Though stunned he was not speechless and he yelled "Hard-a-starboard" as he rushed to the engine order telegraph, which he put first to "Stop" and then "Full Astern".

That was Carsten's account, but it does not seem to fit the facts. If the casualty is reconstructed by working back from the point of collision to the time at which *Andrea Doria* first claimed to have discovered *Stockholm* on her radar at 2245, using the courses steered and the probable courses made good due to a northerly current set of about 3/4 knot, several things become clear. The bearing of *Stockholm* at that time could not have been approximately 272° (heading 268° + 4° relative) but must have been about 270° or perhaps slightly less, putting *Stockholm* a little less than 2° on the bow.

It was claimed by the Italians that the "eyeball" analysis of the 2nd mate showed *Stockholm* would pass about a mile to the north while the relative plot of the 3rd mate of the Swedish ship

---

* The edge of the fog bank sloped so as *Andrea Doria* emerged from it her mast lights become visible while her bridge was still enshrouded, momentarily veiling *Stockholm* (and *Doria*'s sidelights) from the view of those on the bridge of the Italian liner.

gave almost directly opposite results. His plot, though it disappeared and was never produced, gave him a CPA of about three-quarters of a mile to the south of *Doria*.

The reconstruction (see sketch) shows that while the bearings and ranges claimed by the Italians do not match the reconstruction their alleged estimate is the more accurate of the two as regards CPA. If the course change of 4° to port had not been made by *Doria* at 2305 and *Stockholm* had continued on the latter would have passed a quarter of a mile to the north of the former. With the 4° course change the CPA would have been a little over four-tenths of a mile.

The ultimate cause of the collision was the acceptance by both parties of an inadequate passing distance, and for that both must equally share the blame. Having made that initial mistake what the reconstruction surprisingly reveals is that it was not the port turn of *Doria* that brought about the collision but the starboard turn of the Swede. Once that manoeuvre was executed the collision was all but inevitable.

The reconstruction also reveals an even more surprising fact. All the accounts agree that when Carstens first sighted *Doria* at about 2 miles and barely three minutes before the collision she was on *Stockholm*'s *port* bow. *Then* course was changed some 17° to the right to widen the passing distance. It can be seen from the reconstruction that either Carstens made the course change *before* sighting the Italian liner or sighted *Doria* about 10° on the *starboard* bow *before* turning to starboard *across Doria*'s bow.

That places an entirely different slant on the affair. There seems little doubt that Carstens was plotting the relative motion of *Doria*, but measuring the bearings off on the reconstruction we see that the relative bearing at 10 miles would be almost dead ahead while at 6 miles it would be about 1° to starboard, which would give a CPA of about a quarter mile to starboard compared with the ¾ mile to port that Carstens claimed his plot showed. We must remember that the gyro was not stabilised and Carstens had to rely on the helmsman (who he characterised as somewhat unreliable) to tell him when he was on course. We must almost remember that the plotter was not produced as evidence, so Carstens could well have been mistaken in his recollection. Radar bearings may easily be a degree or so off and the helmsman may have misinformed the 3rd mate so that what was actually a very close meeting on the starboard side may have been plotted to show a narrow passage to port.

What seems likely to have happened is that Carstens produced a plot that gave him a CPA, for whatever reason, so close to nil that he felt impelled to alter course to increase it. That plot by his own admission consisted of bearings taken at 10 and 6 miles so he had "computed" a CPA before *Doria*'s 4° change to port. He was well aware of the master's standing orders not to pass closer than a mile off another vessel. His ship had furthermore been setting to the north, and he had twice altered course to the right to compensate for the set. Under such circumstances he would prefer not to alter to port and so get further to the north of the course the master had laid down. Course alterations to port in such situations are also regarded by most seamen with deep distrust (see p. 4), so it would be quite natural for Carstens to opt for a course alteration to starboard to keep clear of the oncoming vessel.

It would also seem plausible that Carstens made the course change to starboard just before sighting *Doria* rather than just after. Only that would explain how *Doria* was first sighted on the port bow rather than the starboard. There is of course the conflicting testimony of Carstens and his helmsman that *Doria* was showing a weak red light when first seen, but what is more likely is that Carstens expected to see a red light and in retrospect convinced himself and the helmsman that they did in fact see one, whereas he probably saw no distinct lights as *Doria* emerged from her murky shroud.

Justifying one's conduct is one of the most natural of human reactions, and an imagined glimpse of a weak red light when *Doria* first came into view would certainly fit that pattern. There is also the tendency for those involved in an accident, though not necessarily responsible for it, to want to be on the "right side". The loyalty of seamen to the vessel on which they serve and their proclivity to "see" things in a light favourable to their vessel was remarked many years ago by an American court where it was observed that,

> The well known loyalty of seamen for their own ship is both natural and praiseworthy. It leads them to unconsciously espouse the cause of the vessel that carries them. Not only the crew, but passengers

also are imbued with the same spirit and seldom see negligence in the navigation of the vessel on which they are temporarily embarked. In such cases it is necessary to have recourse to extrinsic evidence and to weigh the presumptions drawn from the undisputed facts.

Some thirty years later a similar tendency was noted on the part of naval officers in the case of *Silver Palm*. More recently it was taken into account in the collision between *Oriental Hero* and *Castor* in the middle of the Pacific in 1971. The judge hearing that case had been deeply impressed by the testimony of the watch officer of *Oriental Hero*, but when he came to place the statements of that officer against the evidence produced by the plantiffs he could not reconcile the two and was forced to conclude that the views expressed by *Oriental Hero*'s officer, however sincere, had been coloured by the tendency alluded to above.[2]

This case presents a classic example of the commonly made mistakes in "radar assisted" collisions, and in fact the study of it played a significant part in the development of recommendations later incorporated in the Annex to the Rules that came into effect in 1965.

It should be pointed out that the principles of collision avoidance using radar were not widely appreciated at the time of this disaster. Though the "manoeuvring board" plotting techniques had been in use for some time their use was not routine, as the testimony from *Andrea Doria* shows, where it was admitted that the use of their plotting device was not customary.

To accept without question the testimony of those involved as regards such things as radar ranges and bearings without some corroborating evidence is unrealistic as we have noted above. There was no sense of impending doom and hence heightened awareness at the times these ranges and bearings were taken so we must conclude that no great weight can be attached to such evidence. While plotting will not yield answers of great precision it should, if done carefully, give better results than were apparently obtained by the 3rd mate of *Stockholm*. At the least it causes the watch officer to measure bearings and times and so give timely warning of the development of a potentially dangerous situation. In this case a careful plot should have shown that the vessels would pass too close for safety even in clear weather. In any event the master of *Andrea Doria* was confronted at the very outset of this situation, when the Swedish vessel was first discovered approaching on the starboard bow, with an awkward and potentially dangerous predicament. In the accounts of the collision the assumption seems to have taken hold that it was realised almost immediately, or at least very soon after the echo was first seen on the radar screen, that it was an eastbound vessel, yet the point is stressed that the Italian officers were also somewhat nonplussed at the discovery. They were not expecting to encounter an eastbound ship and so it is plausible to assume that it took them some time to realise that the vessel was in fact moving towards them rather than in the same direction.

In a situation such as this unless one pays strict attention to the rate of movement of the target, which means measuring its movement during a given interval, it may take quite some time to appreciate its direction of true motion especially at longer ranges. As *Doria*'s officers did not expect to meet eastbound vessels, and according to later testimony found it "very unusual", it may have been that they did not initially give as much attention to the movement of this target as was later suggested.

But be that as it may, resuming the reputed view from *Doria*, the approach of another vessel fine on the starboard bow on a near reciprocal course, in any kind of visibility, demands the strictest attention. Though it is very common for ships to pass starboard to starboard at sea, at distances of a mile or less such a situation is fraught with risk. The "Collision Avoidance Rules," or "Rules of the Road" as they are commonly called, require that when "vessels are meeting on reciprocal or nearly reciprocal courses so as to involve risk of collision each shall alter course to starboard so that each shall pass on the port side of the other." They go on to say that "Such a situation shall be deemed to exist when a vessel sees the other ahead or nearly ahead. . . . When a vessel is in any doubt as to whether such a situation exists she shall assume that it does and act accordingly."

In the case before us the vessels were not in sight of one another and hence the Steering and Sailing Rules of the Collision Regulations would not apply. The Rule then was also slightly different. In the earlier version the relevant phrase was "meeting end on or nearly end on".

The generally accepted interpretation of that was no more than half a point from dead ahead, or slightly more than $5\frac{1}{2}°$.[3]

The Rules now clearly recognise and explicitly caution against alterations to port in meeting situations in restricted visibility. Though the Rules at the time of this collision had not yet attempted to come to grips with the problems associated with the use of radar, the dangers of close approaches in fog were as well known then as now. Though the art of radar plotting was not the "inbred" skill such as it should be today it was past its infancy, and was a part of the accepted routine navigational procedures. It was practiced on the *Stockholm* and had reached a relatively high state of perfection on at least some of the trans-Atlantic liners.

As previously noted a plot would have revealed a very close approach and the need to take early action to prevent it. The key to successful collision avoidance is to avoid any action that might create uncertainty in the mind of the man at the con of an approaching vessel. And that includes taking no action in a situation where to continue will bring about a close encounter. Basically the objective is to avoid alarming the other fellow so that he is not "triggered" into making a sudden and unpredictable change of course. If you take such action so that you pose no threat to his safety, then you are unlikely to provoke the anxiety and unpredictability you wish to avoid. Early and substantial action will usually accomplish that objective.

While the first mistake made on board *Doria* was the failure to appreciate the hazard of the developing situation and act to forestall it, the second was the change to port of 4° five minutes before the collision. It was not enough to be readily detectable aboard *Stockholm*, nor was it enough to produce an adequate miss-distance or CPA, particularly where the CPA was to starboard. Any evasive action taken at that distance ($3\frac{1}{2}$ miles) should have been of the order of 60° or more. In fact if an evasive manoeuvre is to be delayed to that point probably the most effective action would be to put the other vessel abeam with maximum rudder and then to keep her on or abaft the beam until the distance begins to increase.

The first mistake made aboard *Stockholm* was the 3rd officer's failure to call the master. At 2300 when the vessels were still almost 7 miles apart with an estimated CPA of less than 1 mile and the other ship closing rapidly, fine on the bow and not visible, the 3rd officer had to be experiencing doubts — unless he had such a degree of overconfidence as to bring his judgment into serious question — and it was incumbent upon him to summon the master. If nothing else he needed help, and his failure to call for it proved fatal.

Carstens probably fell into the most common trap of all. He let his pride override his judgment. That is one of the most common and serious mistakes made by watch officers. Even those who have no good reason for it often take an inordinate pride in their skill as navigators. To call the master seems an admission of inadequacy, and though many may themselves know that this is not the case they are reluctant to appear so in the eyes of their subordinates.

Masters are frequently at fault in that they may reinforce the officer's own doubt of the desirability of summoning assistance by their own obvious displeasure. A snide remark or caustic observation made before the helmsman may well make that officer more reluctant to call for help the next time he thinks he needs it. It is a ticklish problem and needs deft handling.

Carsten's next mistake he shared with *Andrea Doria*; his acceptance of what can only be regarded by any standard as a dangerously close approach. Which brings up the question of the speed of the two vessels.

The young 3rd mate was unaware of the fog that hid *Andrea Doria*, but he should have known the meaning of the signal denoting fog that followed the usual directional signal sent out by the Nantucket lightship. He knew, of course, of the high incidence of fog at that time of year in the waters he was traversing, and the master alluded to that likelihood when he specifically reminded Carstens to call him if fog was encountered. His inability to sight the vessel when expected should have suggested the possibility of fog to him but it apparently did not. To plunge ahead at full speed towards a high-speed vessel he could not see, and without making a substantial course change to the right, or without calling the master, or to reduce speed if he rejected the first two alternatives, was a grave error. Admittedly a speed reduction without the master's prior authorisation was not a realistic alternative.

The failure to slow on the part of *Andrea Doria* is an understandable but much less justifiable decision. A token reduction was allegedly made at the onset of fog some eight hours earlier, but that was meaningless and might as well have not been done. It was not the practice of trans-Atlantic liners, particularly since the advent of radar, to slow in fog. Skill and vigilance were felt to be enough protection against the threat posed by approaching traffic, and indeed these ships could not have remained in competition had they slowed appreciably when visibility closed in. Speed was judged an acceptable risk as long as it did not lead to an accident.

Doria's maintenance of speed in fog was hence in conformity with prevailing practice, and no realistic criticism of Captain Calamai can be levelled at him solely on that score. His decision, however, not to utilise his speed to achieve a satisfactory safe passing distance, but to continue on at high speed into a very close meeting situation is another matter. The only justification for maintaining speed is to keep away from an oncoming vessel. If for some reason one chooses to hold course and allow a close approach, the rationale for speed collapses. Prudence demands under these circumstances that speed be drastically reduced. The problem with that, however, is that one has no control over the speed of approach of the other vessel, and to allow any vessel to close, where by maintaining speed that could be avoided, must be the logical choice.

But that does not exhaust the exploration of the causes leading to this tragedy. Why were the principals in this encounter loth to change course, or reduce speed? The answer in large part is quite simply economic pressure. Maintenance of schedule has always ranked high on the priorities of passenger ship operation, and it has become an increasingly important consideration in the operation of the expensive and sophisticated specialist ships of today. A master who is consistently behind schedule is also less likely to be appreciated than one who arrives on time. The ego is thus involved, and that increases the chance that risks will be taken.

There is hence an impulsion not to deviate from one's course if it can be avoided, and with the high cost of fuel there is an added incentive to steam the shortest distance. Plain stubborness may also play an occasional part, but these considerations are probably relatively minor by themselves.

Economic pressures have long been recognised as conflicting with considerations of safety, and while some enlightened operators adopted concessionary policies, the pressure to place safety second to schedule is still a problem.

The collision between *Andrea Doria* and *Stockholm* was at least in part the result of deeply entrenched attitudes that economic considerations take priority over considerations of safety. Perhaps one of the most vivid demonstrations of that is to be found in the sinking of the *Titanic*. Steaming at full speed at night in waters where icebergs had been reported was a gamble, but it was the sort of gamble that was common then and is still common today. The term "risk" is one of the most significant in the mariner's vocabulary. It is the way he earns his livelihood. It cannot be avoided, though the balancing of risk against advantage, and rejecting the risk when the former outweighs the latter, is the mark of the professional shipmaster.

On *Stockholm* Captain Nordensen ignored the 1948 SOLAS recommendation regarding the separation of east and westbound tracks. He flatly refused to abide by an agreement that his employers were not a party to and would add over two hours to his steaming time. It was a risk he had taken dozens of times and he would most probably have vehemently denied that any significant risk was involved.

On *Andrea Doria* a risk was routinely accepted that was in the final analysis responsible for the loss of the vessel. The ship was designed with stability criteria that could not be maintained throughout the voyage without putting sea water into some of her fuel tanks. That would have required bringing a slop barge alongside in New York to pump out dirty ballast before fuel could be taken, and that is a practice that on most ships is avoided like the plague. It is very difficult to strip the tanks completely of water and attempts to burn water even in small quantities have consistently proven unsuccessful.

As the vessel approached her destination then she became vulnerable, and at the most critical point in her voyage: the often fog shrouded and congested waters off Nantucket Shoals. There was no risk, of course, as long as the vessel's hull remained intact. With the required designed stability the vessel could have survived collision with two adjacent compartments flooded, but

6

with less GM* she would list beyond the twenty degrees her design allowed. A collision did occur, it happened on a bulkhead causing two compartments to flood and the ship to list beyond her designed limit, as the compartments filled the water on the low side flowed over the top of the watertight bulkheads into the adjacent compartments, and then into the next ones, and so on until the vessel lost buoyancy and sank.

* * * * * * * *

Notes

1 If the master actually asked the question he displayed a basic lack of understanding of the use of radar, and if the 2nd mate responded as related he also was guilty of similar misconceptions regarding its use. While some very rare individuals may be able to make such assessments by close observation alone it is universally accepted that only some form of plotting can yield reliable information other than that the vessel will pass either to port or starboard depending upon whether the bearing is opening or closing. A tabular value for CPA can be calculated depending upon the degree of change of bearing between specific ranges, but that information was not available at that time.

2 *American Maritime Cases*, 1976, pp. 1288–89.

3 See J. W. Griffin, *The American Law of Collision*, pp. 66–67.

Details concerning the *Andrea Doria/Stockholm* collision are taken mainly from *An Agony of Collisions* by Peter Padfield, a former British Merchant Navy officer, *The New York Times*, August 1956, and "The Mystery of Andrea Doria", by F. C. Bell, *Journal* of The Royal Institute of Navigation, April 1971.

---

* Less than the designed metacentric height occasioned by the loss of bottom weight due to fuel burn off without any compensating ballast.

Andrea Dorea listing heavily before she sank on July 26, 1956

Appendix to Chapter One

Explanation of the Reconstruction of the *Andrea Doria*/*Stockholm* Collision

Based upon the course recorder chart of the *Stockholm* it was established as a fact that the heading of that vessel was 130° when she struck *Andrea Doria*. It has been assumed here that the vessels would have a drift angle of 15° inside the path of their turn. Assuming also that the ¾ knot northerly current set was affecting both vessels equally this would have meant that the courses made good by both ships would have been deflected about 2½° to the north of the courses steered, except on the last leg of *Stockholm*'s track when the course of 117° would have been deflected about 2° to the north (115°). That would mean that *Stockholm* had not yet reached the point of entering her turn and was still moving ahead on a course (made good) of 115° even though her heading had altered from 117° (course steered) to 130°.

While the relevant portion of *Andrea Doria*'s course recorder graph was saved it did not apparently indicate distinguishably the moment of impact, only that she had swung left as far as 154°. All of the testimony and evidence, however, points to an angle of impact of close to 90°, which would therefore mean that *Doria* had to be heading close to 90° to the right of *Stockholm*'s heading (130) at the time of collision. The actual direction of her path in the turn, however, would (using the assumed drift angle of 15°) be 15° less. Others studying the case estimate the *Doria*'s heading to have been about 230° at the time of impact. Using these values the relative position of the two vessels to each other is defined and their positions relative to each other can be derived. The relative positions of the vessels to each other in the minutes leading up to the collision would not be significantly altered if *Doria*'s heading had in fact been as much as 30° further to the left. Given these assumptions and the speeds they were accepted to have been making, their relative positions one to the other in the three minutes prior to the collision are established within very close limits.

With the two ships in the positions thus established *Stockholm* could have seen only a green sidelight and never a red light. For both of the sidelights (allowing for a 3° cross-over for the port sidelight) of *Doria* to be showing let alone the port by itself *Stockholm* would have had to have been almost three-tenths of a mile farther south. Had she been in that position, however, the collision could not have taken place. The *Doria*, had she kept her helm hard over, would have turned through 180° and passed approximately a ship length to the north of *Stockholm*'s path of 115°.

The testimony from the *Stockholm* can in no way fit the established facts. If the distance between the vessels was approximately 1.9 miles when *Doria* was first seen and *Stockholm* then changed course about 17° to the right the Swedish vessel would then move ahead through the water just under 5,600 feet until she collided with *Doria*. Speed loss due to turning for the alterations made by her would be negligible. During the same period *Doria* would travel just under 6,500 feet allowing for a speed loss of 15 per cent during her turn. The only scenario those figures will fit is the one in the sketch that shows *Doria* about 12° on the starboard bow of *Stockholm* at a distance of 1.9 miles from which position only the green sidelight of *Doria* could be visible.

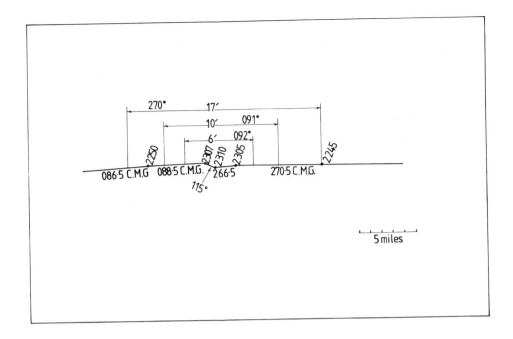

Figs. 1 & 2 *Andrea Dorea/Stockholm* (see preceding chapter)

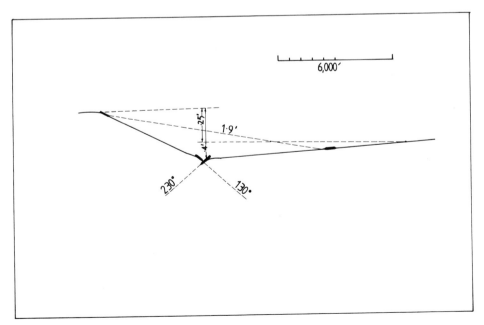

Chapter Two

Restricted Visibility

Though the phrase "radar assisted collisions" was not unknown when *Andrea Doria* collided with *Stockholm* in 1956 it had not yet achieved the notoriety that later led one American company and at least one British to remove radar from their vessels. The studies and publicity that grew out of the *Andrea Doria/Stockholm* disaster raised the consciousness of the maritime community to the mixed blessings of this most marvellous of all modern navigational devices. It came to be recognised as a two-edged sword that sliced through fog on the one hand but could also take a "healthy" cut out of profits if its misuse brought about a collision.

A variety of measures were devised and proposed whereby this "nautical dragon" could hopefully be laid to rest, or at least kept at bay, but the courts continue to provide us with distressing proof that no electronic marvels or sophisticated techniques and procedures are proof against the folly of pseudo seamen. We will find examples of this in some of the cases dissected here though the degree of fault is very wide, and by no means all or even most of the seamen involved can justly be dubbed inept. All, however, were unfortunate, and most were at least careless.

Of the solutions proposed the one that came to be widely accepted and indeed required by law and legal custom was radar plotting. In the hands of a skilled practitioner — which every mariner with a valid claim to competence as a watch-stander must be — radar plotting can usually enable him to avoid close-quarters when he is not hampered by other constraints to navigation. In heavily congested bodies of water, of which the English Channel and the Strait of Dover are two of the most notorious, the volume of vessels underway can on occasion easily tax the skill and stamina of even the most proficient plotter. In the last half-dozen years or so a variety of ARPAs (Automatic Radar Plotting Aids) have appeared on the marine market that enable the navigator to cope with traffic under the most taxing of conditions. By-and-large they do this very well, but while they have solved the plotting problem they have not thereby solved the collision problem (though they undeniably enable the navigator to cope much more effectively), which requires discovery of intention. But that is another story which we will leave for later.

* * * * * * * *

One of the most treacherous of restricted visibility traffic situations is where one vessel is approaching an area of severely restricted visibility from which another is preparing to emerge. The *Andrea Doria/Stockholm* case is a striking example of this and offers dramatic and incontestable proof of the necessity of using radar constantly while at sea except perhaps under the most favourable conditions by day. The fact that their use of radar led them into collision is another matter. We will look at several such cases here as well as some where fog, rain or snow enveloped both vessels from the time of first discovery miles away until moments before the collision.

One of the former occurred a little over a decade after that horrific night off Nantucket in 1956. The *Steel Designer* departed Long Beach, California early on the morning of March 25, 1968 in visibility of about a mile. She was bound for San Francisco and departure was taken at 0642 when the engines were brought up to sea speed of 16 knots and course was set at 245°.

Shortly thereafter fog set in thick and speed was reduced to manoeuvring full throttle, a lookout was posted on the bow, and regulation fog signals sounded. The master, who was new to the vessel and command, noticed a target about a point on his starboard bow and commenced to plot its progress on the reflection plotter on the 4 mile scale.

*Atlantic Trader** had discharged a cargo of oil in Oregon and was returning to Long Beach for another. It was a regular run and the master knew the coast and his vessel well. At 0600 she had come abeam of Point Vicente 3 miles off and course was changed to 105°. The weather was clear though the master was well aware of the possibility of fog, and while he would have probably preferred to remain on the bridge to look after the navigation of his vessel he had some paperwork that required his attention and he left the mate in charge as he went below to take care of that distracting chore. Some time after the master left the mate observed an echo on the radar about a point on the port bow, and after three sightings he concluded that it was an outward bound vessel that would cross ahead at a safe distance. He did not, however, plot it.

Just before 0700 the master returned to the bridge and going to the radar, noted a target about 10° on the starboard bow a little over 3 miles off. The mate informed him that he had been watching the target and it had crossed ahead from port to starboard as he expected. The master made no comment on his failure to plot its track nor did he suggest that this now be done. At about the same time he noticed that his ship was about to enter the fog bank that hid the approaching vessel. He immediately ordered the engines placed on standby followed by a long blast on the whistle before entering the fog. He then went to the starboard bridge wing to see if he could see or hear anything. He blew the whistle twice more before returning to look at the radar. The target had continued to broaden and he concluded that the mate's estimate that the other vessel would pass safely down the starboard side was correct. Though he felt no apprehension at this point he nonetheless wanted a bit more room and he told the helmsman to come left before going back to the bridge wing to observe and listen. Unfortunately that manoeuvre put him directly across the bows of *Steel Designer*, which only moments before had begun a drastic and fatal course change to the right.

At 0700 *Steel Designer* now making a speed of about 12 knots was approaching Point Fermin on her starboard beam from which position the master planned to make a sharp course alteration to the right to put him on the course to San Francisco. As he came abeam of that point at 0705 he commenced the course change coming first to 295, then 300, and finally steadying on 305°. His appreciation of the situation had convinced him that the other vessel, now less than 2 miles away, was on a course that would take her down his port side, and that his new course would open the distance between them. How he reached that conclusion he never successfully explained. He then heard the fog signal of *Atlantic Trader* on his port bow and he began to realise that his assessment of the situation was not what he had thought and gave an order to reduce speed to slow. Not long thereafter he heard another whistle much closer and ordered the engines put "Full Astern", whereupon he saw the bow of *Atlantic Trader* emerging out of the mist on his port bow and ordered the helm put hard left.

The master of *Atlantic Trader* had meanwhile returned to the bridge wing to look and listen after giving the order to come left. He again sounded the whistle twice before returning to the wheelhouse for another look at the radar. As he did so the mate yelled "There she is" and he turned to see the bow wave of *Steel Designer* to port. He immediately ordered hard right rudder and emergency full astern, but before that could take effect the other vessel struck *Atlantic Trader* about amidships. The time was 0708.[1]

There was no attempt to defend the conduct of *Steel Designer's* master.

A more fruitful line was open in attempting to establish some degree of fault on the part of *Atlantic Trader*. Neither the master nor the mate heard any whistle signals from *Steel Designer* until they saw her emerge from the fog, yet there was evidence that she had been sounding such signals for some time before the collision.

---

* *Steel Designer* was a C-2 type general cargo ship of 463' in length and 7,928 gross tons; *Atlantic Trader* was 571' long and 12,428 gross tons.

The routine procedure on *Atlantic Trader* in a situation such as this was for the seaman on standby to take up his post on hearing the first fog signal. That is a very common practice but the Court found it inadequate. The seaman was working to prepare the pilot ladder for the anticipated arrival at Long Beach, and without any prompting to do otherwise he felt a greater urgency to finish that task than to take up his post as a lookout. He later testified that he continued working on the ladder for about three minutes before starting forward to assume his station. He arrived there only about a minute or so before the collision, and the Court concluded that had he taken up his duty sooner he might have heard an earlier whistle signal and been able to more quickly alert the bridge of the impending danger, which might have been in time to have taken successful evasive action.[2]

As already noted the master was well acquainted with the coast and the weather conditions prevailing there. He knew he was likely to encounter fog and the mate must have known they were approaching it when he could not see the target he had on his radar at 4 or 5 miles. Not to have taken steps to have seen that the lookout took his post more promptly was deemed a fault.

The speed of *Atlantic Trader* was next questioned. The master did indeed act with commendable promptness in putting the engines to dead slow when he first entered the fog, but that was not enough to please the court. There was a vessel proceeding towards them whose course and speed, due to the failure to plot, they could only guess. Under such conditions it was incumbent upon *Atlantic Trader* to reduce her way as quickly as possible. The engines should have been stopped immediately and even reversed.

But these faults only assumed significance because of the mate and master's failure to prevent the development of the close quarters situation that gave them their importance. The Court remarked that *Atlantic Trader*'s master had much experience and knowledge of navigation in this area, and he should have known it was a common thing for vessels sailing along the coast to make a turn at Point Fermin. That, of course, is true, but it would be both unrealistic and unjust to fault either of these seamen for failure to anticipate that the other vessel would behave in such an irrational and unseamanlike manner. What is less questionable is their failure to appreciate that *Steel Designer* was no longer passing clear to starboard but was closing rapidly on the bow. The alteration to port several minutes before the collision made a plot meaningless without a stabilised display, which neither vessel had. But if a plot had been made prior to that time, a CPA could have been determined. When that distance was breached and continued to decrease rapidly, the master of *Atlantic Trader* needed no plot to tell him that the other vessel had made a dangerous alteration to starboard, and that might have allowed him enough time to take effective counter measures. While no one disputed that *Steel Designer* was more to blame than *Atlantic Trader* the failure of the latter vessel to keep an effective lookout under the deteriorating conditions of visibility and to use her radar properly made her liable for half the damages.*

* * * * * * * *

Several years earlier a collision occurred off the north-western coast of Spain in somewhat similar circumstances. The *Fabiola* was a twin screw motor tanker on a voyage from Tunisia to Le Havre with a full cargo of crude. She was cruising at her full sea speed of 16 knots on a course of true north as she approached Cape Finisterre in clear weather. The master was an experienced officer who was thoroughly acquainted with the coast and her first officer, who had the watch, though somewhat short of experience appeared to be a competent officer. The master had come to the bridge from time to time as the vessel proceeded on her northerly

---

* In 1975 the Supreme Court of the United States finally brought the practice of American courts into line with those of other nations in the case known as *Reliable Transfer*, a company which owned the coastal tanker *Mary A. Whalen*, which stranded on a sandbar off Rockaway Point in the approaches to New York. A light on the breakwater on which she depended for her navigation was unlit, and suit was brought against the U.S. Government for damages. In the original trial the district court apportioned the fault as 25/75 but divided the damages on precedent, thereby inviting an appeal that went to the Supreme Court for settlement.

course during the early evening hours of July 3, 1964, and at about 2140 he assumed the con and had the engines placed on standby. He knew the visibility frequently became restricted in these waters at this time of year and numerous fishing vessels and heavy traffic was often encountered off that coast where the Atlantic merges with the Bay of Biscay. In addition to the man at the helm there was also a lookout posted on each bridge wing.

Not long thereafter the mate confirmed that visibility was indeed decreasing when *Fabiola* passed two fishing vessels that were sighted when only 3 miles off. Shortly after that a target was picked up on the radar at between 8 and 9 miles about half a point on the port bow and a plot was commenced at 2154 when the range shortened to 8 miles. At 2200 a second bearing and range was plotted on the reflection plotter leaving the first officer to conclude that the vessel was approaching on a roughly reciprocal course down the starboard side at a speed of about 13 knots and would have a CPA of close to half a mile. *Fabiola* was now making a speed of about 15 knots, and though it was quite apparent that the two ships were in a developing close quarters situation in decreasing visibility the master continued on at full speed relying on the excellent manoeuvring characteristics of his vessel and probably not yet aware that the visibility had now closed to less than a mile. He still took no action when the distance between the two ships narrowed to 3 miles without visual contact, but when at 2206 with the range at 2 miles and *Bonifaz** (the other vessel) a good point on the starboard bow he stopped the engines.

Bonifaz was a substantially smaller diesel tanker which had recently discharged a cargo of crude at Corruna. She lay at anchor there for some time after discharge cleaning tanks and ballasting, and she weighed anchor at 1645 of the day of the collision to continue washing tanks as she made her way to Cartegena. She had been in fog for some time and though the master claimed to be turning revolutions for only half speed the Court decided that she was in fact making approximately 13 knots until almost immediately before the collision. There was also some dispute about the courses *Bonifaz* had taken causing Mr. Justice Cumming-Bruce who presided to remark rather caustically that one of the courses claimed by the master would "lead *Bonifaz* on a difficult course over land."[3] The master created a generally unfavourable impression throughout his testimony.

After clearing the Bay of Corruna *Bonifaz* passed about 10 miles to the north-west of Cape Villano. With the master on the bridge was the 1st officer and an apprentice officer who acted as lookout. The master was conning the vessel from the radar, and he apparently saw *Fabiola* at about the same time those on board that vessel discovered his. The bearing was five to six degrees on the port bow, or so it was claimed. The vessel was steered by hand from thence onwards and the master continued to observe *Fabiola* but made no attempt to plot. He alleged that the bearing opened to 18° on the port bow when the range had decreased to 3 miles, and seemingly convinced that *Fabiola* would pass on his port side he altered course 10° to starboard to widen the passing distance. His appreciation of what he saw on his radar bore little relationship to reality, and had he continued on he would in fact have passed closely down the starboard side of the Italian vessel. His change of course to 10° to the right put her dead ahead and took him straight into the jaws of collision.

The master of *Fabiola* was meanwhile anxiously looking for some sight of *Bonifaz* on his starboard bow. The mate reported that the range had closed to a mile and the bearing was still opening though that testimony must be suspect. Moments later at 2209 *Bonifaz* was sighted at eight-tenths of a mile, but instead of showing a green light as had been expected she was showing red and crossing from starboard to port! Having confidently expected the other ship to pass starboard to starboard only to find himself now *in extremis* the master of *Fabiola* ordered hard left rudder and blew two blasts. As his vessel began to swing to port he belatedly realised his blunder, reversed his helm and ordered full ahead on the engines hoping to narrow the angle of blow he now recognised as inevitable. Unfortunately his last manoeuvre brought him broadside to the oncoming *Bonifaz*, and at 2212 her bow penetrated the hull of *Fabiola* spilling oil from her tanks into the sea.

---

* *Bonifaz* was 12,942 gross tons and 560' long and flew the Spanish flag; *Fabiola* was 32,124 gross tons, 772' in length and registered in Italy.

After altering to starboard the master of *Bonifaz* left the radar and went to the port bridge wing to see if he could sight the approaching vessel visually. The radar from that point onwards was left untended. It was later alleged that the engines were put dead slow ahead at that time, were stopped on sighting, and then backed full, but all records were lost in the subsequent casualty and the Court rejected those claims.[4] *Fabiola* was reputedly not sighted until she was about half a mile off at which time the engines were put full astern and the order given for hard right rudder. Whatever happened in the few moments before the bow of *Bonifaz* ruptured the side of *Fabiola* is probably immaterial. In any event a spark from the collision ignited the oil spilled into the sea and within moments *Bonifaz* was enveloped in flame. The gas in her empty tanks was ignited, she exploded and subsequently sank taking all her records with her. She was also assigned three fifths of the blame.

* * * * * * * *

On October 28, 1970 the Greek motor vessel *George S. Embiricos* and the Italian steam tanker *Ercole** collided on courses and at speeds that were almost identical with those of *Bonifaz* and *Fabiola*. *Embiricos* was northbound in the South China Sea laden with a cargo of iron ore for Japan. A typhoon had recently passed nearby and the sea was still quite rough with occasional heavy rain squalls alternating with periods of clear visibility. There was considerable dispute about the direction of the wind with the master of the Greek ship putting it at north–north-east 5 while the Italian master claimed it was south-west 7. There was also disagreement over the visibility with *Ercole* maintaining she was experiencing almost continuous heavy rain while *Embiricos* insisted it was intermittent, which would suggest the passage of a line of squalls. The other pertinent facts were in less dispute though there were the usual inconsistencies.

Ercole was southbound in ballast bound for Singapore on a course of 230° and making about 13 knots. The Greek ship was steering 040° at a speed of between 14 and 15 knots. At about 0120 the watch officers of both ships detected on their radars a target that alerted them to the approach of another vessel close to ahead on a roughly reciprocal course. Neither of them, however, made a proper plot so that both fell into error in their appreciation of what the other ship was doing.

The 2nd mate on *Embiricos* first observed *Ercole* about two to three degrees on the starboard bow, which he believed to be broadening indicating that the vessels would pass starboard to starboard. The watch officer on *Ercole* testified that when he first saw the Greek ship on his radar it was about 6° on the port bow, and as he watched it the bearing opened slowly so that he believed the two vessels would pass port to port. Both Mr. Justice Brandon who heard the case in the lower court and Lord Denning who presided at the appeal thought that the Greek officer had a better appreciation of the situation.[5] In reconstructing the incident using a speed of 13 knots for the Italian and 14¾ for the Greek, and assuming that the course change of 10° to the right was made by *Ercole* when the two vessels were about 3½ miles apart, it can be seen that without that course change the vessels would have passed starboard to starboard about three-tenths of a mile off. If the Italian was going slightly faster the CPA would have been a little less but still green to green.

At 0116 when the two vessels should have been about 20 miles apart *Embiricos* would have been bearing a little over 3° on the port bow of *Ercole* and the Italian vessel almost 6° on the Greek ship's starboard bow. It appears that both officers were out by an equal amount in their assessment, the Greek being too low and the Italian too high, but the passage would have been green to green as *Embiricos'* 2nd mate claimed he assumed.

He also maintained that he saw *Ercole* visually when about 5½ miles away, which should have been shortly before that vessel made her 10° change of course to the right. He claimed further that when *Ercole* was 2½ to 3 miles off she came again into view and he not only saw her mast lights but her green sidelight at that time, and that was accepted by both courts.[6] As the

---

* *Ercole* was 35,168 gross tons and 807′ long; *Embiricos* was 599′ and 19,162 gross tons.

sketch shows, however, *Ercole* could never have been showing her green light alone at any time if the courses accepted by the courts were being steered.*

When the distance between the two ships had closed to 2½ to 3 miles *Ercole* had almost certainly made her course change to 240°. It may have been made as early as 0151 when the master of the Italian ship lost *Embiricos* in "clutter" when the vessels were about 4 miles apart, which was what he indeed claimed,[7] or as little as 3 miles, which was the distance arrived at by the Court. Why the master's testimony on this point was brushed aside was not adequately explained, and indeed if the Greek 2nd mate did catch a glimpse of the green light he would have been likely to have done so more readily at the further distance rather than the nearer one — as the sketch reveals. In any case he would have seen both before the course change, and probably only the red at the nearer distance. After the course change at sometime between six and nine minutes before the collision he would have seen only the red light and never the green.

The testimony from *Embiricos* hence was in error if the accepted courses were steered. The sequence of events would have been either he saw a red light at all times prior to the collision or more likely he saw red and green when the lights of *Ercole* again came into view, followed by the red light when she changed course to 240°. This raises another interesting point that was advanced by counsel for *Ercole* and never satisfactorily resolved. It involved the matter of whether the crossing rules or those applying to restricted visibility were applicable, and that was the main point pressed in the appeal.

In the well known case of *Genimar* and *Larry L,* which is described in the next chapter, those vessels were approaching one another on courses separated by 13° in visibility accepted by the Court as between 3 and 4 miles.[8] Mr. Justice Brandon, who heard that case several months before he sat in judgment on this one, held there that the crossing rule did apply, yet in this case where the visibility was claimed by the Greek to be similar it was held that it was not and the rule governing conduct in restricted visibility governed. It is ironic that counsel for *Ercole* chose to disregard the fact that those on his vessel would not admit to sighting *Embiricos* at any distance greater than 6 to 7 cables and based his case on the testimony of the Greek vessel.[9] He was in effect admitting that his vessel was guilty of a very bad lookout. Lord Denning and his colleagues would have none of that argument and came down firmly on the side of restricted visibility. What is evident, however, is that *if* the 2nd mate of *Embiricos* saw *Ercole* at about 3 miles (or perhaps a little more) after being momentarily obscured after the initial sighting at 5 he could have avoided the Italian ship by turning to the right as late as a minute or two before the collision. It would also seem that there was adequate time for him to evaluate the situation before making a decision, and so he can not be excused for turning to port *in extremis.* Even if he did not sight *Ercole* for the second time until 2½ miles off that was still a full five minutes before the collision.

In the preceding case with the vessels in almost identical positions and with identical speeds, the northbound ship (*Fabiola*) in the position corresponding to *Embiricos* did not sight the southbound vessel until she was less than a mile off yet she was condemned for a turn to port.

What is suggested here is that the 2nd mate of *Embiricos* having once decided that the vessels would pass starboard to starboard seemed unprepared to consider any other outcome. His testimony at least from the time of the second sighting seemed questionable and the Court's paraphrasing of it at this point will fit no set of "facts". To quote:

> At one point the Greek vessel saw the green and red lights; and knew thereupon that the Italian vessel was coming dangerously close to her. She went hard to port at the end to try to avoid a collision. That manoeuvre not succeeding, there was a collision and the damage was done.[10]

We know that the Greek was instead seeing a red light (if he saw anything) and had been seeing it for at least five minutes, and how he could equate that with a starboard to starboard passage is hard to understand. It may well be that he did not realise that a red light on his starboard bow meant the vessel was crossing from starboard to port. The Court was impressed

---

* Though with a sea running the vessel could have been yawing sufficiently to show an occasional green light.

15

by the fact that he seemed to have made an early evaluation of the radar picture that seemed more accurate than that arrived at on *Ercole*, though he had no proof to offer that this was indeed his evaluation at the time. That is very meagre evidence by itself as to his skill as a seaman, and even more important, as to the quality of his judgment. If he had reached the conclusion that the Italian ship would pass three-tenths of a mile off down his starboard side in spotty visibility and was prepared to do nothing about that when he had very poor judgment indeed. His failure to summon the master was not remarked but it does suggest that he may not have realised the danger he was in until he put the wheel hard to port. It is also not unlikely that what alarmed him and caused him to put the helm to port was not the "fact" that *Ercole* suddenly showed a red light when she had been showing red and green (for as already shown she must have been showing red at all times), but the mere fact that she was getting quite close and he turned away from her very shortly before she put her helm over, as the sketch suggests.

The Court held *Ercole* responsible for three-fifths of the damages. Admittedly the master of *Ercole* erred in making a blind turn to starboard on insufficient evidence, but it was an error of degree rather than of principle. He realised that he was in danger of venturing into close quarters and something must be done if that was to be avoided. The 2nd mate of *Embiricos*, however, did nothing until he made his unfortunate turn to port *in extremis*. Even had *Ercole* continued on instead of making a change to starboard the 2nd mate would have still been faced with a close quarters situation yet he took no action. Under the circumstances it seems difficult to justify assigning a greater portion of blame to the Italian vessel unless it was felt that more should be expected of a master than a 2nd mate.

* * * * * * * *

A collision that took place several years earlier on October 22, 1966 off Ushant also had several curious similarities with the ones we have just considered. The German diesel powered bulk carrier *Anneliese* bound in ballast from Emden to a port in Liberia had the 2nd mate at the con. He sighted the Liberian flag *Arietta S. Livanos** at about 6 miles, but lost her again in rain at 2 miles and did not see her again visually until about half a mile off.

Arietta (as we will henceforth refer to her), however, had the master at the con, and though *Anneliese* was sighted by radar at about 8 miles she was never seen visually until about the same time the German ship sighted her just before the collision.

Arietta was bound for Rotterdam with a full cargo of crude she had loaded in the Persian Gulf, and as she rounded Ushant the master set a course of 050°. The 2nd officer had the watch and there was also a seaman on the bridge who acted as helmsman. A lookout was reputedly posted later on the bridge as the visibility deteriorated. She was making her full sea speed of about 15.5 knots. There was little wind and the sea was calm; there were also occasional fog patches and intermittent rain. Both vessels were using radar and *Anneliese*'s was in the true motion mode.

Anneliese was on a course of 237° making 15 knots. Her master had been on the bridge but the 2nd mate was now at the con. The ship was being steered by hand and there was a lookout both on the bridge wing and the focsle head. About sixteen minutes before the collision *Anneliese* detected a target on the radar about 8 miles off, and about four minutes later the 2nd mate sighted the Liberian ship visually 6 miles off; she must have been just about dead ahead at that time crossing from port to starboard. About eight minutes before the collision *Anneliese* altered 2° to the right on the assumption that the two ships would pass close aboard port to port. They would in fact have passed starboard to starboard with a CPA of about ¼ mile if both had held course, but as no plot was made (it could not be done in the true motion mode) the error of the assumption remained undiscovered. Under the circumstances the manoeuvre was not inappropriate though its magnitude was. Perhaps realising that he needed to come further right if he was to achieve an adequate CPA he came another 11° further right three minutes later. The visibility had meanwhile begun to lower as rain moved up from the

---

* *Anneliese* was 19,995 gross tons and 620' long; *Arietta* was 23,626 gross tons and 712' in length.

south, and shortly after the course change he lost sight of the approaching vessel. He started sounding fog signals and called for the master.

During this time *Arietta* had apparently been devoting less than full attention to the movements of the German vessel. The master claimed that when she was first seen on the radar at 8 miles she was 10° on the starboard bow, but that does not accord with any of the other evidence and as he was keeping no notes nor made no plot we can only conclude that he was paying no particular attention at this time or his memory served him very badly. He further claimed that the bearing continued to open until the other ship was about two points on the starboard bow, but by the time the distance had closed to about a mile and a half he realised that the bearing first steadied and then began to close. With *Anneliese* still on the starboard bow he ordered hard left rudder and *Arietta* soon began to swing rapidly to port. After the vessel was well into her turn *Anneliese* was seen about a mile off about 60° to starboard. He thereupon blew two blasts on the whistle and continued his turn. *Anneliese* nevertheless continued to close, and when she was about 100 yards off he ordered the helm reversed to hard right in an attempt to swing the stern clear.

When the master of the German ship arrived on the bridge he went to the port wing where the lookout, a Polish sailor, was stationed and asked him if he heard any fog signals and received a negative reply. The 2nd mate who retained the con reported that the ship was two points on the port bow 2 miles distant, and he estimated she would pass about one-half mile off. The bearing must have been about half that yet when the distance closed to a mile he still maintained that the bearing was opening. He nonetheless altered course another 17° to the right. Not long thereafter the master saw *Arietta* emerge from the fog and rain about half a mile off four points on the port bow and he heard two short blasts of the whistle from the other ship. The engines were now placed on stop, and seeing that the other vessel was swinging rapidly to port the master grabbed the wheel himself and put *Anneliese*'s helm hard-a-port.[11] At the same time the engines were given a triple jingle astern. The bow of the German ship began to swing slowly to the left, but before the reversal of the engines could take effect the stem of *Anneliese* struck *Arietta* at an angle of about 60° leading forward just aft of the bridge and flooded her engine room.

The faults of *Arietta* were clear. She was obviously guilty of a very bad lookout. The visual lookout seems to have been almost totally neglected until the vessels got into close quarters. The master confined his attention to the radar and made no attempt to plot which would have given him an early appreciation of the fact that the vessels were heading into close quarters unless drastic action was taken by one or both, yet in spite of that he kept on at full speed right up to the moment of collision. When the vessels closed to a distance of about 7 cables he entered into a blind turn hard to port that put him across the bows of *Anneliese* and directly caused the collision.

The faults of the German ship were less obvious and more open to dispute, yet the Court found them so serious in nature that in the end Mr. Justice Brandon found himself unable to establish different degrees of blame and hence held both vessels responsible for an equal share of the damages. Both ships were very much at fault for holding their speed as they approached close quarters. The only justification for maintaining speed is to stay out of close quarters, and the defence of speed collapses once the limits of close quarters have been breached. *Anneliese* was also held at fault for not making a bold and substantial course change rather than a succession of small alterations once it became apparent that action would be needed to forestall close quarters, though on appeal this was found a less substantial fault under the circumstances. Where the appeal court differed directly was in their assessment of the importance, and *Anneliese*'s reaction to it, of *Arietta*'s turn to port.

The Lower Court, on the basis of an assessment given by the Elder Brethren of Trinity House, felt that the 2nd mate of *Anneliese* should have recognised at an appreciably earlier stage that *Arietta* was porting and that this contributed to his failure to avoid a collision. The Elder Brethren were of the opinion that it should have become apparent to the 2nd mate after about half a minute, or two minutes before the collision, that *Arietta* had altered to port, which seems a somewhat unrealistically short period of time in which to make an assessment.[12] The Appeals Court, while not rejecting out of hand the opinion of the Elder Brethren on this point, clearly felt more sympathy with the difficulties of the 2nd mate on this issue, and *Arietta* whose conduct in this whole affair was clearly less defensible was accordingly held to be two-thirds to blame.

* * * * * * * *

About a year later in the Strait of Juan de Fuca a collision occurred in thick fog on September 20, 1967 between the Japanese vessel *Chitose Maru** and the Danish ship *Marie Skou* on roughly similar courses to those in the previous case but with roles reversed. The Japanese vessel was a twin-screw bulk carrier on her maiden voyage in ballast from Yokahama to Fort Moody, B.C. *Marie Skou* was a conventional general cargo ship loaded with wood pulp outward bound from Crofton, B.C. She was proceeding at her full sea speed of 16.5 knots with the master at the con assisted by the 2nd officer and a lookout on the bridge. She had been on a course of 288° for some time when the master observed a target on the radar just over 6 miles off at about a quarter past midnight. Why the vessel was not discovered earlier was not satisfactorily explained, but it would appear that a search was conducted only on the 6 mile scale and as no effort was made to plot, earlier detection of the vessel would seem to have had no appreciable effect on the outcome.

The target did not seem to be kept under close observation, but bearings, distances and times were reputedly noted and recorded, which led one of the justices of the Canadian Supreme Court where the case went to appeal to dissent from the majority opinion and conclude that this record was the equivalent of a plot. The fact that the bearings and distances ostensibly recorded at the time could not be made to square with the known facts seems to have been overlooked. In any event *Marie Skou* continued on in thick fog at full speed without utilising the radar in a manner which would have revealed the rapid development of close quarters.

Chitose Maru had been prudently slowed to half her full speed, which amounted to 7.5 knots and was apparently her "slow" speed. That seemingly led her master into the mistaken belief that he could hence trust the navigation of the vessel to the 2nd mate, which assumption was vigorously contested by the Court. The 2nd officer first detected *Marie Skou* about 6 miles off slightly on the port bow, which would only have been possible if *Marie Skou* was in the position shown in the sketch, which suggests that the bearings ostensibly recorded on *Marie Skou* were grossly in error. The 2nd mate of *Chitose Maru* admitted he made no attempt to plot, but if the development of the situation as shown by the sketch is approximately correct then that suggests that his testimony was more accurate than that of *Marie Skou*.

At 0025 he altered course 5° to the right, and a minute or so later another 5° to starboard assuming wrongly that this would bring about a port to port passing; a plot would have disabused him. On this new heading of 125° *Marie Skou* would have appeared almost a point on the port bow, which if she had been on a reciprocal course or nearly so would have placed her in a position for a port to port passage. Had he watched the bearing closely, however, he would have noticed that it was almost steady and in fact narrowing slowly. It appears that he assumed his evasive action was effective and paid little further attention to the bearing of the other vessel until she was about a mile off and dead ahead. At that point he put the wheel hard right and turned directly into the path of *Marie Skou*.

Those on *Marie Skou* claimed that they had *Chitose Maru* under close observation during this time, and produced the record of bearings and distances taken at 0019 and 0025 that had convinced them (so they claimed), as well as a justice of the Canadian Supreme Court, that the approaching vessel would pass well clear starboard to starboard if she kept on as before. Those bearings and distances when plotted show that no collision could have taken place if they were even approximately accurate, and create a strong suspicion that the attention given to the progress of the reflection of *Chitose Maru* across the radar scope of *Marie Skou* was accorded rather less attention than was claimed. The fact that no bearing and distance was recorded after 0025 (when the other vessel changed course) reinforces that suspicion.

---

* *Marie Skou* was 416′ in length with a gross tonnage of 6,262; *Chitose Maru* was 635′ long and 25,254 gross tons.

What is not in dispute is that *Marie Skou* continued on in thick fog at full speed without plotting. When *Chitose Maru* reached a position just under a mile off about 20° or so (though the actual bearing must have been about half that) on the starboard bow she was seen by those aboard *Marie Skou* probably just as the helm had been put hard to starboard on the Japanese ship or very shortly thereafter. The master of *Marie Skou* testified that at about 0029 the lookout on the bridge wing reported a white light about 20° to starboard. When the master looked with his binoculars he saw two masthead lights open to the right which then began to close showing the vessel was turning to starboard, and in a few seconds the port sidelight was also seen.

We quote here from the trial judge's description as to what followed:

> The master rushed into the wheelhouse to the steering pedestal, switched to manual control, swung the wheel hard to port and shouted to the 2nd officer to order the engine full astern. The 2nd officer rang this order on the engine room telegraph but stated he heard some apparent difficulties in reversing the engine. The engine and propeller were in direct drive so that before reversing the engine it was necessary to bring the propeller to rest and after the engine was reversed some time was required before the deceleration took effect as the vessel being loaded would continue to make headway for some time. The chief engineer of the *Marie Skou* stated that the engine orders were as follows: 0030 stop; 0030 full astern; 0032 collision. The master estimated 3 to 4 minutes had elapsed between the lights of the *Chitose Maru* coming into view and the collision.[13]

The Court found a number of faults against both ships. The first was no lookout on the focsle head. In the case of *Marie Skou* this was not seen as contributing to the accident since the master of that vessel was alerted to the presence of *Chitose Maru* before she had begun her swing to starboard. The absence of a lookout on the focsle head of the latter vessel, however, was regarded as contributing to the collision since her bridge was located aft some 500 feet from the bow, and had the lookout been forward he might have seen *Marie Skou* in time to warn the bridge thereby forestalling the disastrous turn to starboard.

In the appeal the Court relied heavily on precedents established in two earlier cases, *Willowbranch/Imperial Halifax* and *Grepa/Verena*. In the former, which had been decided in the court hearing the appeal, i.e., the Supreme Court of Canada, the circumstances were very similar to this case, and the failure of both vessels to plot resulted in their sharing the blame. "The ships involved in this collision," quoted the judge, "detected each other forward of their respective beams before hearing each other's fog signals or sighting each other visually, and they were thus in a position to take early and substantial action to avoid coming to close quarters. In lieu of taking such action, the proper course for both would have been to stop engines and not to proceed again until each had established the position of the other so that both could proceed without risk of collision."[14]

In *Grepa/Varena* a similar judgment was given that if for some reason "early and substantial action to avoid a close quarters situation" is not taken there is no other option for the vessels involved than to stop the engines and navigate with caution.

There was no question but that the two vessels would have passed clear green to green if the Japanese ship had not turned to starboard, but that was only the immediate cause of the collision. Had *Marie Skou* really been on a safe course as she claimed, her approach would not have triggered the unfortunate reaction on *Chitose Maru* that led to collision. The Rules and the habits of prudent mariners lead or should lead them to view any passage of another vessel close down the starboard side with normal apprehension. When they cannot see that vessel's approach due to restricted visibility that apprehension is heightened, and it will be hard to excuse any vessel that allows the development of a close quarters situation where there is sufficient room to allow action forestalling that development.

While the Supreme Court recognised that the various mistakes of commission and omission made by both vessels had contributed to the collision of *Marie Skou* and *Chitose Maru* they were content to rest their opinion on their common fault "that no proper radar lookout was maintained by either vessel and that each failed to take early and substantial action to avoid a close quarters' situation. . . ."[15] The decision that each should equally share in the blame was upheld.

* * * * * * * *

The collisions we have examined here between radar equipped vessels could lead one to conclude that radar itself provides little justification for proceeding at speed in fog. It has become recognised, nonetheless, that when radar is used properly, which entails using the information it provides to obtain a reasonable appreciation of the course and speed of another vessel and the nearness of its approach, vessels can proceed safely at higher speeds than had heretofore been deemed acceptable. That realisation led in the latest revision of COLREGS to the adoption of the term "safe speed" in place of "moderate speed" in the restricted visibility rule. The last case we will consider in this chapter is of interest in that an attempt was made to quantify "safe speed" in a particular case.

* * * * * * * *

On July 21, 1978 two Liberian flag vessels collided in thick fog off the south-west coast of Korea. *C.K. Apollo* was on a voyage from Tsingtao to Mizushima in ballast, and was on a course of 092° making a speed of 13.5 knots. *Sanshin Victory** was bound from Kobe to Inchon with some six thousand tons of general cargo on a course of 285° at about the same approximate speed. There was a tidal current of about 1½ knots setting in a general easterly direction at the time.

At 1027 the 3rd officer on *Sanshin Victory* began a plot of a target on his port bow about 7 miles off that ultimately proved to be *C.K. Apollo*. He took bearings and ranges again at 1030 and 1033 in accordance with accepted practice and plotted them on a manoeuvring board. He calculated that the vessel was on a course of 097° at a speed of 15 knots leading to a negligible CPA. The master then asked the 3rd mate what course was required to give a CPA of 1 mile to port. The answer was 325° if the change was made at 1038. At that time the helm was accordingly put to starboard, but in the interim a number of small targets were discovered about three points on the starboard bow at distances of 1 to 2 miles. The master took these to be fishing vessels so instead of making an alteration of 40° as was necessary for a clearance of 1 mile he made a change of a mere 3° to 228°. Realising that such a small alteration would not result in an acceptable miss distance the master ordered a speed reduction to slow.

The movements of *C.K. Apollo* are somewhat obscure since not only was no oral testimony given but the documents offered as proof for the signed statements submitted in lieu of direct testimony had been tampered with. The master claimed in his statement that he first became aware of *Sanshin Victory* at 1020 when she was about 7½ miles off about 18° on the starboard bow. That testimony itself is a further indication of the unreliability of the evidence offered on behalf of *C.K. Apollo*. As Mr. Justice Sheen, himself a former mariner, remarked, the bearing could not have been as much as that and was probably only about 6°.[16] The distance would also not square with the other evidence, and could only be accurate based upon the tampered evidence which it was no doubt designed to corroborate. There was an entry in the engine room bell book that the Court concluded was originally slow ahead at 1040, but had been changed to dead slow in order to allow a fictitious insertion of slow ahead at 0955.[17].

It was accepted, however, that there was a speed reduction at 0950 by *C.K. Apollo* to half ahead when fog set in and the engines were put on standby. There was a further reduction to slow at 1040. The distance at that point had now decreased to little more than half a mile and was closing rapidly. It was by then apparent that drastic action was required and the helm was put hard to port.

The master of *Sanshin Victory* meanwhile realised that a close quarters situation was rapidly developing. He had planned to make a substantial alteration to starboard as described above, but the discovery of fishing vessels in that direction had inhibited that manoeuver and as an alternative he reduced his speed. By this time the distance between the vessels was closing alarmingly, and at about the same time the master of the other vessel was putting his helm hard left the master of *Sanshin Victory* ordered his helm hard right. As the vessel began to respond *C.K. Apollo* emerged from the fog on the port bow crossing at a broad angle. In an attempt to pass under the oncoming vessel's stern the master of *Sanshin Victory* ordered the wheel

---

* *Sanshin Victory* was a motor ship of 8,813 gross tons and 517' in length; *C.K. Apollo* was also diesel powered, 14,860 gross tons and 552' long.

reversed, but that did little more than check his swing and moments later at 1045 the stem of that vessel struck *C.K. Apollo* on the starboard side aft.

Both vessels were found guilty of proceeding at excessive speed and the Court addressed itself to the question of what a safe speed for both vessels would be. Taking into account all the relevant factors mentioned in Rule 6, and assuming that both vessels were using radar and plotting, being steered by hand with lookouts on both bridge and bow, and that the master was at the con it was decided that 7½ knots would have been a safe speed for both.[18]

The Court also found that both ships should have stopped their engines and reversed if necessary to take all their way off once it became clear that they were entering into close quarters. Finally, *C.K. Apollo*'s action in putting the helm hard to port was characterised as not only contrary to the Rules but "contrary to every instinct of a mariner."[19] *C.K. Apollo* was hence assigned 55 per cent of the fault with the balance to *Sanshin Victory*.

* * * * * * * *

It is an unfortunate choice of words that the term "radar observer" is used to describe the endorsement on licenses signifying that the holder has taken a course in radar plotting and passed an examination in its techniques, for it is precisely because radar was used simply for observation that these collisions occurred. The major fault in almost all the collisions described in this chapter was the failure to acquire an early appreciation of developing close quarters, which stemmed from a failure to plot. Even a simple relative motion plot would have allowed a better though incomplete understanding of the danger developing, but even that rudimentary precaution was neglected in most of these cases. For that there can be no excuse.

In three of the cases at least one of the vessels involved appreciated or believed that the passing would be starboard to starboard at distances of half a mile or less, yet that did not seem to them at the time to occasion concern. Whenever vessels are nearing one another in restricted visibility it is imperative that the conning officer has a clear understanding of whether that approach may lead to close quarters if both vessels hold their courses and speeds. In open sea approaches where traffic is relatively light the prudent procedure is to search on the 24-mile range scale (or its nearest equivalent) to discover advancing vessels at an early moment in order to determine if they pose a possible threat. Searches should also be conducted on smaller range scales at frequent intervals in order to more easily detect small vessels or craft that might only begin to show on the scope at comparatively short ranges.

Where the bearing of the target changes very slowly or not at all it is of course obvious that close quarters will develop if action is not taken. Plotting gives one the basic information on which to act to avoid such a development. If the plot shows that the CPA will be to port but at a distance considered to be insufficient the simple and natural response will be an alteration to starboard to increase that distance. A plot showing a close approach to starboard, however, is bound to provoke apprehension, and that should normally be met by a prompt and bold alteration to starboard.

As was remarked in the preceding chapter the key to successful collision avoidance is to shun any action, which includes inaction, that might awaken the other watch officer from his reveries. If you alarm him he may take action that may be both unexpected and dangerous. If he does this in close quarters it may be fatal, as these examples illustrate. That is most likely to occur if the development of close quarters takes place to starboard. In certain circumstances such as when navigating in confined waters close quarters may be unavoidable, but where sea room is available any mariner who finds himself involved in a collision will find it extremely difficult to avoid blame if he has any appreciable way on his vessel at the time of impact. The solution to the problem is hence simple: avoid close quarters by bold and timely application of helm.

* * * * * * * *

Notes

1 *A.M.C.,* 1970, p. 1374.
2 *Ibid.,* p. 1375.
3 *L.L.R.,* 1967, Vol. 1, p. 326.

4 *Ibid.*, pp. 326, 327.
5 *Ibid.*, 1979, Vol. 1, p. 540; 1977, Vol. 1, p. 518.
6 *Ibid.*, 1979, Vol. 1, p. 541.
7 *Ibid.*, 1977, Vol. 1, p. 523.
8 *Ibid.*, Vol. 2, p. 23.
9 *Ibid.*, Vol. 1, p. 520.
10 *Ibid.*, 1979, Vol. 1, p. 541.
11 *Ibid.*, 1969, Vol. 2, p. 84.
12 Cf. R. G. Curtis, "Determination of Mariner's Reaction Times," *Journal,* Royal Institute of Navigation, **31**, p. 408.
13 *A.M.C.,* 1971, p. 470.
14 *Ibid.*, p. 472.
15 *Ibid.*
16 *L.L.R.,* 1980, Vol. 2, p. 364.
17 *Ibid.*, p. 362.
18 *Ibid.*, p. 363.
19 *Ibid.*, p. 365.

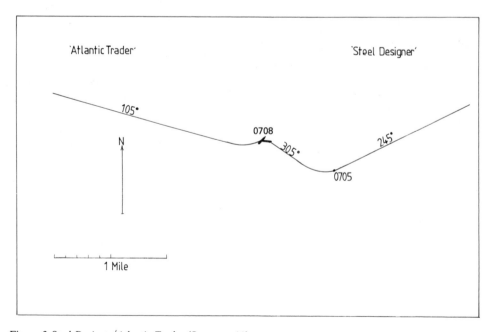

Figure 3 *Steel Designer/Atlantic Trader* (See page 11)

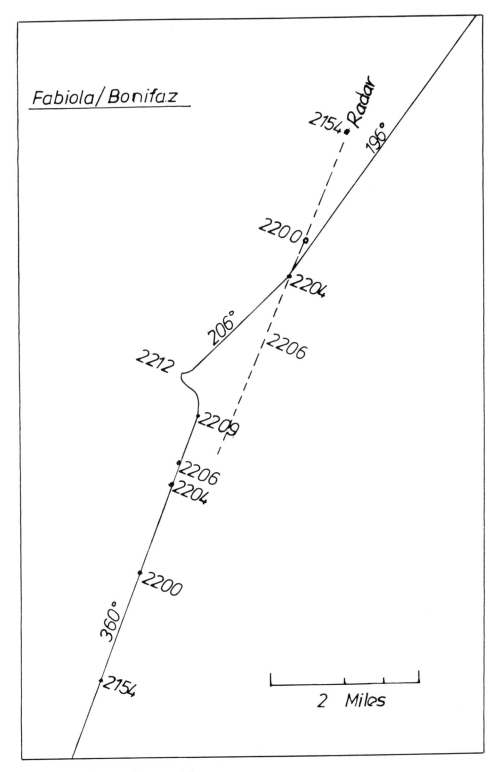

Figure 4 *Fabiola/Bonifaz* (See page 13)

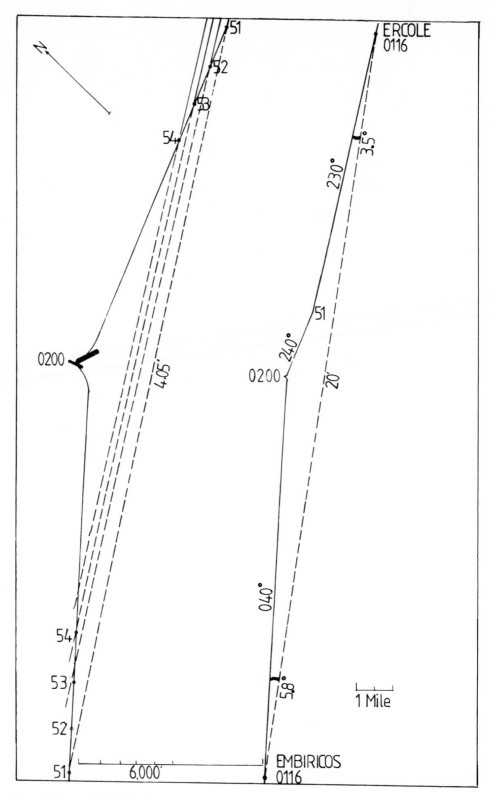

Figure 5 *George S. Embiricos/Ercole* (See pages 14–15)

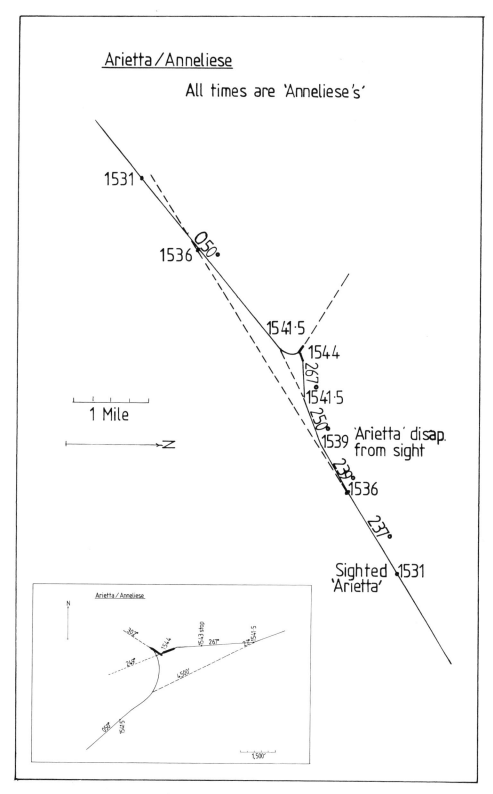

Figure 6 (Figure 7 inset) *Anneliese/Arietta S. Livanos* (See page 17)

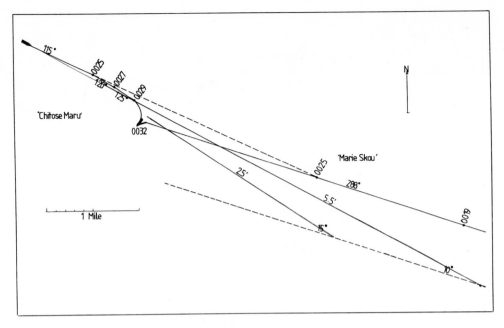

Figure 8 *Chitose Maru/Marie Skou* (See page 18)

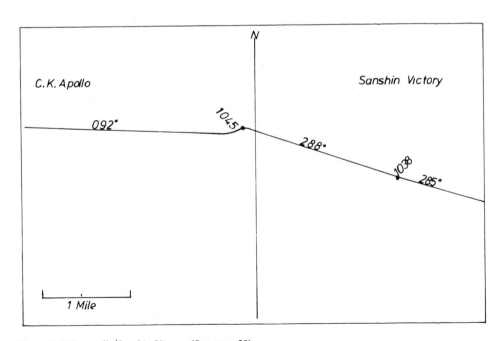

Figure 9 *C.K. Apollo/Sanshin Victory* (See page 20)

Chapter Three

Forestalling Close Quarters in Limited Visibility

One of the most perplexing situations in which the mariner is apt to find himself is when on a course of potential close quarters in limited visibility where he may emerge from the grasp of Rule 19 (Conduct of Vessels in Restricted Visibility) into the grip of Rule 15 (Crossing Situation). That can occur when the visibility is such that the approaching vessel will not be seen until she has closed to a distance of as much as 3 to 4 miles (perhaps more in the case of very fast vessels) or as little as a mile and a half or less (where the vessels are closing quite slowly). In the great majority of cases it will almost wholly depend on the relative speed of approach, and if the vessels involved allow the situation to develop without taking early action to avoid it the vessel that first sights another emerging from for or mist on a crossing course from port to starboard may find herself in a most unenviable position.

Because of the limited visibility Rule 15 will very likely have taken effect on first sighting the oncoming ship, and the stand-on vessel may be obligated to initially hold course and speed. The necessity of plotting the approach of other vessels in such circumstances should be manifest. By so doing an early appreciation of developing close quarters can be gained while the other ship is still not visible and avoiding action can be taken before she comes in sight where the restriction of Rule 15 may remove that legal option. It might be said somewhat paradoxically that one of the keys to successful collision avoidance is to minimise one's exposure to the grasp of the Steering and Sailing Rules, and in few places is that more true than here.

*   *   *   *   *   *   *

Genimar was on a voyage from Newcastle, New Brunswick to Rotterdam carrying a cargo of some forty-seven hundred tons of zinc concentrates while *Larry L** was embarking on a roughly reciprocal voyage in ballast from Antwerp to a port on the St. Lawrence River. The collision occurred in the Dover Strait in the vicinity of the South Falls buoy not long after the change of watch at 0400 on October 1, 1972. There was some dispute about the visibility at the time, *Larry L* claiming that it was only 1½ to 2 miles while *Genimar* maintained it varied from 3 to 6 miles. Another vessel in the vicinity reported visibility of up to 10 miles, while that recorded at the Falls lightvessel was 2.2 miles though that measurement is dependent upon the visibility of certain marks, viz., the Mid Falls and South Falls buoys, and if the closer is visible but the farther not, the visibility is given as the lower distance.

The Court came to the conclusion that the visibility varied between 3 to 4 miles. It was undeniably patchy so that all accounts may have been approximately right at the particular time. From the testimony given by those aboard both vessels at the instant of first sighting the

---

* *Larry L* was a Greek motor vessel of 16,357 tons and 597′ in length while *Geminar* was a Liberian motorship of 3,535 gross tons and 348′ long.

other it would seem that the visibility was at least 2 to 3 miles since *Genimar* claimed to have sighted *Larry L* at 3 miles and she said she saw *Genimar* at 2 miles.

Each ship was constructed with her engines and accommodation aft. Both were equipped with radar, but that on *Genimar* was defective and could only be operated for short periods of time. The tide was setting in a direction of roughly 210° at the time at a rate of about a knot. The masters of both vessels were on the bridge throughout. The chief officers had both relieved the watch at 0400, but the 1st officer on *Genimar* remained on the bridge after being relieved. The latter vessel had both a lookout and helmsman on duty, but there was no mention of a lookout on *Larry L* probably because *Genimar* was under radar observation for some time before she became visible and after sighting was kept under close watch until the collision.

Larry L was on a course of 240° approaching the Dover Strait from the north as the mid watch was drawing to a close. Her speed was 15 knots through the water and she was making a knot better over the ground. At 0353 her position was fixed by the 2nd officer as being 5.2 miles bearing 093° from the Falls lightvessel. At 0405 or thereabouts, with the Falls lightvessel just forward of the beam, course was changed to 235°, the next charted course. At approximately 0410 the vessel was put into hand steering due to worsening visibility, and according to the master speed was reduced from 109 engine revolutions to 100 though that contention was rejected by the Court, Mr. Justice Brandon being convinced by a close analysis of the ship's navigation during the relevant period that her full sea speed was maintained.[1] It was also claimed that fog signals were begun at that time and continued up to the time of collision, but there were no witnesses to back up that claim and it too was rejected.

At about 0420 the chief officer first discovered *Genimar* on the 8-mile scale a bit over 7 miles off, fine on the starboard bow. There was another vessel, *Pearl Creek*, on an approximately parallel course and slightly slower speed about a mile to starboard of *Larry L*. Shortly before 0430 the chief officer, who had been watching *Genimar* for about ten minutes, drew the attention of the master to the target now about 3½ miles off and on much the same bearing as when first discovered. On learning of this the master took over the manning of the radar and switched it down to the 4-mile scale while the mate went to the starboard wing of the bridge to try to sight the vessel visually. At about 0432 course was changed from 231½° to 227½° and a minute later *Genimar* was seen about 2 miles off still fine on the starboard bow.

The master and chief officer watched her for several minutes without any appreciable change of bearing with her masthead lights open to the left and showing a red sidelight. The master thereupon blew five short blasts on the whistle as a warning, being under the impression that it was *Genimar*'s duty to give way as she was proceeding in the wrong direction in a traffic lane. With the distance still closing and no sign of a course change by the rapidly approaching vessel *Larry L*'s master ordered hard right wheel and blew one blast. The helmsman had applied 10° rudder and the ship had begun to swing to starboard when the chief officer on the starboard wing reminded the master of the presence of *Pearl Creek* shouting: "Captain, we close the other ship, very dangerous."[2] The master responded to the warning by ordering hard-a-port.

Genimar had steered a course of 058° from 0345 when the South Goodwin lightship was abeam to port about 1½ miles off until shortly before 0430 when she came abeam the East Goodwin lightvessel 3½ miles off to port. The speed over the ground was calculated to be between 8 and 8½ knots but it appears to have been slightly over 9.[3] At about this time *Larry L* and *Pearl Creek* were sighted some 3 miles off with the former vessel closer on the bow. The latter presented no problem but *Larry L* appeared to be crossing from port to starboard at a narrow angle, and it was decided to haul 10° to the right to attempt to pass port to port.

Genimar held to that course until the distance between the ships had closed to less than half a mile unaware that the Greek ship had altered 3½° to port at almost the same time *Genimar* hauled to starboard. At this point the master ordered hard right rudder and blew one blast on the whistle. *Genimar* responded quickly but a two blast signal was heard from *Larry L* which was now swinging to port. Both vessels swung rapidly through more than a right angle before *Larry L* struck *Genimar* at an angle of about 45° leading forward. The bow of the Greek ship penetrated deeply into the port side forward of the Liberian vessel damaging her fatally. *Genimar* was subsequently successfully abandoned and sank.

28

In attempting to assess the responsibility for this casualty the Court turned its attention first to the traffic separation scheme in which it occurred. The scheme was first adopted in 1967 and afterwards approved by IMCO (now IMO). That, however, did not make compliance with the scheme mandatory at the time of this collision. It nonetheless quickly became recognised that good seamanship required a mariner to follow the scheme unless some other overriding consideration compelled him to ignore it. Compliance with the scheme, however, does not exempt one from adherence to the Collision Regulations, though it does seem to have created that unfortunate impression in the minds of some and was apparently a factor in this collision.

Unlike many cases of landmark status this is one of recent vintage, no doubt because the Rule to which it applies [10(b)(i)] is of recent vintage itself. It had, indeed, not yet been accepted as law since the Rule pertaining to traffic lanes was only incorporated into the new body of rules adopted in the very month and year the collision happened, and only came into force in 1977. Traffic lanes by then (October 1972) had, nevertheless, become so common a feature of the marine landscape (particularly the precedent setting scheme in the Dover Strait), that it was predictable that the first collision that came to trial involving a violation of this "custom" would almost inevitably set a precedent.

It was held that under the conditions of visibility obtaining that the Steering and Sailing Rules applied, and *Larry L* was a give-way vessel and *Genimar* the stand-on ship. Under the circumstances *Larry L* should have made an appreciable alteration to starboard, or, if she felt that the presence of *Pearl Creek* made this unadvisable, a substantial reduction in speed. She did neither and in fact made two small changes to port that further complicated the situation.

Genimar, however, was held to blame for her failure to stand-on, having altered 10° to starboard after first sighting *Larry L*. Her subsequent turn to starboard when *in extremis* was judged proper, but *Larry L*'s hard left turn was understandably condemned. The Court took note of the fact that the manoeuvres of the master of the Greek ship seemed to stem from an attitude on his part that as he was proceeding in the proper lane and the other vessel was advancing against the traffic flow it was up to her to get out of the way.[4]

Mr. Justice Brandon went on to say that while there might well be cases in clear weather where the contravention of a TSS [Traffic Separation Scheme] by a vessel might be a fault it would not necessarily be a causative fault. Such a situation might arise where two ships collided with no others about. The present case, however, was not of that kind. The visibility was poor and threatened to become worse. It was, moreover, night, and the Dover Strait is always a scene of heavy traffic. In this case the presence of *Pearl Creek* to starboard of *Larry L* inhibited the freedom of manoeuvre of that vessel, and "undoubtedly impinged" upon her navigation creating difficulties in her meeting of *Genimar* that might not otherwise have arisen.

Notwithstanding this the judge found that while the presence of *Genimar* in the wrong lane created a situation out of which the collision followed, this fault was comparatively minor in respect to the disregard of *Larry L* of the Collision Regulations. The imprudent and unseamanlike handling of that vessel was judged to be the major cause of the collision and *Larry L* was accordingly held responsible for two-thirds of the blame.

* * * * * * * *

A curious case involving three vessels wherein the restricted visibility rule governed between two of them, but the overtaking rule applied between one of these two and a third ship, took place off the New Jersey coast in a blizzard on the night of February 3, 1961 with attendant storm-force winds from the south-east.

Brott was a Norwegian motor vessel on a voyage from New York to Camden, N.J. via the Delaware Capes. She was in light condition and was at reduced speed due to the strong winds and head seas along with the reduced visibility making about 9 knots. She had dropped her pilot at Ambrose lightship about an hour and a half before and was steering a course of 161° in order to make a true course of 180°. She was sounding the regulation fog signals and using her radar on the 8-mile range.

Nassau*, a twin-screw Liberian steam passenger vessel, had tried unsuccessfully to drop her pilot at about 2300 and then proceeded south on a course of 177° gyro in order to make good 180°. Her engines were on manoeuvring full which gave her a speed of about 12 knots through the water. She too began sounding fog signals though she ceased to do so sometime before the collision. Her radar set was on the 3-mile scale throughout.

About half an hour before the collision *Nassau* was observed by *Brott* to be about 1¾ miles astern fine on the port quarter and overtaking.[5] At about the same time another echo was seen on the radar about 8 miles off 5° on the starboard bow. That target subsequently proved to be *Haminella* which was northbound. The bearing of that vessel remained steady until the distance had closed to 2 miles whereupon *Brott* reduced speed to half ahead. When the distance had closed to ¾ mile *Haminella* was first seen through the binoculars with her masthead lights open to the left and showing a red sidelight about 5° on the starboard bow. At about this time they heard a long blast from *Haminella* and *Brott* altered slightly to the right enough to bring *Haminella* dead ahead, but no signal was made on the whistle to warn the overtaking *Nassau* of that manoeuvre. It was at this time that speed was reduced to half, and about 2323 when *Haminella* had crossed ahead a further reduction to slow was ordered. That was about two minutes before the collision, and a prolonged blast was now heard from *Nassau* which had belatedly become aware of the dangerous situation developing.

The visibility was variable throughout but it seems to have momentarily decreased at this time though the passenger ship still had the stern light of *Brott* in view. *Haminella,* however, was obscured and as *Nassau* had kept her radar on the 3-mile scale since her departure she was unaware of her approach, and indeed did not discover her presence until after the collision.[6]

While *Brott* was aware of the overtaking *Nassau* she had apparently ceased to take much notice of her once the approaching *Haminella* claimed her attention. The long blast from *Nassau* reminded the master of the Norwegian ship that he had more than a single problem. His reduction of speed together with his light draft and the 50-knot wind on his port bow had caused his head to fall off to starboard so that when he looked in the direction of *Nassau* on hearing her whistle he saw her about a hundred yards away heading for his bridge. He ordered half ahead, hard-a-port, and full ahead in quick succession, but before these manoeuvres had time to take effect the bow of *Nassau* struck *Brott* on her starboard side in the way of No. 2 hatch.

As *Nassau* entered the final stages of her approach to *Brott* the bearing broadened on the port bow until the first glimpse of the Norwegian ship's masthead and green sidelight could be seen through the driving snow. The Liberian vessel had shaped up to overtake *Brott* at a distance that must certainly have been considerably less than half a mile, and not long after she had gained her first sight of *Brott*'s sidelight it broke into full view and the master of *Nassau* realised to his dismay that *Brott*'s bow was swinging to starboard. He immediately ordered hard right wheel, but as *Brott* continued to come on he followed that with full astern. He then sounded the long warning blast that awakened *Brott* to her peril to starboard.

The first and obvious mistake was the inadequate lookout being kept on both vessels. Not only was the visibility severely restricted by the swirling snow but the high winds offered an impediment to any manoeuvring. *Brott* was entitled to expect *Nassau* to keep clear and pass at a safe distance, but close attention to the radar would have told those on the Norwegian ship that *Nassau* was on a course that would bring her much closer than was comfortable. She was admittedly in a very difficult position once *Haminella* was discovered close on her starboard bow on a northerly course. Her bearing was steady yet *Brott* could not alter her course as much as she might like to starboard because of the closeness of the overtaking *Nassau* on her starboard quarter and the danger of the storm force winds thrusting her head farther to starboard if it was allowed to broaden on the bow.

Under the conditions obtaining on that wild night it would have perhaps been prudent to have let *Nassau*, which was obviously a faster vessel than *Brott*, to get quickly by to prevent the development of just such a situation as subsequently did transpire. Yet *Brott* cannot be rightly

---

* *Brott* was 485′ long and 6,155 gross tons; *Nassau* was 573′ in length and 15,225 gross tons.

criticised for not being so far-sighted. When she did become aware of the threat posed by *Haminella* her best manoeuvre would probably have been an earlier reduction in speed to let *Haminella* pass ahead, yet the undoubted cause of the collision was the unnecessarily close distance that *Nassau happened* (she did not choose, it simply happened) to pass.

Under any conditions *Nassau* was clearly to blame to allow such a meagre passing distance with ample room to starboard, but under the conditions obtaining it can only be described as a foolhardy venture. She was also seriously negligent in restricting or limiting her search on radar to 3 miles, and the Court so noted that delinquency.[7] The New Jersey coast must necessarily be traversed by all vessels seeking to reach the busy port of New York from the south. It would be unusual not to encounter some northbound traffic as one proceeded south along this coast. Today the Traffic Separation Scheme adopted for that area has all but precluded the development of such a predicament as *Brott* found herself trapped in, but at that time the situation was to be anticipated and had *Nassau* searched occasionally on a higher scale she would have discovered *Haminella* in sufficient time to realise the precariousness of the situation into which she was venturing and could have resolved it by hauling over to starboard to avoid crowding *Brott* as she did. For these faults she was only assigned three-fifths of the blame, which would appear to be a fortunate result indeed in view of the gravity of her misdemeanors.

Notes

1 *L.L.R.*, 1977, Vol. 2, p. 21.
2 *Ibid.*, p. 23.
3 *Ibid.*, p. 21.
4 *Ibid.*, p. 25.
5 *Nassau* was apparently making good a course to the right of *Brott*'s and so overtook her on *Brott*'s starboard side.
6 *L.L.R.*, 1964, Vol. 2, p. 515.
7 *Ibid.*, pp. 514–15.

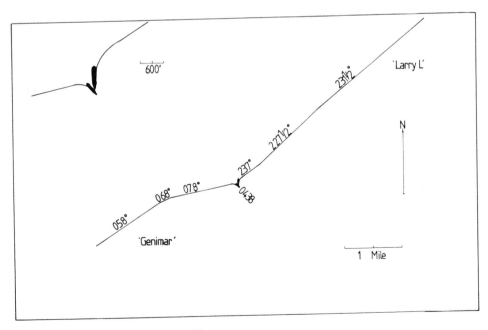

Figure 10 *Genimar/Larry L.* (See page 28)

Chapter Four

The Role of VHF and Harbour Radio in Collision Avoidance

The collision between two T-2 tankers, SS *Arizona Standard* and SS *Oregon Standard* under the Golden Gate Bridge in San Francisco Bay during heavy fog in the early hours of January 18th in 1971 was one of the more publicised collisions of recent years. It is particularly noteworthy in that the Harbour Advisory Radar (HAR) operated by the U.S.C.G. was involved, and that the use of VHF, or rather its misuse, played an unfortunate part in the affair.

Arizona Standard had left Estero Bay, California just after noon on the previous day bound for San Francisco. Shortly after 2200 when about 25 miles south of her destination she encountered dense fog, which extended over the entire Bay area. The engines were placed on standby and whistle signals were commenced. Just prior to entering the main ship channel the master of *Arizona Standard* reported to HAR his position and the fact that he was bound for Long Wharf in Richmond in the northern part of the Bay. As he shaped up on a course of 069° he reduced speed to 13.5 knots. The master was acting as pilot and was manning one of the radar sets while the chief mate used the other. The 2nd officer handled the telegraph and assisted as needed. There was a lookout posted on the bridge wing.

Oregon Standard also piloted by her master, had meanwhile left her berth in spite of the thick fog and HAR advised *Arizona Standard* that her sister vessel was outward bound passing north of Alcatraz Island. The time was 0120. *Arizona Standard* had just changed course to 065° to line up with the channel which passed under the Golden Gate Bridge. At 0215 the lookout, who had meanwhile been sent to the bow, reported the loom of Mile Rocks light about three points on the starboard bow, which according to the radar was about 1 mile off. Two minutes later the chief mate observed an echo on the radar almost 6 miles away a mile south of Point Blunt and commenced to plot it. He established that it was moving along a relative movement line of approximately 264° and that the CPA would be about 1 mile, though the latter information was of questionable relevance since either or both vessels would need to make small adjustments to their courses in order to pass port to port.

At 0130 HAR advised *Arizona Standard* that *Oregon Standard* was a mile to the east of the Golden Gate Bridge and the master of the former now attempted to establish VHF contact with the latter. He tried on the HAR channel 18A, 10, and 16, but had no success. He nonetheless maintained full harbour speed of 13.5 knots. Less than a minute thereafter the Mile Rocks light was abeam a half mile off and course was changed to 056° and speed was reduced to half, or about 11 knots. Not long after the helmsman reported that he was steering with difficulty, probably due to the influence of the strong flood tide. The mate had continued to track *Oregon Standard* on the radar until about 0133 when he lost contact. The master again tried to make VHF contact with the other vessel but without success.

At 0136 hearing the mid-channel signal located on the centre span of the bridge slightly to port

Arizona Standard's master ordered a course change to 058° in an apparent attempt to ease over to the right-hand side of the channel. Two minutes later he informed HAR that he had been unable to contact *Oregon Standard*.

After leaving her berth at Long Wharf *Oregon Standard* proceeded seaward at various speeds, and as Harding Rock buoy came abeam 0.2 mile to port at 0124 the speed was about 11 knots. At that time course was altered to 231°. The master, who was conning the vessel, was at one radar and the 2nd mate at the other. A lookout was on the bow, the engines were on standby, and whistle signals were being sounded. After reporting his departure from Long Wharf to HAR the master had switched his VHF to channel 10, which was used for communication with the owner's office. Though he was aware that *Arizona Standard* was due to take his berth and that they would probably meet on the way out he made no attempt to enquire from HAR about the location of that vessel nor did HAR volunteer that information. Nor was any effort made to use the VHF to contact inbound vessels until he was in imminent danger of collision with *Arizona Standard*.

Some six to seven minutes later as the vessel passed Point Cavallo 0.3 mile off, the master realised he had been set to the right and changed course to 220° to rectify that. At 0133 speed was reduced to 9 knots still unaware of his sister ship's approach. About one minute later hearing Lime Point (the northern end of the Golden Gate Bridge) fog horn apparently abeam he ordered hard right rudder to come to a course of 265° which he amended to 270° during the turn.

As the vessel was turning the master checked the radar and found to his consternation that there was an inbound vessel about two points to port 0.8 of a mile off. He quickly decided on a port to port passing though he was unaware of the heading of the inbound ship. At 0137 the vessel had been steaded on 270° and began to pass under the bridge whose lights were now visible.

Going to the port wing of the bridge the master now began to sound whistle signals manually from that position; no signals were heard from the inbound ship and at 0137½ speed was reduced to revolutions for 4 knots. At about 0139 the 2nd mate advised him that the vessel on the port bow was closing rapidly on a steady bearing. The master went to the wheelhouse and switched the VHF from channel 10 to 16 in an attempt to make VHF contact. Almost immediately *Arizona Standard* appeared out of the fog at a distance of about 200 yards and at 0140, still making 11 knots, she struck *Oregon Standard* at an oblique angle midships on the port side.

It would seem on the face of it that this was a clear case of both vessels proceeding at an immoderate speed. The Court did so hold that the master of *Oregon Standard* was guilty in this respect, but a more lenient view was adopted in the case of the other vessel. Mention was made of the difficulty of steering the ship at a substantially reduced speed in the approaches to the Golden Gate where unpredictable currents and eddies might achieve velocities of as much as 6 knots. The speed of *Arizona Standard* was hence held to be moderate under the circumstances.

From the very beginning the introduction of the Harbour Advisory Radar in San Francisco, and similar installations elsewhere, met with considerable opposition from pilots and ship's masters. It was seen as an attempt to impose guidance and advice by unqualified Coast Guard petty officers on the navigation of vessels, and to the degree that this was true it was a legitimate complaint. Resentment may then explain why the master of *Oregon Standard* ignored the services of HAR after leaving his berth. It does not excuse his failure to obtain information about the other vessel's movements within the Bay relevant to the navigation of his vessel, viz., the presence of *Arizona Standard* approaching the Golden Gate Bridge.

Having embarked upon such a hazardous adventure it become imperative that any meeting he might have with another vessel be so arranged that it would take place at an advantageous place and under the most favourable circumstances practical. That, of course, could not be guaranteed, which was perhaps the most decisive argument against leaving the berth in the first place, but once that decision was made it became imperative that he take every precaution against the hazards inherent in the venture. That he failed to do.

The information regarding the movements of *Arizona Standard*, which was of the utmost importance to the success of his undertaking, he wilfully disregarded.[1] He compounded his error by making no effort to contact that vessel, which he had every reason to expect was underway within the port bound for the berth he had vacated, until he was in a position where collision with her was almost unavoidable. Indeed, it can be argued that his futile effort to contact her on VHF at that time may have conceivably contributed to the collision by drawing his attention away from the conning of the vessel at that critical time.

Having rejected the use of VHF as an aid in determining the approach of other vessels it appears that he furthermore made no systematic effort to determine by radar whether other ships were underway in the vicinity until it was too late.

The worst possible meeting place under the circumstances was where they met under the Golden Gate Bridge. The obvious solution to the problem of where to meet was to communicate directly via VHF to agree on a meeting place within the harbour east of the Golden Gate Bridge. If they were unable to communicate directly then an agreement could have been reached through the agency of HAR, which was precisely one of the reasons for its establishment. It would have been a very simple matter for the master of *Oregon Standard* to have held back so that she was in the vicinity of Harding Rock or somewhat to the east of it when *Arizona Standard* passed under the Golden Gate Bridge.

The actual passage should have been carefully orchestrated so that it not only took place where there was ample room to pass, but both vessels should have slowed substantially (having due regard to the effects of current on steering) as they approached one another so that there would be more time to take corrective action if things did not go according to plan. It would also have tended to minimise the effects of collision.

The major fault on the part of the master of *Arizona Standard* would appear to be his failure to ensure that he did not meet *Oregon Standard* under the Golden Gate Bridge. He knew that the other vessel was underway and they would meet. He had originally hoped that perhaps he could clear the bridge before the other vessel got there, which would have explained his maintaining speed up the main ship channel. At 0120, twenty minutes before the collision, HAR advised him that the outbound vessel was due north of Alcatraz, and it should have been clear then that unless she slowed of her own accord a meeting in the vicinity of the bridge was very likely.

The prudent course at that time would have been to have taken as much way as practicable off the ship while attempting to establish VHF contact so as to reach an agreement on where to pass. When that was not successful then he should have held back and met *Oregon Standard* in the main ship channel after she had passed through the Golden Gate and was on a steady course.

Arizona Standard was admittedly in an awkward position. She was running with a strong flood tide behind her making steering difficult at reduced speed, as was evidenced by the complaint of the helmsman when speed was reduced to half as they neared the Golden Gate. The tide, however, is less a problem in the lower reaches of the main ship channel. About ten minutes before *Arizona Standard* entered the main ship channel her master heard *Oregon Standard* report to HAR that she was leaving her berth. It would have been prudent at that time to contact his outbound sister ship either directly or through HAR to come to an agreement on a place of meeting since it was well within the bounds of possibility, as events confirmed, that they might meet under the Golden Gate. He had of course no way of knowing that he would be unable to establish VHF contact later, but under the circumstances it might be thought questionable to delay the attempt to reach agreement until it was too late to avoid the meeting when VHF contact was not made.

As *Arizona Standard* neared the Golden Gate there was little that could be done about postponing the encounter since an attempt to slow materially would risk losing control of the vessel, and the Court agreed that his speed was moderate at that time under the existing conditions of tide.[2] But as the master could not reduce to as slow a speed as he would otherwise wish it was incumbent upon him to keep as close to the starboard side of the channel as was practical, and that he did not do.

What was never satisfactorily explained is how *Oregon Standard*, which must have been close to 3 miles off at 0133, disappeared from the scope of *Arizona Standard*. There was no rain and little wind, hence no sea to speak of, and if she did disappear on one scope why was no attempt made to find her on the other radar set?

This case demonstrates very clearly the value of VHF communication as a means of dispelling uncertainty in such situations. Direct communication between vessels would have been preferable, but failing that, exchange of intentions via HAR could have sorted things out. The Court in discussing the use of radar in this case pointed out that conditions required a constant guard and intelligent use, saying that intelligent use would also "seem to require a specially assigned watch officer . . . so that the regular watch officer is free to relay and observe orders to the helm and engines, make log entries, audit fog signals and maintain a VHF vigil." It went on to say that, "A vessel equipped with VHF moving in dense fog on heavily trafficked bays is required to use such equipment intelligently as an aid to navigation, and where there is a harbour advisory service available with radar and radio telephone, it is negligent not to use that service."[3]

The case also serves to highlight one of the less widely recognised hazards of VHF communication. Establishing contact with an approaching vessel, particularly where there may be some difficulty in making ready identification, requires a degree of concentration that can distract the conning officer if he takes that task upon himself. It follows from this that the establishment of initial contact should be made well before any subsequent need to manoeuvre so that any succeeding VHF communication can be carried out with an absolute minimum of distraction.

*   *   *   *   *   *   *

Notes

1 *A.M.C.*, 1971, p. 2218.
2 *Ibid.*, p. 2212.
3 *Ibid.*, p. 2214.

Chapter Five

The Avoidance of Close Quarters in Clear Weather

What constitutes a minimum safe distance of approach in an overtaking or meeting situation is a problem that has engaged the interest of seamen since steam began to supplant sail. Prior to that time vessels were often obliged to steer zig-zag courses in tacking against the wind, and although they were undoubtedly no less concerned with avoiding a collision the problem was of a different order.

With the advent of radar and its associated plotting techniques the means of determining the "closest point of approach" or CPA became a routine possibility, and with that development the basis for a relatively precise evaluation came to hand. It is surprising that it took so long to come to grips with this problem but recent work by Dr. R. G. Curtis has finally laid the basis for a systematic approach. [1]

Dr. Curtis has combined his research into the determination of "mariners' reaction times" [2] with a mathematical solution to the problem of "miss distances" in vessels turning across the path of another in close quarters. His concern has been specifically with "minimum safe passing distances" in restricted visibility in the Dover Strait or similar waterways, though it obviously can be applied where vessels are in sight of one another.

However, Curtis' reliance on a quantifiable value for "mariner's reaction times" has limited validity, as he himself has recognised. [3] It is an assumption that holds in the case where the conning officer is aware of the potential hazard and addresses himself to it with skill and diligence. Unfortunately too many mariners on a *world-wide* average would not measure up to such standards. What might to a large extent resolve that difficulty would be to introduce a voice-link by VHF radio in such circumstances so that manoeuvring intentions and actions were not subject to the uncertainty of detection by radar.

The final objective of course is the one Curtis pursued: of resolving the dangers in close approaches in all weathers. We will confine ourselves here to the more modest application of his principles to clear-weather approaches.

The problems of determining minimum clearances, or CPAs, in passing on parallel courses when overtaking or approaching seems obviously closely related to that of a definition of "close quarters". That term the courts and other legal and quasi-legal bodies that study such matters have steadfastly refused to define. Lord Justice Willmer, in a decision handed down in 1961 on the *Grepa/Varena* collision remarked that

> It leaves open to argument what is meant by the phrase 'close quarters situation.' That, I think, must depend upon the size, characteristics and speed of the ships concerned. I think, however, that in the case of ships of the class that we have here it must mean quite a substantial distance, and I venture to think, a distance measurable in miles rather than yards. [4]

The term "close quarters" is ordinarily used in a restricted visibility context, but it undoubtedly also applies to situations in clear weather. But before proceeding further let us look at what some of the experts have to say about "close quarters".

The term itself seems to be of relatively recent derivation. it is not used in Marsden, Farwell or Griffin even though the former two have undergone revision since Lord Justice Willmer discussed it in *Grepa/Verna*, a somewhat curious omission. Perhaps the reason for this is that they view the terms "close quarters" and "*in extremis*" as roughly synonymous, but if that is so it is very odd that very extensive discussions of the latter term contain no mention of the former.[5] Still, there can be no doubt that there is a very close relationship between the terms and a successful definition of one would go far towards arriving at an acceptable description of the other.

Cockcroft and Lameijer have gone as far as most in discussion of this prickly question, and they say that "In the open sea distances of the order of 2 to 3 miles are usually considered as the outer limits [at close quarters] in restricted visibility but smaller distances, probably of the order of 1 mile, would probably be accepted for vessels in sight of one another."[6]

Mr. Justice Willmer's observation quoted above mentions size, characteristics, and speed of ships concerned as the deciding factors in determining the meaning or definition of "close quarters". We have in fact had for many years the means of measuring the speed of an approaching vessel with a fair degree of accuracy by radar — particularly in overtaking situations, and to a somewhat lesser extent in reciprocal meeting cases. More recently the appearance of ARPA (automatic radar plotting aids) systems have made this measurement even more precise. In any event the measurement of speed available is accurate enough for the purposes to be described here.

In confining our examination to clear-weather situations certain reasonable assumptions about ship size and characteristics can be made. Within these limits we then should be able to say with more exactitude than heretofore just how close vessels can approach before the limits of close quarters have been breached. Our goal is not to reach a definition of what would be acceptable to the courts, though investigations into such matters may in time have an effect on what is deemed acceptable, but rather to offer some practical guidance on the everyday problem faced by all officers in charge of a vessel or bridge watch of the approximate degree of hazard to be expected in a certain approach, and when and where it becomes most acute. It is up to the individual navigator then to determine what further margin for error he wishes to add to give him a distance he feels is "safe".

We offer here a provisional definition of "close quarters" as that area around a vessel where a collision with an approaching vessel could not be avoided by the action of the approached vessel alone if the approaching vessel made a major, sudden and unexpected course change. We do not suggest that this might be found acceptable in a court, but it has the advantage of setting parameters for the investigation of the problem before us.

Figures 11–13 show the relationship between a specific vessel A of 700 feet length, 80 feet breadth, and with a tactical diameter of 2,700 feet and other vessels with speed ratios to A of 1.5:1, 1:1 and 1:1.5. Where the other vessel is half again as fast as A a length of 1,000 feet and a tactical diameter of 3,000 feet has been assumed; where the other vessel is of equal speed a VLCC of 1,200 feet and a tactical diameter of 3,600 feet is assumed; where the other vessel is half again as slow as A a length of 200 feet and a tactical diameter of 600 feet is assumed.

A "collision zone" for both overtaking and meeting situations is shown demarcated by the lines OB and OS in the overtaking case and MB and MS in the meeting one. With the other vessel's stem along the lines OB or MB and that vessel entering a turn toward A at that point under maximum rudder, the bow of the other vessel would just catch the stern of A if A continued on course. A speed loss through the turn of 15 per cent has been assumed for the other vessel though it would almost certainly be more. The position of the lines OB and MB are only marginally dependent upon the size and turning characteristics of the other vessel. As the length and tactical diameter decrease the lines OB and MB will move slightly ahead, or in the direction of the motion of vessel A.

The lines OS and MS mark the other limit of the "collision zone", and with the other vessel's stem along this line the bow of A would just catch the stern of the other vessel as it crossed ahead if A continued on course and took no evasive action. An overall speed loss of 30 per cent through the turn has been assumed in this case thought it should be somewhat less. The position of this line, unlike lines OB and MB, will vary substantially, depending upon the length and turning circle of the other ship, since the position of this line is dependent upon the distance the *stern* will have to travel to cross ahead of A.

As is well known, when a vessel begins to turn, its heading alters substantially before it actually enters into the turn. The drift angle will normally be at least 15° and may be appreciably more. The vessel will also range ahead for from three to five ship lengths in this manner before entering her turn, and it is assumed that A will discover that deviation in course and react to it by the time the other vessel enters her turn.

With the bow of the other vessel anywhere within the cross-hatched area a collision would be all but unavoidable regardless of any action taken by A. With the other ship within the "collision zone" but beyond the cross-hatched area. A's ability to avoid collision would be proportionate to the distance the other vessel's bow is clear of the cross-hatched area.

As can be seen from the diagrams, it is further assumed that once the other vessel has turned through 90° she will then continue on at right angles to the initial course of A. Should the other vessel continue to turn through 90°, as she might due to a steering gear failure, the effect would be to increase the miss-distance if A turned to avoid the other vessel. The same would be true if the other vessel turned with less than maximum rudder through a larger circle.

A turn through 90° and then continuing on at right angles is hence the most dangerous eventuality, but it is unlikely that a vessel would long continue on such a course if it were almost certain to bring about a collision. It would, however, take her from three to five ship-lengths to recover from the initial turn and enter into a turn in the opposite direction, so in this case we will assume that the right-angled course will continue for at least five ship-lengths.

Conditions are approximately similar in a parallel meeting situation. The distances between the lines demarcating the "collision zones" are practically identical. The difference is that due to the greatly increased relative speed of approach in a meeting situation the "collision zone" for this situation will begin and terminate further ahead.

The cross-hatched area of the "collision zone" extends out furthest the greater the relative speed of approach, whether overtaking or meeting. Balanced against that consideration, however, is the reduction in exposure time, or length of time it takes the other vessel to transit the "collision zone". In the case of meeting vessels this length of time will be relatively short — less than a minute in almost any event. In an overtaking situation, however, the "exposure time" can be the major consideration. The smaller the difference in speed between the vessels the greater the need to achieve a "comfortable" passing distance.

The configuration of the diagram would not be affected to any significant degree by a change in the dimensions of vessel A. If the length of A was smaller, the trailing edge of the collision zone in the diagrams would be advanced by a slightly lesser distance than the difference in length, and be retarded by a comparable amount if the length was greater. The extent of the collision zone would, however, be lengthened due to the increase in tactical diameter of a larger vessel and shortened with a smaller vessel.

It should be clearly understood that the data obtained from the diagrams is only as valid as the assumptions on which it is based. In so far as actual conditions deviate from the predicted assumptions so will the predictions. Nor can it be too strongly stressed that a passing distance outside the limits of the cross-hatched area of the collision zones (assuming the assumptions fit) does not necessarily render a vessel safe. Beyond these distances there is more room and time for manoeuvre, but the possibility of a collision developing is no less likely.

It may not, however, be practical in some cases to achieve the minimum passing distances defined by the cross-hatched areas. The traffic-separation schemes in many straits may make it awkward (the scheme in the Strait of Gubal is one such) if not impossible to attain such a clearance. Under such circumstances one should consider delaying passing until a more advantageous position is reached. This is particularly true if the passing distance is near the cross-hatched area, wherein any mistake or mishap would allow no margin for recovery.

If one is being overtaken in such circumstances the only safe alternative may be a marked

38

reduction in speed in order to minimise the exposure time as well as the effects of interaction.[7] Unfortunately it not infrequently happens in such cases that other overtaking ships may be coming up astern and complicate matters. The most practical, and indeed almost imperative, prelude to such a manoeuvre is communication by VHF radio with the vessel or vessels astern, initiated perhaps by a visual signal on the Aldis lamp. Where direct voice communication can be established in an overtaking situation it can be more safely undertaken, if necessary, at a lesser distance than might otherwise be advisable. In such case one would not need to rely upon visual detection of a major course deviation by an approaching vessel since that vessel could, and indeed would be obligated to, advise of any deviation no later than the time of its execution.

It would seem no more than prudent that any ship overtaking another within a distance of, say, one mile should attempt to establish voice contact by VHF radio. There is, of course, the problem of attracting the attention of the overtaken vessel, but if the overtaking will be so close as to indicate such a precaution it will perhaps also be close enough to read that vessel's name on its stern or, alternatively and by night, a whistle signal could achieve that purpose.

The chief value of the diagrams is that they give a clear indication of those areas wherein another vessel must only be admitted under the strictest scrutiny, and if practicable denied access. It is a much more precise ship domain as compared with the observed ship domains developed and defined by Goodwin. It could in a sense form a basis for a definition of the elusive term "close quarters" in that it can show within fairly close limits the minimum distance of approach within which one can still avoid collision by one's own action regardless of the action of the other.

As already noted, from a practical operating standpoint the "minimum safe passing distances", deduced from such information as given by the diagrams, can often not be achieved. On the high seas where plenty of sea room is available the aforesaid "minimum safe passing distances" should be adhered to as a matter of course. Indeed, the minimum distances suggested may well seem scanty to many experienced seamen.

The distances will of course *be* scanty if their limitations are not strictly observed. Perhaps the most common fault of seamen whose navigational deportment may be flawless in every other respoect is to tend to neglect if not ignore a passing vessel once he has determined that it will pass clear *if conditions do not alter*. This is possibly one of the most frequent causes of collision and it is commonly known as "failure to keep a proper lookout".

Our object here has not been to attempt to define precise limits for "minimum safe passing distances". What has been attempted is to show with a fair degree of accuracy those areas within which the danger of collision would be certain should either vessel make a major course alteration. With that information available a mariner can then make a more realistic assessment of what he deems to be a minimum safe passing distance for his vessel.

* * * * * * * *

Notes

1 Curtis, R. G., "The probability of close overtaking in fog." *Journal*, The Royal Institute of Navigation, 1980, September.
2 Curtis, R. G., "Determination of mariner's reaction times." *Ibid.*, 1978, September: "Analysis of the dangers of ship's overtaking," *Mathematical Aspects of Marine Traffic*, Academic Press, 1979.
3 *Journal, ibid.*, p. 408.
4 Cockcroft, A. N. and Lameijer, J., *A Guide to the Collision Avoidance Rules*, p. 139.
5 *The Law of Collisions at Sea*. In both Marsden and Farwell the term is not used in the text. Its only appearance is where the Rules themselves are reproduced, wherein it appears. Since Griffin died in 1948 the omission there is more understandably since it would seem that "close quarters" is a radar related term. The term was apparently coined by Wylie where it was used in an article by him, "Radar and the Rule of the Road at Sea," in the *Journal* of the Royal Institute of Navigation in 1950. I am indebted to Michael Richey for this information. Also

cf. Capt. H. Topley, "Radar and Moderate Speed," *Journal of the Honourable Company of Master Mariners*, July 1964, pp. 78–88; and Kapitan Walter Helmers, "The Close Quarters Situation," *Ibid.*, October 1964, pp. 166–74; IMCO Sub-Committee on Safety of Navigation, 24 Dec. 1981, Note by the Government of the German Democratic Republic, "Matters Related to the Collision Regulations Definition of the Term 'Close-Quarters Situation'".
6 *Op. cit.*, p. 66.
7 *Ibid.*, p. 79.

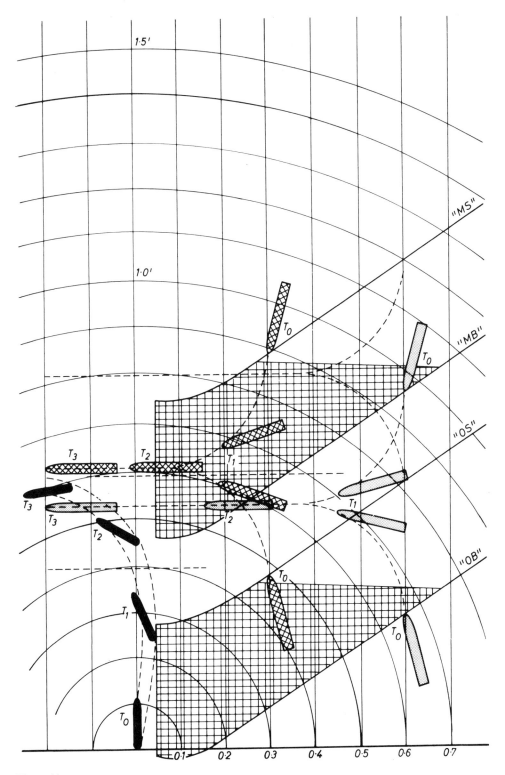

Figure 11

41

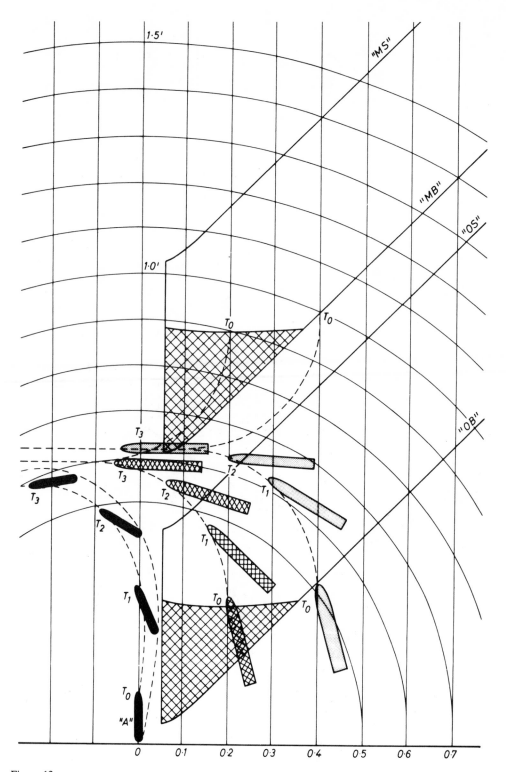

Figure 12

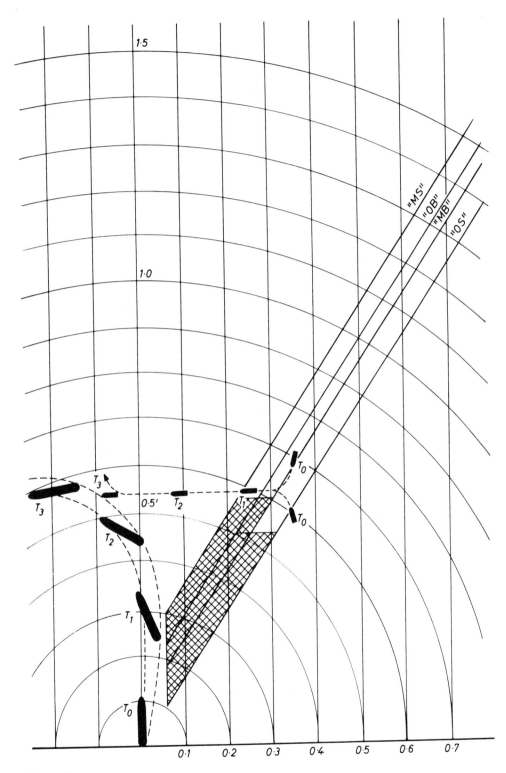

Figure 13

Chapter Six

Starboard Bow Reciprocal Meeting

Of all encounters perhaps the most worrisome is that where the mariner finds another vessel approaching fine on the starboard bow on a reciprocal course. Here again a border line case can lead to disaster if one vessel interprets the Rules as applicable and the other does not. Such was the case when two very nearly identical diesel powered super-tankers, the Brazilian *Horta Barbosa* and the South Korean *Sea Star** met in the Gulf of Oman north of Ras al Hadd as the mid-watch neared its end on the night of December 19, 1972.

The visibility was excellent at the time with a light north-easterly wind and no current of sufficient strength to have had any material effect. The *Sea Star* had loaded a full cargo of crude in the Persion Gulf and was outbound on a course of 142° with a speed through the water of close to 16 knots. The 2nd mate was on watch assisted by a cadet† and two seamen one on the wheel and the other on lookout. It was the practice in such a situation to fix the vessel's position at half-hourly intervals, which the 2nd officer did at 0330 using a radar bearing and distance off a point of land. As he did so he noticed an echo on the radar screen about 14 miles off, slightly on the starboard bow. He looked with the binoculars and saw *Horta Barbosa* with her masthead lights in line or almost so and he altered course to 145° which placed the oncoming vessel about two to three degrees on the port bow.[1]

Horta Barbosa was in ballast out of Rio de Janeiro to Khor al Amaya in the Gulf. She also has a sea speed of 16 knots and was on a course of 322°. The 2nd officer also had the watch on the Brazilian ship, and with him was a cadet and a seaman who acted as lookout. The vessel was in automatic steering. He too saw the other vessel at about 0330 at a range of 16 miles bearing 10° on the starboard bow, or so he claimed. When the distance had closed to 8 miles he saw her masthead lights open to the right with the bearing about the same. No plotting was done but he estimated the CPA to be between three quarters to a mile.

At around 0345 both the cadet and the lookout left the bridge to call their reliefs leaving the 2nd mate alone on the bridge. He now saw the green sidelight of *Sea Star* some 3 to 4 miles off on a bearing he estimated to be about 30° on the bow but must have been only a third of that. Satisfied that she would pass safely down his starboard side about a mile off he went into the chart room where the radar was located to obtain a fix for 0400 in preparation for handing over the watch. The lookout had meanwhile returned to the bridge though the cadet had not. He remained below to have a cup of coffee in the galley before giving his relief another call before returning to the bridge a minute or two before 0400.

---

* *Sea Star* was 63,988 gross tons and 893′ in length while *Horta Barbosa* was 62,619 gross tons and 891′ long.

† The cadet was the sole survivor of those on the bridge of the *Sea Star* and his testimony constituted the sole evidence of events as seen from that vessel.

When the lookout returned shortly before the cadet he claimed that he found *Sea Star* still showing her lights open to the right, but when she had closed to 2 miles, which would have been about four minutes before the collision if his account is accurate, he saw her masthead lights close and her red sidelight come into view. On seeing that he went into the wheelhouse to report this to the 2nd mate but found no one there, and then he heard the shouting of the cadet.

When the cadet returned to the bridge he passed through the chart room where he found the 2nd mate working on the chart. He paused momentarily for a look before entering the wheelhouse where he saw to his horror the red sidelight of *Sea Star* and her forward masthead light almost dead ahead. She was obviously trying to cross from starboard to port and was just as obviously not going to make it. He ran back to the chart room shouting and gesticulating wildly. The 2nd mate rushed into the wheelhouse and saw the ship attempting to cross his bow. He immediately rang full astern on the engine order telegraph and told the lookout to take the wheel and switch from automatic to manual steering. No sooner had that been done then *Horta Barbosa* struck *Sea Star* almost at right angles just forward of her bridge. She exploded in a sheet of flame and the fire that finally left her a gutted wreck took the lives of eleven of her crew including all who had been on the bridge except the cadet.

What transpired on *Sea Star* is even less clear since the account is based entirely on the testimony of the cadet. Some time after *Horta Barbosa* was first sighted the 2nd officer instructed the cadet to write up the deck log. Probably about nine or ten minutes before four the chief officer passed through the chart room on his way to the wheelhouse to relieve the 2nd mate. What happened during the next few minutes is unknown since all who were witnesses perished in the fire. *Sea Star*, however, was on a course of 145° when the cadet went into the chart room.[2] When he came out somewhere around three to four minutes before the collision the ship was on a course of 160°. At very close to three minutes before the collision the 2nd mate told him to check the distance off *Horta Barbosa* by radar. The cadet switched down to a shorter range to do so and found the distance to be between 1.3 and 1.4 miles. He claimed that when he re-entered the wheelhouse the other ship was about 25° on the port bow showing a green light, but the bearing must have been much less. At the time he measured the distance she must have been no more than 3 to 4 degrees on the bow, and at that time the 2nd mate told the helmsman "starboard more" followed shortly thereafter by "hard a starboard". He blew one blast on the whistle at that time and then just before the collision ordered "hard to port".

We can only conjecture as to what caused the 2nd mate to act as he did. His change of course to 3° to the right on first discovering *Horta Barbosa* is an almost certain indication that he expected to pass port to port, and it would seem that he assumed that this action would succeed until the chief mate's arrival on the bridge.

The mate most probably felt some alarm at the situation facing him and perhaps voiced a certain disbelief when the 2nd mate informed him that he expected to pass the other vessel on his port hand on the course he was holding. He may have done more than voice mere disbelief but whatever transpired in those final few minutes the 2nd mate was inspired or provoked into a course of action that was not only disastrous but fatal. Perhaps his pride was wounded in the exchange and to keep from granting full acknowledgment to the mate's assessment of the seriousness of the situation he responded by only ordering an alteration of 15° more to the right. But by now it was too late to dally, and it immediately became apparent that this first effort would not succeed leading him to complete his folly by ordering full right rudder.

With the fault of each so gross the division of blame may have occasioned a certain perplexity, but *Sea Star* was judged to be guilty of the grossest violations and so was assigned liability for three-quarters of the damages. The best that can be said of the 2nd mate of *Sea Star* for his attempt to cross ahead of *Horta Barbosa* at such a late stage was that he was foolhardy. Having embarked on such a course, however, not to signal that venture until it was too late warrants even harsher condemnation.

The Court then took the 2nd mate of the Brazilian ship to task. He was guilty of a most flagrant neglect of duty for spending six to seven minutes in the chart room plotting a fix just as the other vessel was coming into a position where any deviation by her would be most dangerous.

As has been pointed out in Chapter Five the assumption that an approaching vessel having been observed to be on a seemingly safe course will maintain that course is a very common but hazardous supposition.

The Court somewhat surprisingly took no note of the failure of either vessel to try to ascertain the CPA of the other ship by plotting, or at the very least to keep a visual check of the bearing of the approaching ship. They were both lax in that respect, but both vessels demonstrated a lamentable degree of laxness in their attitude in general. The failure of both ships to try to determine how close they would pass especially in a green-to-green approach is one indication. The neglect of the chief officer of *Sea Star* to study the chart before relieving the watch is another. But it was the evidence from *Horta Barbosa* that came in for most of the criticism. There seemed to be an irresponsible attitude and understanding of the importance of keeping a lookout on that vessel. To allow both the cadet and the lookout to leave the bridge at the same time with a vessel nearing on the starboard bow just as the 2nd mate planned to spend some time in the chart room was unforgivable. But as Mr. Justice Brandon remarked, "he seemed, even by the date of the hearing, to see little wrong in retrospect with his having done so."[3] Failure to put the vessel in hand steering at the prospect of a close approach was a further fault.

As already remarked, when two vessels are approaching one another in a situation such as we have here there is always the danger that one will not see the situation as the other does. If one feels that it is an acceptable starboard to starboard passage but the other regards it as a nearly reciprocal meeting that requires an alteration to starboard a very dangerous situation may develop as did here. Now the governing Rule (14) states: "(a) When two power-driven vessels are meeting on reciprocal or nearly reciprocal courses so as to involve risk of collision each shall alter course to starboard so that each shall pass on the port side of each other." And, "(b) Such a situation shall be deemed to exist when a vessel sees the other ahead or nearly ahead and by night she could see the masthead lights of the other in a line or nearly in a line and/or both sidelights and by day she observes the corresponding aspect of the other vessel." Cockcroft and Lamiejer state: "Rule 14 is apparently not intended to apply to cases in which, from a vessel which is ahead or nearly ahead, one sidelight can be seen but the other is obscured."[4]

To preclude the existence of a theoretical "dark lane" wherein the sidelights of a vessel (particularly one of great breadth) could not be seen from dead ahead the Rules provide that these lights shall be so screened: "that the rays of light from the outer part of the filament . . . may cross the fore and after line and be visible to a vessel approaching from an angle of up to 3° on the opposite bow."[5]

Now sidelights are often seen at distances considerably in excess of the 3 miles prescribed by the Rules, but one should not count on seeing them beyond that distance and at 3 miles a vessel approaching another on a reciprocal course from 3° on the bow would pass between one and two-tenths of a mile off abeam, clearly an unacceptable distance by any standard if sea room is available.[6] Yet under the Rule a starboard-to-starboard passage seems to be allowable at that distance.

There are obviously only two ways out of this dilemma; either an alteration of course to starboard or to port. In the instance just referred to the masthead lights of the approaching ship would be showing not more than 2° on the bow until the distance had closed to less than 5 miles (see Diagram A).

They would normally show at a distance substantially beyond the 6 miles required by law, and 8 to 9 miles in clear weather is probably a reasonable average while distances appreciably in excess of 10 miles are not unusual.

The first consideration is to determine by careful observation of the bearing of the other vessel or radar plot whether her course is sufficiently close to a reciprocal of own course to allow her to pass starboard-to-starboard. If the bearing remains steady or closes very slightly to the left the situation of course calls for an alteration of course to starboard. But if a close green-to-green passage is indicated there is a legitimate option.

There is a strong and well-founded prejudice among many seamen with a proper understanding of the Rules, reinforced by innumerable court decisions, against any alteration of course to port for the purpose of avoiding traffic under normal circumstances. Once the Rules *begin* to govern that stance becomes almost unassailable in meeting and crossing situations, but to rule out alterations to port in circumstances such as we are considering here is to unrealistically restrict one's practical manoeuvring possibilities. Having taken that possibly controversial position it should quickly be qualified by saying that such alterations should almost without exception be taken early on and at a point before the rules would begin to apply if it were a meeting or fine-crossing situation.[7] The alteration should also be sufficient to be clearly recognised as such with a minimum of perhaps 10°. With vessels of equal speed that would increase the CPA by 0.3 of a mile if executed at 4 miles and by 0.45 miles if done at six. The separation would of course be proportionately less if the other vessel is faster and greater if it is slower.

As the diagram shows quite clearly vessels on reciprocal courses can pass much closer than prudence and good seamanship would dictate without being specifically required by the Rules to manoeuvre. As already noted when two ships are meeting on reciprocal courses so that each sees only a single sidelight the rule governing head-on meetings (14) does not apply. There is hence no obligation to alter course to starboard to pass port-to-port, yet to continue on where the lateral separation when abeam may be less than 0.2 of a mile, as it could be where the sidelights are not seen before 3 miles, would clearly be unseamanlike. The inescapable conclusion is that an alteration to port to achieve a safe distance must not only be permissible but required by good seamanship, unless of course one opts for a red-to-red passing.

As Cockcroft and Lameijer, however, have remarked, "Whether power-driven vessels are meeting on reciprocal courses or crossing at a fine angle it is important that neither vessel should alter course to port. If it is thought necessary to increase the distance of passing starboard to starboard this implies that there is risk of collision."[8] There would seem to be some conflict here but Cockcroft and Lameijer are discussing conduct *within* the Rules while the action we are suggesting in this instance is action taken, as emphasised above, before the Rules apply.

In heavily trafficked areas such as the Red Sea where most of the traffic encountered seems to fall under either Rule 13 or 14 (overtaking and head-on) stubborn adherence to red-to-red meetings, where the green-to-green option is permissible, can readily create problems where none existed before. Where one is frequently meeting several vessels as well as being overtaken or overtaking several more one must take advantage of the option, where available, of an alteration to *either* port or starboard simply from the standpoint of practical seamanship.

Lateral separations of a mile in such situations as we have been considering here can almost certainly be regarded as sufficient providing of course that the conning officer watches the transit of the approaching vessel through the "collision zone" (see diagrams in Chapter Five) with undivided attention. Lesser distances down to a minimum of half a mile can be adequate in some cases, but distances below that should be avoided if at all possible.

This should not be construed as approval of passing distances of less than one mile. Where sea room permits one should not ordinarily accept CPAs forward of the beam of less than a mile, but as already noted, in many places and instances heavy traffic and other navigational constraints make it impractical to achieve passing distances that one would otherwise desire. Where one is forced by practical necessity to accept marginal passing distances a correspondingly higher degree of caution and vigilance must be exercised during the passing interval.

Notes

1 *L.L.R.*, 1976, Vol. 1, p. 120. This was the testimony of the cadet. The reconstruction would indicate *Horta Barbosa* was about dead ahead after the course change.

2 *Ibid.*, p. 122.

3 *Ibid.*

4 Cockcroft & Lameijer, *op. cit.*, p. 109.

5 *Ibid.*, pp. 144–45.

6 Cf. diagrams in Chapter Five. Sidelights in the author's recent experience are frequently seen at 7 miles. During a period of several months in the spring of 1982 the distances at which

sidelights could be seen in clear weather was intensively studied. It was found that sidelights of sea-going vessels could commonly be seen at distances of 7–8 miles. It was not unusual to see them at 9–11 miles and in two instances they were seen at 13 miles. They could usually be seen with the unaided eye at 5–6 miles and where ordinarily clearly seen at 4–5 miles.

7 The question of attempting to define the point at which the Rules begin to apply in any particular situation is a complex one. It would first of all be a matter of speed of closing, which would then be translated into distance. A factor should then be allowed for a reasonable amount of time before one would discover an alteration of heading of an approaching vessel, and next a reasonable amount of time for response. A minute and a half for both together should be reasonable, providing the officer concerned is giving his undivided attention to the matter.

In commenting on the action to be taken by the give-way vessel in a crossing situation Marsden says: "Whatever action she takes, it must be seamanlike, timely and substantial, so as to leave the stand-on vessel in no possible doubt as to what she is doing." (P. 566.) The same should hold true for any manoeuvres undertaken by a vessel in a meeting situation.

In his unpublished doctoral thesis, "Factors in the Prevention of Collisions at Sea" J. F. Kemp described the results of experiments conducted on the radar simulator at London Polytechnic into meeting situations such as we are concerned with here and found that the most "natural" response was a turn to port. He had earlier commented that "The current rules state that vessels meeting nearly end-on so as to involve risk of collision should each alter course to starboard but, as indicated by experiments to be described in the next chapter, many mariners faced with the above situation prefer to alter course to port to increase the existing miss distance. They justify this action by suggesting that, since there is not initial risk of collision the Rules do not apply; i.e. they choose quite deliberately and consciously to operate under anarchical conditions in which they may do as they please. The counter to their argument is to suggest that, if there were really no risk of collision there would have been no need to alter course at all; but argument and counter-argument are inconclusive in the absence of a precise definition of the phrase "risk of collision". Suffice it to be said that an alteration of course to port is safe and expeditious in good visibility when action taken by either vessel is immediately obvious to the other; but the same manoeuvre could be dangerous in the absence of a facility for mutual observation or an equivalent exchange of information" (p. 78).

Diagram A (see opposite).
The line labelled 3° ——— is the bearing of own vessel from a vessel approaching on a reciprocal course (the angular cross-over allowed by COLREGS for sidelights) and other vessel's bearing from own vessel. At a range of 6' if both vessels maintained course the CPA would be 0.3'. The line ——— (17°) indicates the c/c needed if the wheel is put over at that range in order to achieve a CPA of 0.5' to port if the spd ratio between vessels is 1:1. The similar line (26°) is c/c needed if spd ratio is 1:1.5, and the line (12.5°) for a spd ratio of 1.5:1. The line to port labelled 4° indicates c/c needed to port to achieve. 0.5' CPA at a 1:1 spd ratio.
The line ——— (19°) indicates c/c needed at 6' to achieve ½' CPA to port if original CPA to starboard. was 0.4' and line ———— (21°) is c/c if original CPA was 0.5' to starboard.

Diagram A (See p. 48)

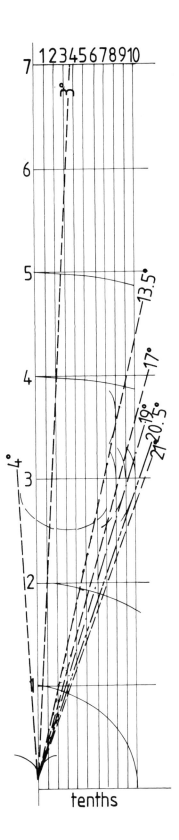

tenths

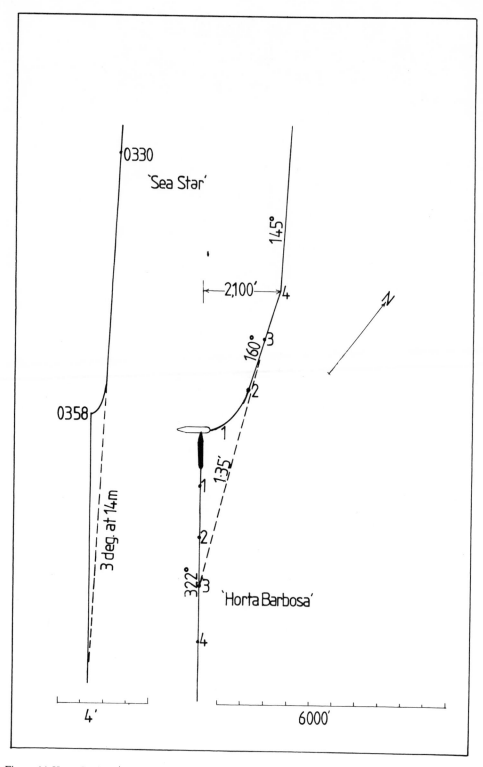

Figure 14 *Horta Barbosa/Sea Star* (See page 45)

50

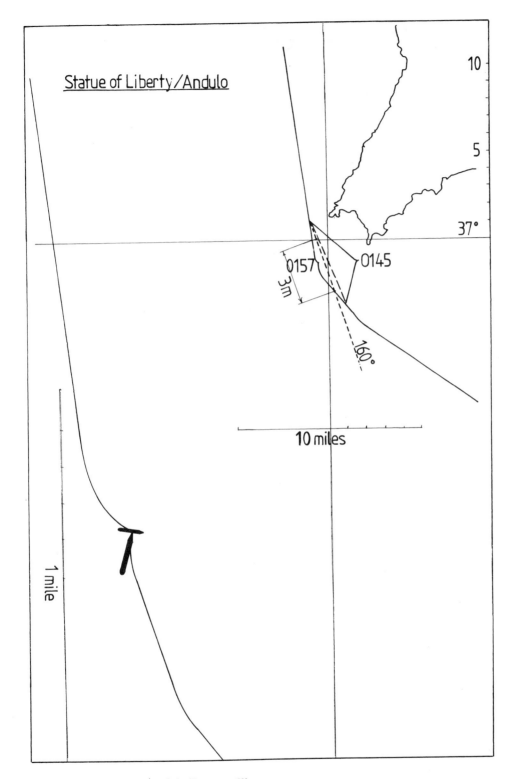

Figure 15 *Statue of Liberty/Andulo* (See page 62)

Chapter Seven

In extremis and Close Quarters

The term *"in extremis"* is a close cousin if not a sister of that somewhat nebulous expression "close quarters", and while every mariner knows that he should avoid falling within their clutches he has no guidelines to tell him what defines their limits. In Chapter Five an attempt was made to arrive at a practical boundary for "close quarters" using a hypothetical vessel of specific characteristics and dimensions, but it would seem questionable that any worthwhile purpose could be served by attempting to do the same for the even more elusive limits of *in extremis*.

If the object of The Collision Avoidance Rules is to prevent the development of a close-quarters situation the concept of *in extremis* can have little practical meaning to the prudent mariner as if he can succeed in staying out of close quarters, he will then never be found *in extremis*. [1a] Nonetheless, while the term may seem very abstract to the average seaman it can take on a harsh reality in an admiralty court, and for that reason alone warrants the mariner's attention.

The related concepts of "close quarters" and *"in extremis"* might be conceptualised in a "target-like" diagram wherein the "bullseye" represents collision, the adjacent circle the area of *in extremis*, the next the domain of special circumstances and close quarters, the next beyond — the zone of applicability of the Rules, and the outer ring the area in which the Rules do not apply. It would differ from the conventional "target", however, in that the lines of demarcation between the concentric rings would not be sharply differentiated but hazy as between the colours of a rainbow.

In such abstract areas hard-and-fast rules are usually best avoided, but certain rules of conduct *in extremis* can be distilled from court decisions that have more than a casual applicability. In the "agony of collision" — that vivid phrase used to describe the reality of *in extremis* — the conduct of the stand-on vessel is understandably granted a degree of tolerance usually denied the give-way ship.

In commenting on the earlier Special Circumstances Rule (27) Marsden remarked that,

> It must always be a matter of difficulty for the officer in charge of the vessel which has kept her course and speed to determine when the time has arrived to take action. If he acts too soon, he may disconcert any action which the other vessel may be about to take to avoid his vessel, and be blamed for so doing, and yet the time may come when he must take action. The precise point when he should cease to keep his course and speed is difficult to determine, and some latitude is allowed him in determining this. When it is shown that he was carefully watching the other vessel and endeavouring to do his best to act at the right moment, he will not be held to blame, though it afterwards appears that he waited too long or acted too soon. . . . [1]

The American authority, the late John W. Griffin, in his book *On Collision*, was adamant that, ". . . if a vessel, without her own fault, is placed in a position of sudden danger, she is not condemned if the action which she takes in the stress of emergency proves to have been erroneous."[2] He cites numerous decisions in support.

Conversely he maintains, "A vessel which is herself to blame for the existence of the emergency cannot use it as an excuse for her own erroneous action. If her antecedent fault [failure to give way in ample time] has caused or contributed to the danger, she cannot invoke the principle of error *in extremis*."[3]

What seems quite clear from numerous court decisions is that once a *give-way* vessel finds herself *in extremis* any course alteration to port is almost certain to be condemned, unless, against all the odds, it is successful. Backing the engines, though often little more than a futile gesture, is the manouevre most likely to go uncensured.

The Rules themselves give little practical guidance as to how to judge when a position of *in extremis* is reached though it would seem that Rule 17(b) "When, from any cause, the vessel required to keep her course and speed finds herself so close that collision cannot be avoided by the action of the give-way vessel alone, she shall take such action as will best aid to avoid collision," prescribes theoretical parameters.

The wording of the Rule is perhaps unfortunate. If one does not have to take action until "collision cannot be avoided by the action of the give-way vessel alone . . . ." then one must also be able to surmise what action the give-way ship will take (so that one can take complementary action), and assume that this action will be taken. That is a very questionable supposition.

Fortunately the Rules now allow an escape from such an unenviable position. Rule 17(a)(ii) allows the stand-on vessel to ". . . take action by her manoeuvre alone, as soon as it become apparent to her that the vessel required to keep out of the way is not taking appropriate action in compliance with these Rules." Although it was not always recognised under the old Rules it was, nonetheless, always permissible to take action at long range before risk of collision materialised. It was permissible precisely because the applicable Steering and Sailing Rule did not apply until there was risk of collision. It was a point, however, that recieved little attention, and many seamen felt that once they sighted a vessel on the port bow crossing from port to starboard they had no option but to trust to fate that the other vessel would obey the Rules and give way.[4]

Under the new Rule the stand-on vessel can of course still haul off before the distance has closed to the point at which the Rules have taken hold. Cockcroft and Lameijer have suggested that this distance might be as much as 8 miles (where the speed of closing is rapid) or as little as perhaps 5 miles where the relative speed of approach is more modest. This stage where the stand-on vessel is obliged to maintain course and speed would then hold down to a maximum of around 3 miles and a minimum of about 2 miles depending again on the speed of closing.[5] At that point she is again permitted to take action to avoid the development of close quarters, and that should almost always be a radical alteration to starboard. The most effective action in most cases would be to put the helm over smartly until the other vessel is on the port beam and then not let her get forward of the beam until it is safe to resume course.

Should a mariner be so foolish as to venture into *in extremis* he then *must* take action. A turn to starboard under such conditions may then not be the safest course with a vessel approaching from close aboard at an oblique angle from the port bow. If a collision appears to be unavoidable a turn to port may be the best manoeuvre under the circumstances. A turn to starboard would not only place one broadside to an oncoming vessel thus putting a much larger obstacle in her path, but would be more likely to result in damage fatal to both vessel and crew.

The vessel approaching from the port bow should put her helm to starboard. In such case both vessels will present their narrowest aspect thereby increasing the possibility of escape or sideswiping the other, or at the worst a blow taken on or close to the bow and hence less likely to be fatal.

During this period when the stand-on vessel is obligated to hold course and speed there are several measures that can be taken to help ascertain if the burdened ship intends to give way. While the vessels are still separated by a distance of at least 5 miles or so an attempt to establish contact by VHF can be made, and if the other ship fails to respond that can be taken as an initial indication that she will perhaps not respect her obligation.* If at night that can be supplemented by directing a serious of quick flashes on the Aldis lamp towards the give-way vessel. If, on repetition of this signal and a further attempt to establish VHF contact after the distance has closed another mile or so, the give-way ship does not respond this would suggest that she is not going to give way in a timely manner and the stand-on vessel should then (assuming no other vessel, hazard or condition exists to interfere) take action as indicated above to prevent the development of close quarters.

From a realistic standpoint one may wonder why, if the Rule allows the stand-on vessel an option of altering course once it seems apparent the give-way vessel is reluctant to heed its obligation, there can be any practical necessity to stand-on any further as long as one turns away from the oncoming ship. In rephrasing this Rule the rule makers were faced with a dilemma. The old Rule was obviously unsatisfactory since compliance with it could lead the "privileged" vessel into close quarters if the "burdened" vessel did not abide by her obligation to give-way. Yet the distinction between "burdened" and "privileged" could not be cast aside since that would lead to confusion about which vessel should give-way and when. So the distinction had to be maintained. In effect the intent of the Rule seems to be thus: In a crossing situation where risk of collision is present the vessel on the port hand shall give way, but if that vessel does not do so in a timely manner so that a close quarters situation threatens to develop unless one of the vessels acts, then the starboard hand vessel can take such action as to best forestall the development of close quarters, and that action will normally be a substantial alteration to starboard.

If the object of the Rules is not simply the prevention of collision but the forestalling of the close quarters that is their necessary prelude then no artificial constraints should be placed upon the working of these Rules that might impede that objective. In two cases, viz., overtaking and crossing we have a situation where some temporary constraint has been deemed necessary to prevent the so-called "privileged" vessel from taking action that might frustrate the avoiding action of the "burdened" one. In the latter case it was finally recognised that the Rule as it then stood occasionally led a conscientious seaman into the close quarters the Rules are supposed to prevent, and that led to its amendment.

In the case of an overtaken vessel the situation is somewhat different since the overtaking can be done on either side. It is hence necessary that once the stand-on vessel has been overtaken by the give-way ship that she hold her course and speed once the overtaking vessel has "come up" with her. That phrase is a troublesome one, as we shall see in Chapter Eleven. From a practical standpoint it would seem that an overtaking ship has "come up" with the vessel she is overtaking once she has reached a position where she is committed to passing on a particular side. At that point the overtaken vessel must hold her course and speed until the other vessel has reached a position ahead from where she can manoeuvre without embarrassment to the overtaken ship. The overtaken vessel, however, need not blindly and irrevocably hold her course and speed simply because she is in the process of being overtaken. She must do so only to the extent that a course or speed change might interfere with the overtaking vessel passing safely.

If she is being overtaken on the starboard side she must not alter course to starboard until the other vessel is past and clear, but there is nothing to prevent her from altering to port in order to increase the passing distance. She also must hold her speed if the overtaking vessel is coming up on an oblique course so as to pass astern of the overtaken ship, but if she is being overtaken in the ordinary manner on a parallel or nearly parallel course she is not prevented from reducing speed,[6] and indeed good seamanship would oblige her to do so if she is about to be overtaken in a narrow channel. It would also be advisable to slow if she is being overtaken by a vessel of very nearly equal speed as the period of running alongside one another would otherwise be prolonged. If in the process of being overtaken she is nearing a point at which the progress of

---

* There is of course the possibility that the conning officer speaks no English or does not have his VHF set on, but that does not invalidate the general proposition that failure to respond to such a transmission can be taken as some evidence of lack of alertness on the part of that vessel.

her voyage requires a course change in the direction in which she is being overtaken a reduction in speed is her only practical option.

In interpreting or applying the Rules there is one infallible principle that should always govern: is the action or manoeuvre one intends to follow or execute likely to increase or decrease the risk of collision? If the answer is the latter then that action must be allowable within the Rules since it is in obvious accord with the principles of good seamanship, and the practice of good seamanship can never be in conflict with the Rules. Ordinarily the practice of the Rules will be simple and straightforward but where ambiguity begins to creep in, as we will witness in a number of cases investigated here, then the situation should be considered with the above principle in mind.

But before leaving this subject we should finally consider the proper conduct of the give-way vessel. The problems and difficulties we have been studying arise out of the failure of the "burdened" ship to respect her obligation, so we would be remiss if we left the topic without some comment and observation on the manner and means whereby this obligation is met.

The first thing we will consider is the prickly question of crossing ahead. Rule 15 governing "Crossing Situations" provides that where there is risk of collision "the vessel which has the other on her own starboard side shall . . . if the circumstances of the case admit, avoid crossing ahead of the other vessel." The problem of course is deciding where risk of collision begins and ends. Risk of collision will normally be greater the narrower the angle of crossing and the slower the speed of the give-way vessel.* A faster ship crossing at a right-angle might safely pass a mile ahead, but a slower ship crossing at a narrow angle might be ill-advised to attempt to pass ahead at the same distance.

This is one of the most dangerous situations in which a mariner can find himself: a fine angled crossing situation with another vessel on the port bow. If in addition the stand-on ship is a VLCC that may range ahead for close to half a mile once the wheel is put over the situation can become very hazardous if the inner limits for positive action for the stand-on vessel suggested above are ahered to. If to all this the vessel in the give-way position will pass narrowly ahead, say a quarter of a mile, if she maintains course, we have a recipe for disaster.

Should the give-way vessel be tempted to pass ahead, but, feeling some apprehension about passing so close, decides contrary to the dictates of the Rules and the canons of good seamanship, to make a slight adjustment to port to increase her margin of clearance at about the same time the "privileged" VLCC decides to haul what she thinks a substantial though—due to the "burdened" vessel's adjustment to port—inadequate amount to starboard a collision may be very difficult to avoid.

In a case such as this once one has let slip the opportunity to manoeuvre so as to forestall close quarters before the Rules have taken hold, and stands down to the inner limit wherein action is again allowed (as defined above) the only safe option is to bring the oncoming vessel abeam to port as quickly as possible and keep her there until safely across her bows. Nor in such a situation should one be bothered about niceties of interpretation as to whether one has held on to that point where one is no longer obliged to stand on.

In a position such as this where the give-way vessel will only narrowly pass ahead if she stands on there may also be a temptation for the stand-on ship to alter to port if it appears that the other vessel may try to cross ahead. If the stand-on vessel does adopt such a dubious course then she should make certain that she does so before she becomes a stand-on ship within the Rules, and the course change should be sufficient to show the vessel which was approaching from port a broad green light so there can be no mistake of intention.

What is almost certain is that where two vessels are crossing on such courses the stand-on ship will become anxious at a fairly early stage if the give-way vessel has made no move to resolve the potential development of close quarters. In such a case it is foolhardy of the "burdened" ship not to give way in good time otherwise she may discover that when she makes her belated

---

* When the angle becomes very narrow the vessels are of course no longer crossing but meeting.

move she may by her dilatoriness have frightened the stand-on vessel into a manoeuvre that conflicts with her own. She should thus not only give way at an early stage but should alter sufficiently to starboard so that the stand-on vessel is now seeing her port sidelight.

The stricture against turning to port to evade an oncoming vessel is part of the tradition of good seamanship perpetuated in the Rules and particularly by those who judge their infractions. Though the courts have on rare occasions overlooked a port turn executed *in extremis* in restricted visibility they are almost unanimous in their opinion that where the other vessel can be seen a turn to port will outweigh almost every other fault. As we see in so many cases here a port turn is almost inevitably condemned in the harshest terms.

Practical seamen know, however, that things are not that simple. Where there are only two vessels involved a turn to starboard will almost always, when executed in good time, achieve the result the Rules intend. But where more than two ships are involved or a proximate hazard to navigation interferes, a refusal to consider a turn to port as an option may subject a vessel to almost insuperable difficulties (see Chapter Nine). In many such cases a substantial reduction in speed may resolve the situation, but the effectiveness of a speed reduction is hampered by its imprecision. That is of no real moment if the objective is to let another vessel or vessels draw ahead, but in multiple traffic situations, a reduction in way to avoid one vessel may create a traffic problem with another that did not exist before. And that may not be readily determinable until after the reduction. In such a case a turn to port may be the only practical alternative, (cf. Chapter Nine, p. 70) but because this manoeuvre is so decisively condemned wherever it has been attempted and collision resulted many mariners will consider it only with the greatest reluctance, and adopt it only as a last resort. That attitude and approach is apt to make the manoeuvre a very chancy one indeed as the natural reluctance may tend to delay the response to the point where a port turn is no longer a safe option. We are not suggesting that port turns be adopted casually as part of one's normal "manoeuvring repertoire", but there are certain circumstances in which a port turn may be a legitimate option.

If one is to turn to port as an evasive measure then it should only be done "legally". There is of course no restriction against a turn to port when overtaking another ship, but where vessels are on crossing or meeting courses, though the Rules do not expressly forbid, they clearly and decidedly discourage, any port turn. When one becomes enmeshed in special circumstances, however, no manoeuvre is forbidden, but no prudent mariner will allow himself to become trapped in special circumstances if he can prevent it.

The clear and simple answer to this problem is if one is to "legally" have recourse to a turn to port as a means of avoiding close quarters then one should execute that manoeuvre before the Rules apply. Some may reply that it may not be apparent early in the development of a traffic situation that it will present any unusual difficulty. That it may not be *readily* apparent can be no excuse.

In every encounter the conning officer should try to visualise how it will develop. Radar plotting is the obvious answer in most cases, and recourse to that technique is an absolute must in clear weather traffic situations if the difficulties we are examining here are to be avoided. It is the great advantage of ARPAs that they can predict or forecast those situations that may require other than a straightforward response. It can also be done by manual plotting, but that requires more skill and close attention than many conning officers are willing or able to offer. But unless one does avail himself of these predictive devices or techniques one may find himself faced with the development of an imminent close quarters situation that cannot be readily solved by a simple and direct recourse to the Rules. By the time it becomes apparent it may be too late for the early action suggested above that could have easily resolved the matter.

One of the guiding principles of the Collision Avoidance Regulations is to so prescribe the conduct of vessels in encounters that the action of one can be successfully predicted by the other. This concept of predictability is so central to the successful operation of the Rules that any suggestion of allowing exceptions encounters an almost instinctive rejection on the part of those who judge and preside over the casualties that stem from their infraction.

So entrenched is this attitude that one of the major objections to the use of VHF radio for the purpose of reaching agreement between ships in traffic situations is that they might come to an agreement contrary to the Rules. That might be a valid objection if vessels willy-nilly cast the Rules aside in reaching agreements, but no thinking mariner is likely to casually relinquish his privilege to hold course and speed unless it is to his advantage. Similarly, in those cases where an element of ambiguity is present as to whether the Rules apply, or whether this or that rule applies, the use of VHF in such a context can be of indisputable value — as we can see from a number of cases investigated here.

No mariner in his right mind would willingly proceed into a position of *in extremis*, and in many cases it is only when the Rules become ambiguous of application or are misconstrued that vessels find themselves in this unenviable and dangerous posture. One way the development of such situations can be avoided is if the vessels concerned are able to communicate in an effective manner. Admittedly there are difficulties attending the use of VHF in such a context and the interchange of information by means of a visual display would probably be preferable in most cases. But the development let alone the acquisition of such equipment by the average merchant vessel awaits the future while VHF is at hand and increasing in use — or misuse. The exploitation of the potential of this device can provide the means whereby the haphazard development of *in extremis* situations can be minimised and avoided, and where circumstances preclude such avoidance the timely establishment of communication between the vessels involved can allow the complementarity of action within *in extremis* that is required if collision is to be avoided.

*   *   *   *   *   *   *

Notes

1a While the prudent mariner will normally avoid close quarters and thereby *in extremis* situations, he cannot prevent exposure when venturing into narrow channels and waterways. Such "normal" exposure is not what we are concerned with here.

1 Page 564.

2 Page 529.

3 Page 534.

4 See "The Burden of Being Privileged", R. A. Cahill, U.S. Naval Institute *Proceedings*, Jan. 1965.

5 Pages 110–16.

6 See note 7.

7 Page 466. Also compare P. Aranow *et al*, "Rules of the Road training investigation" CAORF 1977, page 8 where they state that the best legal advice given at the 1972 Conference was "that courts would interpret the provision of Rule 17(a)(ii) at about $2\frac{1}{2}$ miles to 5 miles depending upon the circumstances, size and speed of the vessel." (P. Aranow, Dr. T. J. Hammell, M. Pollack, DoT U.S.C.G. Office of Research and Development CAORF.)

Chapter Eight

Crossing/Meeting

Where vessels are crossing in such a position that the range lights are distinctly open and one sidelight clearly visible there should be no room for misinterpretation of the Rules and there should be no confusion and hence no collision, yet this is one of the most common types of collision. The causes are several, but probably the predominant one is the higher speed of approach, viz., the greater the relative speed of closing the less time for correct assessment of the hazard and the more likelihood of mistake.

In the cases we will examine here the difference between the original courses on first sighting was from about one to three points. In all these cases the vessel having the other on her starboard hand could easily have resolved the situation by a simple alteration to starboard so showing a red light where she had shown a green. Such a measure would ordinarily be taken when the vessels are still separated by at least several miles and preferably more. To delay action beyond that point can create uncertainty in the mind of the conning-officer of the stand-on vessel, and may cause him to behave in an unpredictable manner. Avoidance of uncertainty is the basis of the Rules so any action, or inaction, that may introduce uncertainty into a situation is almost sure to be found blameworthy if brought to the attention of a court.

* * * * * * *

A case that illustrates this vividly is the collision that took place between the American naval aircraft carrier U.S.S. *Saratoga* and the German motor vessel *Bernd Leonhardt** just south of the Virginia Capes on the night of May 25, 1960. The case was unusual in that the carrier, which was the stand-on ship, was the one that so thoroughly confused the give-way vessel that a collision occurred that should by any reasonable standard have been easily avoided.[1]

Saratoga had left the naval base at Norfolk, Virginia, that afternoon for manoeuvres off Mayport, Florida. After clearing the Virginia Capes a course of 174° was set to take her well clear of the shoals off Hatteras. She was cruising at a speed of 26 knots on a clear, calm night with ample sea room and nothing to impede her navigation other than vessels she might encounter on her way. At about half-past eleven three ships were picked up on her radar. One of them was *Bernd Leonhardt*.

At the time the German vessel was not yet in sight and was slightly on the port bow of the carrier. Had *Saratoga* kept her course *Bernd Leonhardt*, which was steering a course of 330° on her way to Baltimore from Trinidad with a cargo of bauxite, would have crossed her bow with almost a mile to spare. Unfortunately a vessel to the south of the German ship was in a meeting situation with *Saratoga* causing her to alter 16° to starboard at 2348 in order to pass port-to-port.

The German freighter and the American naval vessel were a little over 7 miles apart at that time. Each had the other in sight by now and were rapidly nearing the point where the Steering

---

* *Bernd Leonhardt* was 485′ long and 6,135 gross tons; *Saratoga* was 1,063′ in length and displaced 75,900 tons.

and Sailing Rules should govern the courses they would steer. On the course of 190° that *Saratoga* had taken to pass the vessel she had just met the carrier would have passed ahead of *Bernd Leonhardt* by about the same distance the latter would have cleared ahead of her on the old course.

The 3rd mate of the German ship checked the bearing of *Saratoga* and found it to be closing so he was led to believe that this was a routine crossing situation whereby he would pass astern. Unfortunately he was not using his radar as it was not yet (1960) a common practice to do so in clear weather. The carrier, following a customary routine at that time aboard American naval vessels asked the identity of the German ship by blinker and identified herself, signing off with a "bon voyage."

While that exchange was taking place the Officer of the Deck (OOD) on *Saratoga* decided to return to his base course though he chose later to explain it as a manoeuvre to pass astern of *Bernd Leonhardt*.* Whatever the reason it was a clear violation of the rule that required him to stand on since the vessels were little more than 3 miles apart when he altered left to 170° at 2355.

The watch officer on the German ship, who was attentive to his duties and obligations, had checked the bearing of the naval vessel when he finished signalling and found to his surprise that the bearing was approximately the same as the previous one. As a steady bearing is a clear sign of danger — particularly at such a rapid rate of closing — he ordered the helmsman to come right in order to place the stand-on ship on his port bow. What he did not realise was that the bearing only *appeared* steady, and with the course change to 170° the bearing of *Saratoga* was actually opening to the right.

Bernd Leonhardt had executed her turn to approximately due north at 2358. Unfortunately the OOD conning the carrier seemed determined to pass astern (or so later phrased his intention) of the German ship and altered a further 10° to the left to 160° at the same time *Bernd Leonhardt* hauled right to a northerly heading. It appears that neither conning officer had the other under close observation with binoculars since by this time they should have been able to see clearly not only the range lights but the sidelights of the other, and that would have told them beyond any doubt that the assumptions they had made about the other vessel's behaviour were false.

The curious phraseology of the OOD of the carrier, about wanting to "pass under the stern" of *Bernd Leonhardt*, suggests that he may have been confused as to her approximate heading so that he thought she was on a broad-angled crossing course. But whatever his intentions they had assumed an alarming aspect since no sooner had the carrier swung to a 160° heading than the OOD told the helmsman to keep coming left to 150°. When she reached a heading of about 155° he finally realised that he was headed for a disastrous collision and ordered the helm reversed to hard right.[2]

The 3rd mate of *Bernd Leonhardt* came to the same conclusion at almost the same time and ordered the wheel of his ship put hard to starboard. Luckily there was just time for the vessels to swing enough to avoid a head on collision that would almost certainly have proved fatal for the German ship. As it was *Saratoga* struck *Bernd Leonhardt* a glancing blow with the overhang of her flight deck striking the port side of the deck house of the freighter. It appeared as if a giant steel fist had landed a blow on the midship of the German ship crushing the whole port side at a 45° angle.

The District Court had originally reached the remarkable conclusion that the German vessel was alone to blame. The Appellate court not surprisingly overturned that decision and found both vessels at fault. One of the judges of that Court in fact dissented from the majority decision and laid all the blame on *Saratoga*.[3] The majority, however, agreed with the District Court's findings of fault on the part of *Bernd Leonhardt*, but found at least equal fault with the conduct of the carrier. The failure of the 3rd mate of the German ship to observe the port turns of *Saratoga* led him to misjudge the situation and turn into her path. He could not of course

---

* The distraction of the frivolous blinker exchange may have prevented the German mate from noticing the carrier's course change. The practice is a dangerous one and should be forbidden.

anticipate that she would turn further to port when he altered to a northerly heading at 2358, but if he had observed her closely he could not have failed to notice that she was now showing a green sidelight and had departed from her obligation to hold her course of 190° which if held would have brought her clear across his bow. Furthermore, both vessels failed to signal their turns by blowing the appropriate whistle signals.

Nonetheless, it is hard to escape the conclusion that the major fault lay with *Saratoga*, whose "whimsical" departure from her obligation to hold her course and speed created the circumstances out of which the collision developed. Had the American Court had available to it the more flexible doctrine adopted a decade later in *Reliable Transfer** whereby damages proportionate to the degree of fault were assessed *Saratoga* well might have been assigned a higher portion of the blame.

* * * * * * * *

Early in the morning of the night of June 8, 1965 the motor vessel *Andulo* of Lisbon was approaching Cape St. Vincent on a course of 172° bound for Casablanca. The 3rd officer had the watch with the master at the con. It was a fine moonlit night with excellent visibility and the Portuguese vessel intended to alter course to 161° for her port of destination on coming abeam of the light on Cape St. Vincent a little over a mile off. While still some miles north of that location, however, the range lights of a northbound ship were seen a point or so on the port bow, and the master believing he was in a stand-on position decided to postpone his course change until the approaching vessel was past and clear. Unfortunately no visual or radar bearings were taken of the northbound ship to ascertain whether the bearing was opening, closing, or remaining steady. Had that elementary step been taken it would have been discovered that the other vessel was in fact passing ahead and a course change to the left when abeam Cape St. Vincent would in fact have been quite safe. But the master chose to proceed on assumption rather than ascertain the fact, and that led him into collision.

The northbound vessel was the steam propelled tanker *Statue of Liberty*† registered in Monrovia. She was on a course of 320° and was on a voyage from the Persian Gulf to Rotterdam with a full load of crude. The 2nd officer was alone on the bridge at the time until only moments before the collision, the helmsman having gone aft to call his relief. The master had been earlier on the bridge at which time the ship had been steering a course of 304° which was designed to take the vessel about 3 miles south of Sagres light. When it was found that the ship was to the left of her track the master laid down a new course of 320° to take the vessel 2 miles off Cape St. Vincent from where a course of about 340° would be required. The master then left the bridge to work on charts in the chart room.

About 0145 the 2nd mate relieved the helmsman so he could go aft to call his relief. *Andulo* was 6 miles or more off at the time, and as the 2nd mate took over the duties of the helmsman he apparently abandoned any attempt to keep a lookout, nor did it seem to occur to him that it was necessary to summon the master. The procedure appeared to be part of a well-established routine that only an emergency could break. The remark of Lord Reid, who presided when the case was appealed to the House of Lords, that "It seems to me very probable that the officer on the bridge of the *Statue of Liberty* had never seen *Andulo* at all until that moment" [just before putting the helm hard-a-starboard little more than a minute before collision] indicates the attention devoted to the lookout.[4]

Not long before the seaman returned to take the wheel the 2nd mate altered course to about 340° for a reason that was never adequately explained.[5] What is more certain is that just about the time the helmsman returned to the bridge *Andulo* was seen close ahead and the helm put hard right.

Andulo had meanwhile watched *Statue of Liberty* approach on the port bow and draw slowly

---

* See footnote on p. 12.

† *Andulo* was 450′ long and 5,503 gross tons; *Statue of Liberty* was 707′ in length and 22,610 gross tons. Both vessels were making about 14 knots.

ahead. It appeared to the master of the Portuguese ship that the tanker would pass narrowly ahead if she held course and he held to his — as he was now obliged to do. About three minutes before the collision he noted the course change of *Statue of Liberty* to 340°, but that did not apparently alarm him. With her now showing a narrow green light fine on the starboard bow he made his delayed course change to 161°. At that time, or possibly a moment or so earlier, the 2nd mate on *Statue of Liberty* put her helm hard-a-starboard. The master of *Andulo* watched with horror the rapidly accelerating swing of the northbound vessel to starboard as his own head swung to port and he shouted to the helmsman to put the wheel hard left. It was too late and the bow of the big tanker knifed into the side of the smaller freighter penetrating to two-thirds her breadth. She sank the following day while under tow.

Here was a case where two ships were both approaching a headland where both expected to change course. It was an area that was heavily trafficked, and one which should be approached with more than normal caution since the vessels one would expect to meet could also be expected to change course. *Andulo* indeed had *Statue of Liberty* under observation for a long time before they met. She was using her radar set yet she inexplicably failed to attempt to plot the movement of the other vessel. Had she done so she could have determined by the time she came abeam Cape St. Vincent that *Statue of Liberty* was passing ahead without risk of collision and she could make her course change with safety. But those aboard her ignored that precaution and chose to stand on, so increasing the likelihood of a close quarters situation.

Statue of Liberty made that most common of fatal mistakes and neglected her lookout at the very time its vigilance should have been increased. Here again as we have seen so often in the cases under study a single seaman doubled as both lookout and helmsman. That violation of the spirit of the Rules was then compounded by allowing him to leave the bridge to call his relief at a period when his services were most required. Under such circumstances it was imperative that the watch officer summon the master to assist. He was making a close approach to land where it was incumbent upon him to fix the ship's position at frequent intervals. That meant that he would not be able to give the lookout the strict attention that prudence and good seamanship demanded. Yet he abandoned both of his most important responsibilities to take up the duties of the helmsman. To add to this already considerable catalogue of mistakes he had two radar sets neither of which was in operation.

In his testimony the 2nd mate of *Statue of Liberty* claimed that he was aware of the approach of *Andulo* for some time before the collision and he made the curious statement (as did the OOD of *Saratoga*) that he changed course to 340° "with the object of passing under the stern of the *Andulo*."[6] How he proposed to carry out that manoeuvre from the position he was in at the time he did not attempt to explain. *Statute of Liberty* was also faulted for failing to signal the execution of her course change.

The 2nd mate of *Statue of Liberty* "expressly disclaimed any inhibition against altering to starboard by reason of the nearness of the coast,"[7] but that is a venture that would give many seamen pause and it would have been a highly questionable undertaking with the conning officer alone on the bridge fully occupied with steering the vessel.

One of the reasons for giving a wide berth to shoal water, particularly off a busy headland, is to allow ample room for manoeuvre in case it is needed. One of the advantages of Traffic Separation Schemes is that they are usually so designed as to prohibit through traffic from passing so close to a headland as to inhibit if not foreclose the possibility of a course alteration in that direction in order to keep clear of an oncoming vessel. That is a consideration that could not be overlooked in this case.

It was accepted from the beginning and never challenged that the applicable rule was the old Rule 22: "Every vessel which is directed by these Rules to keep out of the way of another vessel shall, if the circumstances of the case admit, avoid crossing ahead of the other." However, there is the interesting question of whether the Rules were applicable at the time that *Andulo* came abeam of Cape St. Vincent?

The Assessors were asked the question: "If *Andulo* had taken bearings more accurately at an earlier stage and had observed *Statue of Liberty* while she was changing course instead of only seeing that *Statue of Liberty* had changed course from 320° to 340° after that manoeuvre had been completed, would *Andulo* have been in a better position to make a decision whether or not to change her course to port when she did."[8] Their answer to this was no. But had a similar question been asked whether *Andulo* would have been in a better position to judge if it were safe to change course when abeam Cape St. Vincent if she had taken accurate bearings of *Statue of Liberty* prior to that time a credible case for an affirmative answer could be made.

The question here is: was there risk of collision at 0145 when *Andulo* was abeam Cape St. Vincent, and the answer to that must clearly be no. If the answer is no then there was no legal or practical reason why *Andulo* should not make her course change at that time, especially as we can see from the sketch that *Statue of Liberty* would have crossed ahead of *Andulo* by 3 miles in that event.

One must always bear in mind that the objective of the Rules is to prevent the development of close quarters, and common sense is essential in their application. Marsden maintains that an alteration made for greater safety when there is no risk of collision is held not to be a fault, which of course is only common sense.[9] It is clear that *Andulo* was in such a position when abeam Cape St. Vincent. To stand-on and press her privilege so close to land where the give-way vessel would have to turn towards shoal water a bare 2 miles or so away in order to pass clear is certainly a very questionable enterprise. It would be unrealistic to expect the courts to condemn her action but it led to collision and can hardly be classed as an example of good seamanship. The damages were divided 15 per cent for *Andulo* and 85 per cent for *Statue of Liberty*.

*　*　*　*　*　*　*　*

About a year earlier the Panamanian flag steam tanker *Pentelikon* collided with the twin-screw Italian passenger-cargo vessel *Verdi** in the Strait of Gibraltar. *Verdi* was westbound in the Strait on the early hours of April 16, 1964 having taken a course of 242° after passing abeam of Tarifa at 0202. The weather was clear with good visibility with an east–south-easterly wind blowing about 10 to 15 knots. She was making a speed of about 19 knots at the time when she observed two vessels on her starboard bow at 0212 crossing from starboard to port. The farthest was *Pentelikon*, which according to the master of *Verdi* appeared to be broadening. The nearer vessel, which was never identified, was not, however, and was the object of immediate concern. To pass clear of this vessel, course was accordingly altered to 257° to pass under her stern, whereupon the course of 242° was resumed.

This deviation had apparently brought *Verdi* onto a collision course with *Pentelikon*, and her master according to later testimony became concerned about the risk of collision. He seemed to have become immobilised by his concern, however, for he did nothing to dispel it.

Pentelikon was on a course of 090° making about 13 knots through the water against a contrary current and head wind. Her master claimed he also sighted *Verdi* at almost the same time as *Verdi* sighted *Pentelikon* at 0212.† The situation was clearly a crossing one, with the Panamanian vessel in the stand-on role. Perhaps because of her privileged position those on *Pentelikon* felt no need to check the bearing of the Italian ship, but whatever the reason no bearings were taken nor was the radar in use so the progress of *Verdi* could not be plotted.

As the vessels closed the master became aware that *Verdi* was on a collision course or nearly so and though she was kept under close observation he continued to stand-on. As the distance continued to close with the give-way vessel holding her course he began to become concerned and he flashed the International Code signal "U" (You are standing into danger) on his blinker light. When there was no answer or action taken by the burdened ship he repeated the signal and followed that with the danger signal on the ship's whistle, but still there was no action or response from the *Verdi*. In spite of the impending danger *Pentelikon* continued to stand-on in the increasingly vain hope that the Italian vessel would starboard her helm and come under the stern.

---

* *Pentelikon* was 726′ long and 24,502 gross tons; *Verdi* was 528′ long and 13,225 gross tons.

† There was a discrepancy between the times of the vessels. The times used here are *Verdi*'s.

The obvious inaction of the burdened ship caused *Pentelikon*'s master increasing anxiety but did not spur him to any action. Impressed by his duty and privilege to stand-on he held his course until unable to ignore the inevitability of collision he ordered hard right rudder and a double jingle astern. He had delayed too long. *Verdi* had finally reacted and compounded her fault by going hard-a-port. She struck the Panamanian vessel amidships causing extensive damage to both ships.

It would have been futile to deny *Verdi*'s blame in this affair and counsel wisely admitted her fault. She did nothing right but it did not follow from this admission that *Pentelikon* did nothing wrong. Her lookout had earlier left the bridge wing where he was stationed and went below for a cup of coffee, and though this was admittedly a fault it was rightly ruled non-contributory. He could have supplied no information that was not acquired by the master or watch officer so the lack of a lookout did not affect the result.

The Panamanian vessel did not use her radar, and that was seen in a different light. Failure to utilise the radar in such a heavily trafficked place as the Strait of Gibraltar was ruled a fault on the grounds that good seamanship and prudence dictated its use.

Her most serious deriliction, however, was her failure to act once the point of *in extremis* was reached. The Court ruled that "the master of *Pentelikon* should have taken action immediately after he gave the second "U" signal and blew the danger signal, since his vessel was *in extremis* at that time."[10]

This is one of the most vexing decisions with which a master can be faced, and the obvious solution is to stay out of *in extremis* since it is so difficult to judge when one has gotten within it. First of all an action that succeeds will not be criticised because it will not be judged while one that fails will bear the harsh scrutiny of the court. Had *Pentelikon* been using her radar, and once the distance separating the two ships had closed to 1 mile (see sketch) she had put her helm hard to starboard and kept it there until *Verdi* was astern, there would have been no question raised as to whether she acted too soon as there would have been no collision. One cannot, of course, set an arbitrary distance at which to take evading action; each case must be assessed on its "merits", but in taking such action one principle can be enunciated: it should ordinarily be designed to increase the distance between the two vessels, which would normally mean a turn to starboard with full rudder.

* * * * * * * *

Toni was a motor ship belonging to the port of Mogadishu in Somalia, and she was on a voyage from Port Sudan to northern Europe via the Cape of Good Hope when she had the misfortune to encounter the Norwegian tanker *Cardo*,* though those on that vessel probably felt that the misfortune was more properly theirs. It was early on the eight to twelve watch in the evening of St. Valentine's Day of 1969 when the junior 1st officer of *Cardo* first sighted *Toni* on his radar at about 14 miles fine on his port bow. On looking in that direction with his binoculars he saw her mast lights with the lower to the right of the higher. She was crossing from port to starboard and in that position at that distance she should easily have made it across *Cardo*'s bow if nothing were done to disturb her progress.

Though *Cardo*'s radar was in use no attempt was made to plot the movement of the other vessel, nor was any effort made to check her bearings visually. As in the previous cases reliance was placed solely on that imprecise instrument known as the "seaman's eye". According to later testimony the bearing did not change much and what change there was seemed to be a slow movement to the left, which indicated to the watch officer that the vessels would pass port to port. How he arrived at that conclusion was another of the unexplained mysteries of this case, but that was his conclusion and it led him into a series of disastrous mistakes.

Toni, let us remember, was slightly on the port bow with her range lights open to the right, which meant that she was steering a course to the right of *Cardo*'s reciprocal. When the distance

---

* *Toni* was 470' long and 7,919 gross tons while *Cardo* was a much larger vessel of 41,444 gross tons and 830' in length.

had closed to 5 miles the mate saw the green sidelight in addition to the range lights yet he still persisted in the belief that the vessels would pass port to port, and at 2110 when he claimed *Toni* was 4.7 miles away, but more probably just over four, he altered course 5° to the right in order to widen what he misguidedly though was a port to port passage.

Toni was under the con of her Yugoslav master who was standing a watch because he was short of a watchstander. Whether the added burden of standing a watch — a questionable practice on an ocean-going vessel — had induced fatigue we do not know, but his powers of concentration were obviously suffering from the ill-effects of something during the period leading up to this disaster. When he took over the watch at 2000 the ship was being steered by gyro pilot on a heading of 221° at a speed of 10 knots, and that was the course probably being steered when she was first seen aboard *Cardo*. There was a south-westerly current set of about 2½ knots opposed by a 15 knot wind.

At about 2048* the AB, who was serving as both lookout and standby helmsman, drew the master's attention to a vessel about 10° on the starboard bow that was undoubtedly *Cardo*. The master later maintained that the masthead light was to the left of the range light and that the green sidelight shortly came into view. If that were the case there could have been no collision, but these were not the only inconsistencies.

Cardo was not only a much larger ship but also a faster one making about 15½ knots through the water. While neither vessel was apparently fitted with a course recorder so that the courses steered and the changes made could be ascertained within narrow limits the Court accepted as a fact that *Toni* made a course change to port sometime during the approach, and that she was at all times on the port bow of *Cardo*. Given these circumstances and their respective speeds she had to port at sometime during the approach or the collision could not have taken place, and it was probably shortly after the time *Cardo* made her first alteration to starboard.

At 2115 or thereabouts *Cardo*'s watch officer, still holding blindly to his belief that the other vessel would pass port to port, altered 28° more to starboard. Mr. Justice Brandon before whom this case was heard remarked that this officer "seemed not to understand what a crossing situation under the Collision Regulations was or what ships in such a situation were supposed . . . to do. He seemed to understand as little of these matters by the date of the trial as at the time of the collision."[11] The Judge nonetheless believed he was trying to tell the truth as he saw it. What would appear to be the case was that he originally assumed that he was in a meeting situation and all his subsequent manoeuvres were based upon that assumption.

Whatever the situation aboard *Cardo*, *Toni*'s master seemed to be burdened by no assumptions at all and was, in the words of Mr. Justice Brandon, keeping "only the sketchiest of lookouts." He further remarked that he would "not be altogether surprised if the fact were that there were times when the master was not looking out at all."[12]

About two minutes before the collision with *Cardo* little more than half a mile away the AB again drew the master's attention to the vessel close on the starboard bow. Now fully but belatedly alert to his danger the master blew the danger signal on the whistle and flashed his blinker light a number of times. The master's previous appreciation of the danger he was standing into is indicated by the fact that the vessel was still in automatic steering. He hurriedly disconnected that device and ordered the seaman to take the helm and put it hard right. He had rung full astern on the engines and he now gave them another jingle.

Cardo's mate seemed equally oblivious to his peril as the vessels neared. When the master of *Toni* was jolted into action he apparently first signalled his intention by blowing a single blast on the whistle. That awakened *Cardo* to her hazard and the watch officer ordered the helm hard-a-starboard. *Toni*'s whistle also was heard by the master of *Cardo* in his cabin and he rushed to the bridge to find his vessel *in extremis*. He found the helm hard to starboard and blew the danger signal followed by a single blast; he also ordered the engines placed on standby,

---

* The times differed between the vessels. These are *Cardo*'s times.

which was followed by stop and a reversal of the helm. At 2122 the vessels collided with *Toni*'s bow striking *Cardo* on her port quarter at an angle of about 50° leading forward. The blame was shared equally.

* * * * * * * *

In three of these collisions there was no attempt made by either vessel to check the visual bearing of the other ship or plot her motion on radar. The visual lookout was also defective in that there seemed to be no effort made to gain a true appreciation of the aspect and hence general heading of the approaching vessel. In short the basic and simple tasks that should form part of the watch officer's routine in meeting another vessel on the high seas were neglected.

All of these ships were moreover equipped with radar yet no endeavour was made to make even a relative motion plot to establish CPA,* and on two of the vessels the radars were not even switched on. Neglect of plotting seems an endemic fault among a large number of watch officers, and that is a fault no court today is likely to condone should a collision ensue.

* * * * * * * *

Notes

1 See *A.M.C.*, 1968, p. 914, and esp. the dissent of Justice Bryan who felt that *Saratoga* should be held solely to blame.
2 *Ibid.*, p. 912.
3 Pages 915–19.
4 *L.L.R.*, 1971, Vol. 2, p. 280. Justice Brandon thought it might have been slightly earlier, cf. *L.L.R.*, 1970, Vol. 2, p. 159; another curious feature is that with only a single sailor on watch with him no use was made of the automatic steering, which would at least have allowed the 2nd mate to continue doing his job.
5 It may well have been simply a routine course change. The normal procedure in rounding this headland on approaching from the east is to make a course change somewhat west of south of Sagres for a point roughly south-west of St. Vincent from where a course is shaped for Cabo Roca. That course would be about 340°, which suggests that the 2nd mate made his course change to 340° not to "pass astern" of *Andulo* as claimed but as a matter of simple navigation before he became aware of the approach of the southbound ship.
6 *Ibid.*, 1971, Vol. 2, p. 284.
7 *Ibid.*, 1970, Vol. 2, p. 159.
8 *Ibid.*, 1971, Vol. 2, p. 280.
9 Marsden, *The Law of Collisions at Sea*, p. 406.
10 *A.M.C.*, 1970, p. 1140.
11 *L.L.R.*, 1973, Vol. 1, p. 82.
12 *Ibid.*

---

* *Saratoga* undoubtedly was carrying out a plot in CIC but there seems to have been insufficient attention paid to the information being developed there.

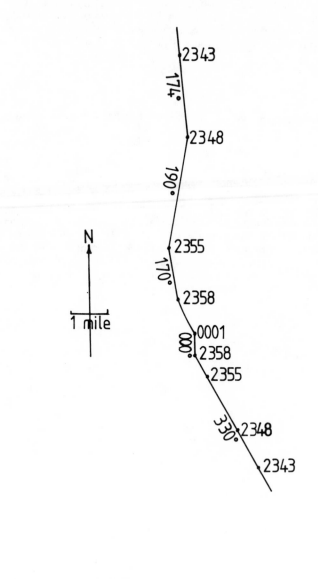

From 2358 to time of collision 'Saratoga' was swinging slowly from 170° to about 155°

Saratoga/Bernd Leonhardt

Figure 16 *Bernd Leonhardt/Saratoga* (See page 58)

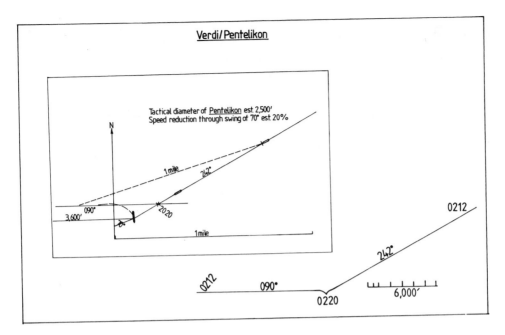

Figure 17 *Pentelikon/Verdi* (See page 63)

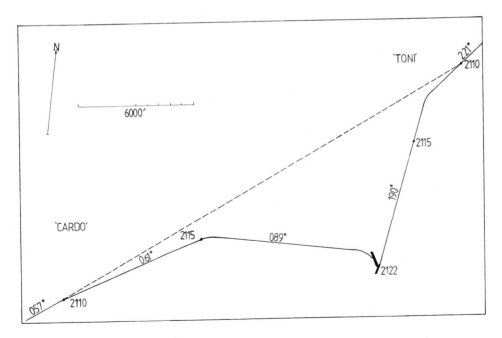

Figure 18 *Cardo/Toni* (See page 64)

Chapter Nine

Fine Crossing/Overtaking/ Special Circumstances

On a fine clear night on July 24, 1976 the VLCC *Brazilian Faith* was under tow in the Malacca Strait on a base course of 125° at a speed of about 5 knots. A somewhat smaller but still very large Philippine motor tanker *Diego Silang* (hereinafter referred to as *Diego*) was overtaking her on her port side. The Philippine vessel was on a course of 120° making about 13½ knots through the water with *Brazilian Faith* a couple of miles off fine on the starboard bow when she sighted a westbound vessel very fine on the same bow about 10 miles off around 2321. This vessel was the Russian freighter *Vysotsk** out of Singapore bound for Tuapse, a port on the Black Sea.

The first reaction of the master of *Diego* was to come right to 123°, but he quickly realised that this would put him too close aboard *Brazilian Faith* and he came back to his original course. He continued to watch the westbound ship closely, but he did not observe the elementary precaution of instructing the watch officer to either check the visual bearing of the approaching vessel or to plot her movement on the radar.

The master of *Vysotsk* also sighted *Diego* at about the same time around 10° on the port bow. He too neglected to have her bearing checked or her motion plotted, nor did he or anyone else on his vessel pay her the strict attention the circumstances warranted. That carelessness would have had no untoward effects had he kept his course and speed,† but for some reason that was never discovered or explained (no doubt because he chose to deny it) *Vysotsk* altered course to port at about 2330, first to 304° and not long thereafter to 290° when the vessels were some 4 miles apart.

As both vessels were equipped with course recorders the reconstruction of the casualty should have been straightforward affair and the trial, if it came to a trial, a speedy one. It was not. The master of *Vysotsk* on reflecting on his predicament after returning to Singapore for survey after the collision apparently decided to fiddle with the evidence, and he cut off the incriminating portion of the course recorder chart showing the course changes after 2330 and altered the times on what remained. That at least was the way Mr. Justice Sheen saw it. He concluded "that this document [was] tendered by [the master] to the solicitors acting on behalf of the owners of *Vystosk* with the intention of deceiving all concerned about the true facts that led to the collision."[1] The disgruntled judge thenceforth refused to accept any statement of the Russian master that was not supported by other evidence.

The master of *Diego* observed *Vysotsk* turning to port about nine minutes before the collision so as to show first both sidelights and then only her green. That placed him in a most unenviable

---

* *Brazilian Faith* was 1,026′ long and 90,930 gross tons; *Diego Silang* 829′ and 51,835 gross tons; *Vysotsk* 494′ and 9,454 gross tons.

† The CPA would have been 0.7 mile if both vessels had kept course and speed.

position. *Brazilian Faith* was close aboard to starboard foreclosing the possibility of any sharp turn to the right. A turn to port was against his seaman's instincts and he was probably reluctant to have recourse to his engines (if it was indeed considered at that point) in the hope that this was just a temporary aberration of the helm or con of the approaching ship. He confined his action at this point to indicating his alarm by flashing his blinker light at the errant vessel and perhaps a little heavy sweating. When the distance had closed to 2 miles he first rang stop on the engines followed by half and finally full astern. The engine room had received no prior notice of any speed changes and so were possibly not as prompt in backing as might otherwise have been the case. In any event the momentum of the heavily laden Philippine tanker could not be so quickly reduced, and when *Vysotsk* then swung to port the collision became inevitable. At 2342½ the bow of *Diego* struck the starboard after side of the Russian vessel.

On impact the master of *Diego* stopped his engines. His head had fallen off to starboard as would be expected due to the reversal of the engines. The forward movement of *Vysotsk*, who had maintained her speed, no doubt slewed the bow of the Philippine tanker further to starboard as the vessels came together. The first concern of the distraught master was the possibility of fire and explosion, but after the vessels came free and there was no sign of conflagration in the following few moments the danger of collision with the VLCC under tow, which he had just overtaken on his starboard side, tossed him from the crest of one crisis to another.

Within half a minute after the collision he again ordered the engines half astern followed by a double ring full astern. Three minutes later he gave another jingle on the telegraph to spur the engineers to make maximum revolutions astern. He had probably become somewhat disoriented following the collision and he now had no clear idea of the position of *Brazilian Faith*. One of his first reactions was to tell the mate on watch to fix the position of collision where the more pressing problem was to fix the position of the VLCC. But that consideration escaped him at the moment and such a mistake is understandable in the confusion then reigning.

It was later said that he should have put the engines slow ahead and the helm hard left in an effort to avoid the vessel under tow coming up on his starboard side, but when the Elder Brethren of Trinity House were asked for their view as assessors they said that the prudent measure in such a position of extremity was to take all way off the ship, and that was the course adopted by the master of *Diego*.[2] Unfortunately this probably accentuated the vessel's swing to starboard bringing her broadside across the path of *Brazilian Faith*. About seven minutes after the first collision the damaged Philippine tanker was struck on her starboard side by the lumbering *Brazilian Faith*.

In arriving at a judgment Mr. Justice Sheen was confronted with no ordinary set of circumstances. There was no question but that *Vysotsk* was guilty of the gravest faults and mistakes not to mention the conduct of the master. It was a foregone conclusion that the learned judge would deal heavily with her, but first what of the conduct of *Diego*? It was certain that there would have been no collision without the inexplicable and unseamanlike behaviour of the Russian vessel, but part of the proper conduct of seamanship is to make allowances for the possible unseamanlike conduct of other seamen.

While the judge seemed reluctant to add to the discomfort and distress of the Philippine master whom fate had dealt with so harshly already he nonetheless felt he should have been more prompt in responding to the perilous position into which he had been thrust. What had not been done that could or should have been done? The answer to that was obvious: had he been more prompt in backing down or stopping his engines his vessel would have been less far ahead at the moment *Vystosk* tried to cross his bow and the collision might have been thus avoided. *Diego* was hence held responsible for 20 per cent of the damages though one is left with the impression that Mr. Justice Sheen was somewhat pained to lessen any part of the blame that belonged so overwhelmingly to *Vystosk*.

But then there was also the second collision to be dealt with. That misfortune was an outgrowth of the first, and while it was agreed that the activities and the attention of the watch officer would have been more prudently employed in discovering the whereabouts of *Brazilian Faith* than the position of the collision the action that the master took in attempting to take all way off the vessel was the approved one. As *Vysotsk* had put *Diego* in the position whereby she collided with *Brazilian Faith* the Russian ship was assigned damages in the same proportion as in the collision in which she was a direct participant.

In arriving at his judgment Mr. Justice Sheen indulged in some interesting speculation and reflection. *Vysotsk* was indubitably in the stand-on position when the two vessels first came in sight of one another, though whether she ever came within the grasp of the Rules while she was on her original course is another matter. The distance, certainly at the first, was too great, and it would be difficult to argue that there was risk of collision while she kept to the course of 310°.

He did not, however, choose to discuss that but instead directed his attention to events as they unfolded after *Vysotsk* reached that point about 4 miles distant from *Diego* when she chose to make her fatal alterations to port. This was a clearly inexplicable act, and one that was impossible to foresee without some method of direct communication between the vessels. Faced with such a surprise the master of *Diego* was entitled to a few moments reflection before he decided what if anything to do about this perplexing and perilous development.

The nature of the dilemma with which the master found himself faced in this situation can perhaps be appreciated best by turning to the arguments of the opposing counsels.

> Mr. Thomas [for *Vysotsk*] submitted that because *Diego* was the "give-way" vessel from the moment of first sighting,* she must remain the "give-way" vessel until the vessels were past and clear. Mr. Thomas sought to rely upon the decisions of the House of Lords in *The Otranto* . . . and *The Statue of Liberty* . . . both of which cases deal with the duty of the stand-on vessel to maintain her course and speed. She is not entitled to alter her course or speed at a moment when there is ample time for the ship which is bound to give way to discharge her duty. Mr. Thomas further submitted that when two ships are meeting there would be utter confusion if the ship which starts as the "stand-on" ship were subsequently to become the "give-way" ship. Mr. Clark submitted that once *Vysotsk* had altered course to port and put *Diego* on her starboard bow, *Vystosk* assumed the role of the "give-way" ship. The fact that two advocates so familiar with the collision regulations felt able to make submissions which are so totally in conflict, the one with the other, highlights the difficulty in which the [Philippine master] found himself.[3]

The Judge himself indicated that he saw it as a case of special circumstances, which the conflicting views of the two advocates would tend to support. He cited the presence of the *Brazilian Faith* just forward of the starboard beam as the first factor. The inexplicable behaviour of *Vysotsk* in altering to port so as to put herself in an undeniable give-way position wherein she had prior to that manoeuvre been in as equally an undeniable stand-on position. She could by any reasonable criterion be expected to "give-way" or revert to her original course. Lastly, the size and weight of *Diego* proceeding at her full speed prevented any rapid reduction in her way.

He thereupon referred the matter to the judgment of the Elder Brethren who did not take issue with any of his assumptions, but went on to, among other things, state with the greatest emphasis that "Under no circumstances should [*Vysotsk*] alter course to port."[4]

Alterations to port, except in the agony of *in extremis*, are viewed by admiralty courts in much the same way that the local ladies' sewing circle views social disease. There is of course a very good reason for this, but the admission of special circumstances should open all doors in the search for an escape from collision. Admittedly an alteration to port should ordinarily be the last option considered, and it should only be contemplated when there is sufficient information available to ensure it can be carried out with success. That information would include the distance of advance of the vessel in turning through 90°, the distance off the approaching ship, and the relative speed of approach whereby an appreciation can be made of the room needed to turn out of the way of the oncoming vessel despite any manoeuvre she might make. With that data available one cannot dismiss a turn to port in such an agonising situation when it offers the only reasonably certain option of avoiding collision.

Admittedly backing down the engines at an early moment could accomplish the same objective without the stigma of an "unseamanlike" turn to port. That manoeuvre, however, relies on a

---

* A questionable claim.

prompt response by the watch engineer, who has probably been taken unawares, as well as a fairly precise knowledge of the reduction of way and the closure distance during the available backing interval.

As long as mariners are denied the means of safely and effectively ascertaining the intentions of an approaching ship in a positive manner they will occasionally be confronted with such daunting dilemmas.

* * * * * * * *

Notes

1 *L.L.R.*, Vol. 1, 1981, p. 442; also cf. 443–45.
2 *Ibid.*, p. 451.
3 Page 449.
4 *Ibid.*

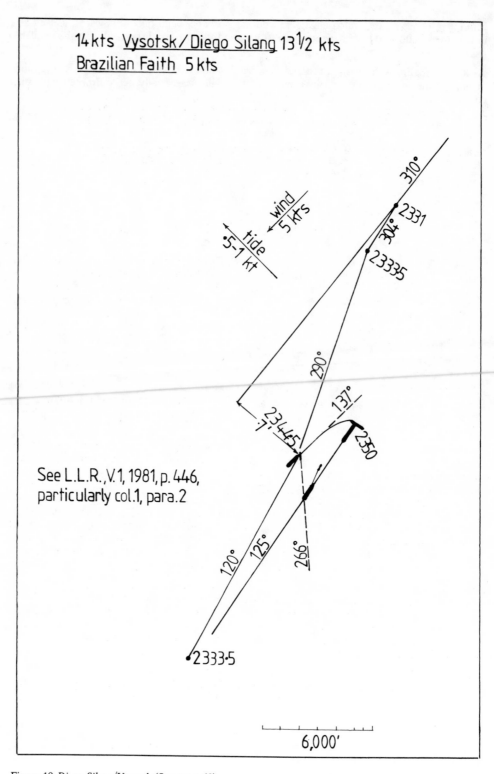

Figure 19 *Diego Silang/Vystosk* (See page 68)

Chapter Ten

Crossing, Overtaking or Special Circumstances

In the early hours of April 20, 1973 the American container ship SS *American Aquarius* was proceeding on a course of 115° bound from Kobe to Yokahama. At the time she was south of the headland known as Shiono Misaki on the main Japanese island of Honshu, and was crossing through an unofficial (not recognised by IMCO — now IMO)[1] traffic separation scheme drawn up by the Japan Captains' Association through which the Liberian bulk carrier MV *Atlantic Hope* was passing on a course of 253° on her way from Chiba to Oita, Japan. *Aquarius* was making a speed over the ground of some 23½ knots compared to approximately 11½ for *Hope*. The visibility was good, being estimated at from 6 to 8 miles though it was dark and overcast with some light rain.

A Japanese vessel, the MV *Sadoharu Maru*,* was also in the vicinity on a similar course to the *Hope* making 14 to 15 knots, and overtook her on *Hope*'s port side about three-tenths of a mile off shortly before the collision. *Hope* later tried to involve her in the blame for *Hope*'s subsequent collision with *Aquarius*.

Aquarius had sighted the lights of three vessels (the third was the American steamship *Colorado*) on her port bow at about 0309, and shortly thereafter the master commenced a plot of the ships showing on the radar at distances of from 5½ to 6½ miles in order to determine their courses, speeds and CPAs.[2] As he regarded himself as privileged he accordingly kept his course and speed.† It soon became apparent that *Colorado* would pass clear well ahead, but the other two ships were observed to be on collision courses or nearly so. In spite of the fact that the meeting would take place in the TSS (Traffic Separation Scheme) the master of *Aquarious* did not consider that to affect the applicability of the Steering and Sailing Rules of the Collision Regulations, and he expected the two crossing vessels on his port bow to keep out of his way. He nonetheless very prudently kept them under very close observation.

Sadoharu Maru was at this time on the port quarter of *Hope* and passed that vessel on her port side at a distance of about 1,800 feet at approximately 0305. The master had been closely observing *Aquarius* and was aware that he might have to manoeuvre to clear her. When the Japanese ship had drawn ahead of *Hope* about three-quarters of a mile she altered course to starboard[2] to 295° at around 0315 after blowing one blast on the whistle. Shortly thereafter she passed the American ship to port about three-quarters of a mile off.

Hope was under the con of her 2nd officer, the master having gone below about 0230 though he was aware of other vessels in the vicinity and the likelihood of encountering other traffic in that area. There was a helmsman on the bridge with the 2nd mate but no lookout was posted.

---

* *Sadoharu Maru* was 467' long and 8,789 gross tons; *Atlantic Hope* 635' and 18,389; while *American Aquarius* was 705' and 19,127.

† At 0319 *Aquarius* changed 4° to starboard to 119°.

Though she was proceeding in accordance with the TSS on the present leg it was her intention to continue on when she reached its end and cut across the next leg of the TSS towards her destination. The radar was not in use at the time nor at any time up to the collision.

After being overhauled by *Sadoharu Maru* the helmsman sighted *Aquarius* on the starboard bow showing a red light. The time was about 0310, and when approximately five minutes later the Japanese ship turned to cross *Hope*'s bow the 2nd officer ordered 10° left rudder but did not signal that action by the required two blasts of the whistle. As it took only moments for the Japanese vessel to cross from port to starboard *Hope*'s helmsman had hardly finished putting the wheel over before the watch officer told him to put it back amidships. He thereupon summoned the master as it was becoming obvious that he was in a developing close-quarters situation. He did not, however, advise the master of the approach of *Aquarius*, merely that a ship was crossing close ahead after overtaking.

The master arrived on the bridge in two to three minutes with *Sadoharu Maru* almost a mile on his starboard bow on a course of 295° and the American vessel just beyond and crossing. The 2nd mate still made no mention of *Aquarius* though the master became almost immediately aware of her presence.[3] Whether *Hope* was still swinging left a bit under the influence of the 10° left rudder is unclear, though it would seem unlikely if the helm had been returned midships several minutes before. In any event the master claimed that he was under the impression she was as he attempted to rapidly analyse the swiftly developing situation.

It was starkly apparent that some evasive action had to be taken immediately if a collision was to be averted, and under the impression that *Hope* was still swinging left he ordered hard-a-port and full astern sounding three blasts.[4] The master of *Aquarius* had meanwhile watched with escalating alarm *Hope* bearing down on him, and when the burdened vessel was about a mile off he sounded the danger signal of five short blasts on the whistle. Hearing no response and seeing *Hope* continuing to stand on *Aquarius*' master blew another five blasts and almost immediately thereafter ordered hard right rudder after blowing a single blast followed by slow and stop on the engine order telegraph. At approximately 0321 *Hope* collided with *Aquarius* on her port side aft.

There are a number of interesting aspects to this case that we will deal with in due course, but when the case was first heard by the Honourable Chas. E. Stewart in the Southern District of New York the major portion of the fault was clearly seen to lie with *Atlantic Hope*, and she was accordingly assigned 80 per cent of the blame. In holding the American vessel responsible for the balance of the fault Justice Stewart turned for precedent to the example of *The Genimar* where an English court several years before had held that vessel responsible for one-third of the damages for navigating in the wrong direction in a traffic lane, albeit an IMCO approved one (see Chapter Three). Though the Court recognised that the scheme was not compulsory for the vessel contravening it the presiding judge, Mr. Justice Brandon, held that good seamanship alone demanded compliance with the Scheme. Counsel for *Aquarius* maintained that the TSS in question, though known to the master, was not IMCO approved and hence not compulsory for any vessel, and moreover was not even reproduced on the chart. Justice Stewart, however, felt that these arguments were not persuasive and held that the master of *Aquarius* had failed to comply with the precepts of good seamanship in not following the TSS even though it was not compulsory.

Hope in trying to plead special circumstances[5] in excuse for her failure to abide by her clear duty to keep clear of *Aquarius* claimed that Rule 19 [crossing] (now Rule 15) is applicable only when two vessels are involved, and as *Aquarius* was already at fault for being in the wrong lane it was up to her to avoid the other ships. That argument was given short shrift.

Hope then tried to shift the blame to the Japanese vessel by claiming the *Sadoharu Maru*'s turn across her bow was in violation of Rules 24 and 22 thereby placing *Hope in extremis* and so justifying her successive turns to port.[6] That argument was similarly summarily dismissed since the Court ruled that the Japanese ship was past and clear at the point at which she altered course to starboard as required by Rule 19.

These arguments were advanced under the grave handicap of *Hope*'s gross negligence in other respects. She was proceeding without a lookout through waters normally subject to such congestion that the Japan Captains' Association had devised a TSS to alleviate its effects. It might also be thought that her master had personally contributed to the generally negligent manner in which she was being navigated by leaving the bridge at a point where there was a patent need for so high a degree of vigilance as to require his personal attention. He himself testified that if he had arrived on the bridge two minutes before the actual time at which he did appear he could have avoided the collision. All during the period leading up to the casualty no attempt was made to use the radar though the circumstances were such that a prudent navigator would have used it as a matter of course. Finally the 2nd mate's failure to blow two blasts when he ordered the helm put to port followed by the master's neglect to blow two blasts before the three blast signal deprived *Aquarius* of valuable intelligence of *Hope*'s action.

The arguments put forward by *Hope*'s counsel regarding the constraints inhibiting her ability to change course to the right ignored the obvious but common refusal to consider the option of a reduction in speed. In any situation such as this where there may be any doubt about the advisability of a helm action to comply with the Steering and Sailing Rules it is no more than common prudence to advise the engine room of the possibility of a speed reduction.[7]

When the case was appealed in the Second Circuit of the U.S. Court of Appeals in the autumn of 1980 the higher court modified the judgment of the lower exonerating *American Aquarius* of all blame and holding *Atlantic Hope* 100 per cent liable. The Appeals Court noted that the trial court had correctly found that "while some sailing rules not having official status can achieve the force of law by custom and usage . . . the Shiono Misaki TSS had not attained the status of a custom."[8] They observed that "mere knowledge of the existence of a traffic scheme lacking the force of law does not create an enforceable duty to observe it." The Court went on to say moreover that "even if we were to find that *Aquarius* was bound to follow the TSS, our disposition of this appeal would not be altered." The conclusion was hence inescapable that the obligation to observe the provisions of the Steering and Sailing Rules of the Collision Regulations once they begin to apply took unarguable precedence over any obligation imposed by law to follow a TSS. There is an attempt afoot to make that interpretation explicit.

The British court had, moreover, ruled in *The Genimar* that: "There may well be cases of collisions in clear weather, where contravention of a traffic separation scheme by one of the colliding ships though a fault, will nevertheless not be a causative fault. A typical case of that kind would be where, although the area is usually busy, no other ships than the colliding ships are about at that time, and they see one another clearly at a distance of several miles."[9]

This case is yet another illustration of the vexing problem arising out of crossing situations where one vessel is, in the language of the earlier rule (21), "burdened" by the obligation to keep out of the way of another crossing from starboard while the latter ship is "privileged" and equally obliged to hold her course and speed. The dilemma that such a situation can pose has been a source of anxiety to the mariner almost from the time of the adoption of the "starboard hand" rule, and the dubious nature of the so-called "privilege" of the vessel on the starboard hand led to an amendment of that rule in 1972 and the adoption of the terms "give-way" and "stand-on" to replace the words "burdened" and "privileged."

The amendment of the rule whereby a stand-on vessel, faced with a give-way ship which seems disinclined to heed her obligation to keep out of the way, is allowed to take early action to prevent the development of a close-quarters situation is in effect a recognition of a practice long followed by many mariners when faced with an oblivious give-way vessel. It appears, however, that this situation is still a source of some confusion in the minds of many mariners, and particularly so when a third vessel is in the vicinity that might create an impression of the intrusion of special circumstances into the situation.

The rarest form of casualty is that collision where neither vessel is found guilty of an infraction of the Rules, particularly on the high-seas. Infractions of the Rules are, however, all too often not deliberate or the result of inattention but due to misconception. The Rules work almost perfectly where they are properly understood and applied, but there are far too many instances where two vessels have conflicting views over which Rule is applicable, as was claimed to be the case here. Situations such as this one are likely to become increasingly common, and there is probably no comparable common encounter where there is a greater chance for confusion than the case where one vessel overtakes another and has to manoeuvre for a third. The widespread acceptance and establishment of traffic separation schemes has greatly increased the probability of such encounters.

The question also arose as to why *Aquarius*, a vessel of greatly superior speed, persisted in holding to her "privilege" knowing full well that she was in the wrong lane of the TSS, and why with no traffic to inhibit her at that time she did not haul sharply to the right to get into the recommended lane when *Colorado, Sadoharu Maru* and *Hope* were first discovered. An expert witness testifying at the trial said that if it were possible to avoid the situation he would not have allowed himself to get into the position *Aquarius* subsequently found herself in, but if it could not be avoided he would give way to starboard. The point was also made with some reason that if the master had searched on the 12-mile scale instead of confining his observation to the 6-mile one he could have picked up those vessels earlier and been able to determine their direction of movement some time prior to their becoming visible. There would have been no question then of being restricted by Rule 19.

This case also serves to illustrate a current weakness in the application of the Rules. There is clearly scope for ambiguity as to which Rule applies in such situations, and while it may be of critical importance in law in establishing which seaman's interpretation was "right" or "wrong" it is only incidental in the avoidance of the collision that would render that determination redundant. That danger can be overcome if the ships involved *can* establish effective communication. That can be done with VHF radio. That there are substantial problems associated with its use in this context in no way changes the fact that it is capable, if used properly, of dispelling the confusion and uncertainty that contributes so heavily to collisions.

* * * * * * * *

Notes

1 The scheme had not been submitted to IMCO for approval due to opposition from the Japanese fishing industry. It was, however, known to all parties involved and *Aquarius* had followed a similar scheme on a previous leg of its passage but had been forced to the north and into the opposite lane when overtaking another unidentified vessel somewhat earlier. See *A.M.C.*, 1980, pp. 2536–37.
2 The Japanese vessel actually made two earlier slight course changes to the right of 2° while overtaking as a prelude to crossing. See *Ibid.*
3 Counsel for *Hope* maintained that a further reason for ordering left rudder was the presence of another ship to starboard on a parallel course. None of the other vessels in the vicinity observed such a ship and that claim was rejected by the Court.
4 *A.M.C., ibid.*, pp. 2541–43.
5 Rule 24 is now 13 while Rule 22 is encompassed by Rule 15.
6 Some diesel engines and very high pressure steam turbines when in the sea steaming mode cannot be readily backed without risk of damage.
7 *A.M.C., ibid.*, p. 2534.
8 *L.L.R.*, 1977, Vol. 1, p. 525.

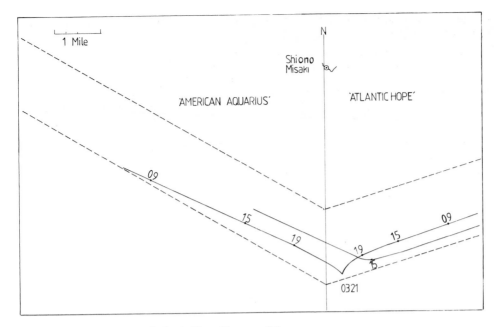

Figure 20 *American Aquarius/Atlantic Hope* (See page 74)

Chapter Eleven

Converging Overtaking/ Crossing

Within the space of less than a year (February 1972–January 1973) two collisions occurred off the west coast of the Iberian Peninsula that vividly illustrate the hazard and confusion that so often attends converging overtaking and crossing situations. Another had happened about a year earlier off the Isle of Wight. As many of the points raised in the court actions and investigations stemming from these incidents were similar and interrelated we will consider these cases in tandem.

The first took place some 20 miles to the south of Cape St. Vincent shortly before 0400 between the Polish motor ship *Nowy Sacz* and the Cypriot motor vessel *Olympian*.* The Polish ship was on a course of 341° making a speed of 12½ knots on a voyage from Casablanca to Gdynia. The Cypriot vessel claimed to be steering a course of 290° at a speed of about 13 knots, but these contentions were challenged by the Court and it was concluded that her speed must have been close to 14½ knots and her course about 331°. She was on her way from Malta to a port in West Germany.

The weather was fine with excellent visibility as *Nowy Sacz* made her way towards a landfall off the Portuguese coast. The 2nd officer had the midnight to 0400 watch assisted by two quartermasters who shared the duties of helmsman and lookout alternately. At approximately 0245 the lookout reported the lights of a vessel to starboard. The 2nd mate claimed that *Olympian* was at that time about 30° abaft the beam and around 3 miles off. He further testified that about 0300 the red light of *Olympian* came into view and the ship was abeam 1 mile off at about 0330. He finally asserted that she had drawn ahead to a position close to 30° forward of the beam at 0345, at which time the lookout was ordered to take the wheel and steer by hand.

Some four or five minutes later he tried to attract the attention of the other vessel by five short flashes on the signalling lamp but had no response. Shortly after he rang half ahead followed by slow, dead slow and stop. About that time he heard a signal of one short blast on the whistle by *Olympian*, which was then very close aboard, and he responded by putting the engines first half and then full astern. The bow of the Cypriot ship was now swinging to starboard and though no helm was applied on the Polish vessel it appears that her bow also began to swing to the right probably due to the reversal of the engines accentuated by interaction as her bow neared the stern of *Olympian*. They collided at approximately 0358.

The distances given by the 2nd mate were all based upon visual estimates, and in spite of the fact that he had used radar to fix his ship's position he apparently made no attempt at any time to ascertain the movements of *Olympian* by plot. Mr. Justice Brandon, who considered the 2nd mate a reliable witness, accepted the testimony of that officer as substantially true, yet if it was accurate *Olympian* would have passed ahead of *Nowy Sacz* by over half a mile and there would

---

* *Nowy Sacz* was 357′ in length and 3,809 gross tons compared to 520′ and 12,211 tons for *Olympian*.

have been no collision (see sketch A). When the case subsequently went to appeal the Court also accepted the 2nd mate's testimony regarding times of bearings. That error could, and most probably would, have affected the conclusions drawn in the original trial (see Appendix).

The case presented by *Olympian* was certainly riddled with inconsistencies, and earlier evidence taken from the deck log relating to her passage through the Strait of Gibraltar showed that the records kept aboard that vessel were far from precise.[2] The working chart, which could have supplied some valuable clues in trying to sort out the movements of *Olympian*, had disappeared, and neither the master, who appeared on the bridge about 0330, nor the 2nd officer were available as witnesses. There can be little doubt but that Mr. Justice Brandon formed a very unfavourable opinion of the navigation of *Olympian* and the apparently slovenly manner in which she was operated. Relying upon the testimony of the 2nd mate of *Nowy Sacz* he notwithstanding reached a somewhat ironic conclusion.

He found that though *Olympian* was indeed on an overtaking course when first sighted by *Nowy Sacz* she had not yet "come up" with her, and relying on the precedent established almost a century earlier in *The Banshee* (1887), he concluded that risk of collision, on which the applicability of the overtaking rule depended according to the principle laid down by Lord Esher in the above case, was not present at that early time. Turning to the Elder Brethren for advice he was told that such risk had only materialised when the distance between the two vessels had closed to 1 mile and they were abeam of one another. According to the testimony that was at approximately 0330. He accordingly found that *Nowy Sacz* was the give-way vessel in a crossing situation and was at fault for failing to keep out of the way of *Olympian*.

Olympian, however, was not held blameless. The Court found that she delayed too long in altering course to starboard thereby contributing to the collision. Had she changed course more slowly several minutes earlier collision would almost certainly have been averted regardless of what action was taken by *Nowy Sacz*. Mr. Justice Brandon accordingly found *Nowy Sacz* 75 per cent to blame and *Olympian* 25 per cent.

When the case was appealed before Sir David (subsequently Lord) Cairns the judgment and the apportionment of blame were both reversed. The reasoning by which the Appeal Court reached that decision was intriguing and significant in that it challenged the venerable precedent laid down by Lord Esher in the case of *The Banshee*.

Sir David accepted the facts as found by the lower court, but he then decided to examine the long established proposition that the overtaking rule is dependent upon risk of collision before it takes effect. He pointed out that whereas all of the applicable Steering and Sailing Rules take effect only when vessels are in sight of one another, four of these, including the crossing rules, are only applicable, according to explicit provision, when vessels are proceeding so as to involve risk of collision. This provision is not mentioned in the overtaking rule, hence it would seem that there need be no immediate risk of collision for vessels to fall within its grasp.

He went on to say, however, that there was "impressive authority" implying that risk of collision did in fact determine whether vessels in an overtaking situation were governed in their conduct by the overtaking rule. He cited the case of *The Banshee*, and then proceeded to subject it to intensive analysis. He quoted Lord Esher where he ennunciated the principle, long regarded as governing, that none of the regulations apply until a position has been reached where risk of collision exists.[3].

From there he went on to look at the unusual case of *The Manchester Regiment*, which while in the process of adjusting compasses collided with *Clan MacKenzie*. The latter vessel was approaching the former from a position about two points abaft the beam from 2 to 3 miles distant when *The Manchester Regiment* turned to starboard in the course of her manoeuvres so that the ships were then crossing at right angles, and then subsequently collided. The crossing rule was found to apply, and the President of the Court, Sir Boyd Merriman, relied on the precedent of *The Banshee* for his decision, noting particularly that in that case a mere 800 yards separated the "overtaken" and "overtaking" vessels yet the Rules were not seen to bind their conduct. He went on to observe that "the distance astern at which the overtaking rule becomes applicable must vary according to circumstances,"[4] depending upon the respective speed of the ships. The lateral interval between the courses of the vessels was also deemed material, but he emphasised that it was the principle that matters (see preceding paragraph).

It was the contention of counsel for *Olympian* that the principle of *The Banshee* governed, though it was conceded that without the weight of the authority of that precedent "a different view might well be taken."[5] The Court then boldly took upon itself to question that precedent, and reached the conclusion that the provision that "no subsequent alteration of the bearing between the two vessels shall make the overtaking vessel a crossing vessel within the meaning of these Rules" clearly suggests that "the rule applies before there is risk of collision."[6]

If that was the case then it remained to determine at what point the overtaking rule began to apply, and that was seen to be defined by the phrase "coming up with another vessel." That in turn was reckoned to be a matter of physical proximity. In the case at hand the Court put the question to their Assessors: "at what stage could it be fairly said that risk of collision arose?" They answered: "About 0330 when *Olympian* was about abeam of *Nowy Sacz* and continuing to close."[7] According to the calculation of the Court the ships were separated by a distance of about a mile at that point.

It was hence clear that if none of the Rules were applicable before this point then the crossing rule had to apply since *Olympian* should have had the green sidelight of *Nowy Sacz* clearly in view, and it was that consideration that had apparently led Mr. Justice Brandon to conclude that the crossing rule applied. But that was not the end of the matter.

The point at which the vessels had "come up" with one another and become bound by the overtaking rule was then considered. Lord Esher had found that distance to be less than 800 yards in the case of *The Banshee,* and that was not challenged in the present judgment. The two vessels there were making 6 and 7 knots respectively. Nevertheless, in a case several years before *The Banshee* the Court held that "the overtaking rules applied when two ships were on courses so nearly parallel as to involve no risk of collision, and applied at a time when the ships were three or four miles distant from each other."[8]

Sir David Cairns in attempting to reach a determination as to what point *Olympian* "came up" with *Nowy Sacz* turned again to his Assessors for advice, asking them to assume that if when *Nowy Sacz* came into sight of *Olympian* her stern light was visible "would a competent mariner consider that *Olympian* was coming up with *Nowy Sacz*?"[9] They answered in the affirmative. Since the Rules provided that the stern light be visible at a distance of 2 (now 3) miles it would seem reasonable to assume that a vessel overtaking another should consider herself bound by the Rule at this distance.

Such a conclusion would, however, seem to contradict the unchallenged decision in *The Banshee* that the Rule did not apply to the overtaken vessel at 800 yards when the difference in speed between the ships was only a knot. Sir Boyd Merriman we will remember had observed that not only must the respective speeds of the vessels involved be considered, but the lateral distance between the courses had to be taken into account in arriving at a minimum distance. Current, wind, sea state and turning characteristics of the vessel manoeuvring might also enter into the calculation. But while difference in speed between ships might seem to play a very significant part in the calculation a closer examination casts doubt on that assumption.

No matter at what speed a particular vessel is moving it requires only a certain approximate area in which to effect an evasive manoeuvre,[10] and it is that expanse of sea that has the most relevance in this matter. The length of that area, or distance ahead, would in most cases be something of the order of four ship lengths more-or-less. Admittedly, where the difference in speed is very great, say of the order of 20 knots or upwards, that difference has increasing significance in that the acceleration of speed of closing can bring vessels from a position of relative safety to one of hazard in a matter of a few minutes. Nonetheless, it would seem that the distance at which the overtaking rule begins to hold would be nearer a mile than a greater distance. It would, nevertheless, be imprudent to ignore the implications of the Rule until one reached that point. Once it becomes evident that one is proceeding into an overtaking situation one should consider the manner of passing long before reaching a point at which the Rule applies.

The overtaken ship should also pay close attention to vessels overtaking. While it is the duty of the latter to pass at a safe distance it would be imprudent to allow oneself to be closely crowded by an overtaking vessel if there is room to move over, and where the overtaking occurs in a narrow passage one could be held guilty of poor seamanship to force another to pass closer than advisable if there is room for the overtaken ship to alter away from the overtaking ship.[11]

It would seem then that the interpretation of the overtaking rule arrived at by Sir David Cairns is thus: A vessel coming up with another vessel from such a position that her stern light is in view on first sighting, and though while risk of collision may not exist at that time it might develop if both ships hold their courses and speeds, shall be considered an overtaking vessel within the meaning of the Rules. He hence found *Olympian* to be overtaking *Nowy Sacz* and reversed the findings of the lower court.

Unfortunately any interpretation that relies solely on the time of sighting of the stern light without taking into consideration the relative speeds of the vessels gives rise to serious difficulties, as Mr. Justice Brandon pointed out in the next case to be considered. Perhaps the only practical resolution of this difficulty is to take a most unorthodox view of the matter by suggesting that the overhauling* vessel becomes an overtaking one on first sighting the stern light of the overhauled ship, but the overhauled vessel does not necessarily become an overtaken ship at that time.[12]

If that view is adopted, the overtaking vessel is given no additional burden. She is free to manoeuvre as she sees fit as long as she keeps clear of the vessel ahead, as good seamanship would require in any event. In this view the overhauled vessel is relieved of the potentially absurd restriction of having to hold her course and speed for perhaps a matter of hours if she happens to be overhauled by a ship of very nearly equal speed. The time at which she becomes the stand-on vessel will be determined by the relative speed of the two vessels.

* * * * * * * *

Less than a year after this collision the Italian ship *Auriga* collided with the Spanish vessel *Manuel Campos*† off Cape Finisterre in somewhat similar circumstances, and it so happened that Mr. Justice Brandon was called to hear that case before the earlier one came to appeal.

The MV *Manuel Campos* was on a voyage from Bilbao to the Canary Islands when on the evening of January 11, 1973 she came abeam Cape Villano light 10½ miles off bearing 149°, at which point she changed course to 205°. The time was 1808‡ and the master was on the bridge with the chief officer who was feeling ill and was shortly relieved by the 3rd mate. Her speed was about 12 knots.

Auriga was bound from Gdynia to Bagnoli, Italy, on a course of 212° at a speed of about 14 knots. The chief mate had the 1600 to 2000 watch assisted by a cadet and two seamen who alternated as helmsman and lookout. At 1845 *Auriga* came abeam of Cape Villano 10.4 miles off. *Manuel Campos* was then about a point forward of the starboard beam some 2 miles off and being overhauled.

The officers of that ship were aware of the presence of *Auriga* at least since the time of *Manuel Campos*' change of course at 1808.[13] *Auriga* at that time was approximately broad on the starboard quarter of the Spanish ship before that vessel changed course when some 3 miles off, and *Auriga* was about 70° abaft the beam after the course change. She was clearly regarded as an overtaking ship and those aboard *Manuel Campos* proceeded to take no further notice of her until shortly before the collision.[14]

Aboard *Auriga* the chief officer had apparently been keeping a less than diligent lookout as he did not become aware of the presence of the Spanish ship until about 1910 when he claimed

---

* We will use the term "overhauling" to signify a vessel that is overtaking but not necessarily an overtaking vessel within the meaning of the Rules.

† *Manuel Campos* was 387′ in length and 4,259 gross tons; *Auriga* was 574′ long and 12,740 gross tons.

‡ The vessels were keeping different times and for simplicity's sake we will use that kept by *Auriga* throughout this account.

he observed her about 4 miles off abaft the port beam though she must have been in fact slightly forward of the beam. He also estimated her course to be about 220° and her speed at 17 knots. At no time, however, was there any attempt to make even the most rudimentary plot on the radar, nor was any use made of the radar for determining the distance off of *Manuel Campos*; nor for that matter was it used aboard the Spanish vessel. Based upon this completely fallacious estimate the chief mate of *Auriga* concluded that *Manuel Campos* " . . . was coming from the port side aft sector more than 22° astern of the beam and was overtaking the *Auriga* having a greater speed."[15]

At the trial counsel for *Auriga* in fact claimed that no particular attention was paid to the Spanish ship until some time later at about 1946 when the chief mate of the Italian vessel took a round of bearings to fix his ship's position. He maintained that the true bearing of *Manuel Campos* at that time was 122°. Mr. Justice Brandon took a somewhat more caustic view observing that the claim that no particular attention was paid before that time was, " . . . if anything, an understatement. I think it would be nearer the truth to say that no attention was paid to her at all."[16]

In any event *Auriga* had on coming abeam of Cape Torinana 10.2 miles off by radar changed course to 181° at 1922. That altered what had been heretofore a simple and safe overhauling situation, and beyond the reach of the overtaking rule since the ships were then on diverging courses that would have resulted in a minimum lateral separation when abeam of about 3 miles,[17] into a collision course crossing situation.

About ten minutes after this change of course *Auriga* altered briefly to starboard to avoid another approaching vessel, and then resumed her heading of 181°. *Manuel Campos* was then almost broad on the bow of *Auriga* and about 2 miles off, and the Court held that at that point the crossing rule took hold and the Spanish ship was obliged to keep out of the way of the vessel overhauling her over a point abaft her port beam.

Unfortunately scant attention was paid by either vessel to the movements of the other. Not only was no attempt made to make a radar plot but no effort was made to check the visual bearing of the other ship. The Court found the lookout on board vessels to be "seriously defective," and, "Because those on board either ship were not aware of the situation, then neither of them took any measures to deal with it. By the time those on board either ship realised that risk of collision existed, and took action to avert it, it was too late for such action to be effective."[18]

There was perhaps more than "bad lookout" at work here. Counsel for *Manuel Campos* indeed claimed that as she had originally been overtaken by *Auriga* that vessel's subsequent alteration of course to 181° did not thereby change her status from that of a burdened vessel to a privileged one. The Court rejected that argument, but insofar as *Manuel Campos* considered the movements of *Auriga* she very likely regarded herself to be the privileged ship, which would help to explain — though not justify — her apparent unconcern about the navigation of *Auriga*.

It is a notorious fact that the aspect of a vessel's lights can convey a very erroneous impression as to her heading, and without availing oneself of the information available by radar it may be impossible to tell if another vessel is converging, diverging or on a parallel course. Nonetheless, as the distance closed to under a mile careful observation would have shown that the courses were converging dangerously, and while it was clear to the Court that *Manuel Campos* was directly to blame for failing to give way it was just as clearly recognised that *Auriga* contributed to the collision by failing to take action until it was too late.

Mr. Justice Brandon hit the nail squarely on the head when he said:

> In this connection it is to be observed that, whereas in many crossing situations it may well be dangerous for the stand-on ship to act early under the proviso [note that the new rule allowing early action was not yet in effect], because her action may frustrate belated action to keep out of the way by the give-way ship, no such danger was likely to arise from the *Auriga* taking reasonably early action to alter her course to starboard away from the *Manuel Campos* in this case.[19]

Nonetheless, that consideration alone would not have rendered *Manuel Campos* any less culpable had it not been for the fact that this dangerous crossing situation did not arise fortuitously, but had been brought about by the deliberate act of *Auriga* when they were only

3 miles apart in clear sight of one another. A question of seamanship was involved here, and the Court turned to the Elder Brethren for advice. They suggested that *Auriga* was entirely at fault for setting such a course as to "take the water" of *Manuel Campos*, and it was not in accord with good seamanship.

Justice Brandon went on to cite Lord Justice Wilmer in the case of *The Tojo Maru* in 1968 where he said:

> It seems to me that no vessel is entitled, in face of another vessel seen to be approaching, to put herself deliberately on a crossing course in the position of a stand-on vessel, so as to force that other vessel to keep out of her way.[20]

While that case was related to a harbour collision where the vessels were in much closer proximity at all material times he, nevertheless, felt that the principle involved was clearly applicable. It would be difficult to quarrel with that view.

In consideration of all these facts the Court found that *Auriga* was mainly to blame, primarily due to the final consideration, and her share of the damages was assessed at 60 per cent.

* * * * * * * *

Before offering any conclusions we will turn briefly to one last case involving two large Liberian flag tankers which collided with disastrous results some 10 miles or so south of the Isle of Wight several years before.

Pacific Glory had diesel engines that drove her at a speed of about 15 knots. She was of 77,648 deadweight tons and carried a full cargo of light crude on a voyage from Nigeria to Rotterdam. She had embarked a North Sea pilot at Brixham on the afternoon of October 23, 1970 and was on a course of 087° designed to take her about a mile south of Bassurelle lightship.

Allegro was propelled by a steam turbine that gave her a speed of about half a knot more than *Pacific Glory*, and she was somewhat larger having a deadweight tonnage of 95,445 tons and had a full load of crude out of Libya to Fawley, England. She had passed abeam of Casquets on a course of 050°, which she maintained until 1940, when she altered to 060° about half an hour after sighting St. Catherine's light. Her master was on the bridge throughout assisted by the chief officer until relieved by the 3rd mate at 2000.

Pacific Glory was approaching the Isle of Wight on the port hand as the watch was changing at 2000 with the 3rd officer relieving the 2nd mate. The weather was fine with the visibility about 10 miles. The master had come to the bridge occasionally but around 1900 he retired to his cabin and remained there until the collision. There was an able seaman at the wheel but no lookout was posted. The tide had turned and was running down the channel at about half a knot. There was some conflict as to the use of the radar, the pilot said it was in use while the 2nd mate testified it was on standby. It was agreed, however, that at no time was it used to plot the courses of other vessels.[21]

Allegro was first noticed by the 2nd mate at about 1940 showing a red sidelight and open range lights at a distance he estimated at about 1 mile (it was actually over 4 miles). He reckoned its bearing to be a little abaft the beam, and though he had never seen her bearing more than two points abaft the beam he said she was gradually drawing ahead and he regarded her as an overtaking vessel. The pilot claimed he noticed her somewhat earlier about 25–30 degrees abaft the beam some 5 miles off, and he was sure she was seeing *Pacific Glory*'s stern light, though he admitted she might have had an occasional glimpse of the green sidelight and masthead light. He agreed under cross-examination that this meant that she was in a marginal position more-or-less than two points abaft the beam, but he insisted that she was an overtaking vessel throughout. Just how he could justify that conclusion since no visual bearings were taken and no attempt was made to plot her on radar he did not explain.[22]

At the time of *Allegro*'s course change *Pacific Glory* must have been between 4 and 5 miles off. Though the lights of a number of small vessels were seen to starboard during the hour prior to the change of the watch at 2000, and shore lights were seen to port, neither the master or the chief officer, who had the watch, was aware of any vessel to port.

When the 3rd officer relieved the mate at 2000 he said he scanned the horizon but did not see the lights of any ships. The master, however, contradicted that testimony saying that there were many ships around, though mostly to the south and none constituted any danger. The radar was apparently in use as the master obtained a position with it at 2000. Some idea of the alertness of the watch being kept was that in spite of the radar being in use and the fact that *Pacific Glory* was at that time little more than 2 miles off no one on *Allegro* was allegedly aware of her presence.

Shortly after eight o'clock a seaman came to the bridge with a cup of coffee for the 3rd mate and took up a station on the port bridge wing to keep a lookout.[23] He said that very soon after taking up that post he reported the lights of *Pacific Glory* a little abaft the beam but received no acknowledgment. He then moved nearer and shouted "Vessel to port" but could not say whether that was heard. Obviously it was not because the master remained unaware of the close approach of *Pacific Glory* until 2017 when he suddenly saw the lights of that vessel about 20° forward of the beam at a distance he estimated at 1 mile. He immediately ordered the engines placed on standby and sent a series of quick flashes on his masthead "blinker".

Pacific Glory, nonetheless, continued on her collision course yet the master of *Allegro* delayed taking any action himself. The Board of Investigation convened by the Liberian government in London found that neither vessel took any evasive action until about a minute before the collision at 2022. As they were little more than 1,500 feet to the point of collision at that time and would barely begin to enter their turn then it was too late. The master of the *Allegro* claimed that when the vessels were ten to twelve hundred feet apart, which would have been about a minute and a half before the collision, he rang stop on the engines and hard right rudder. The engine room bell book showed stop at 2022.

Pacific Glory had come abeam of St. Catherine's at 2015. *Allegro* was then roughly a mile off, and the pilot claimed she was then some five to six points on the starboard bow. She was in fact a point forward of the beam. For some time *Pacific Glory* had been overtaking a coaster about a point on the starboard bow and shortly after coming abeam of St. Catherine's the pilot decided he would have to haul over a bit to clear the vessel ahead. He accordingly came left to about 080° and after steadying on that course he said he observed *Allegro* now swinging sharply left as though under hard-a-port wheel. He responded to that threat by ordering hard left wheel and blew two blasts. The vessel answered very quickly to her helm but not long after she had commenced her swing the pilot seemed to detect a movement back to starboard by *Allegro*. The vessels were very close together now and in an attempt to avoid their sterns coming together he ordered the helm put hard to starboard, but it was to no avail and they came together on very nearly parallel headings. It was later concluded that the vessels came under the influence of interaction, as do all vessels in the moments just prior to collision, but it seems unlikely that interaction was any part of the cause.

These examples demonstrate very vividly the danger in the converging overtaking or crossing situation where close attention is not given thereby permitting an accurate appreciation of the applicable Rule in the particular case. But even where a determined attempt is made to evaluate the approach, ambiguity can be difficult to dispel. Where a ship is overhauled on the port side there is, of course, no problem as the overhauling ship will in all cases be burdened and obliged to keep out of the way. But an approach from the starboard side can be quite a different matter.

By night there should be less danger of ambiguity since the overhauling vessel's obligation should be defined by the lights of the overhauled ship. Conversely the bearing of the overhauling vessel will tell the overhauled ship which Rule should govern. Unfortunately where the bearing is very close to two points abaft her beam the overhauled vessel cannot be absolutely sure which of her lights are being seen by the other ship. Admittedly Rule 13(c) does provide that "When a vessel is in doubt as to whether she is overtaking another, the shall assume that this is the case and act accordingly," but the overhauled vessel cannot be certain as to whether the overhauling ship regards her situation as doubtful.

By day the risk of confusion is even greater since the overhauling vessel cannot know with any degree of assurance whether she is overtaking or crossing unless the course of the overhauled vessel is known. It is hence imperative that a careful plot be made early in the approach (unless unambiguous confirmation of the course has been obtained by VHF) in order to determine the ship's course as closely as possible. Manual plotting techniques undeniably lack precision, but in a situation like this where the plot can be developed during an extended period of time the course of the other vessel should be able to be determined within two or three degrees.

The overhauled vessel in this case may find herself in an awkward position. She cannot know whether the ship on her starboard hand will stand-on or give-way though she may herself feel quite certain that she is in a privileged position as an overtaken vessel. If she persists in insisting on her privilege she may find herself approaching close quarters before she has firm evidence that the other vessel does not agree with her assessment. It would hence be prudent to take action to avoid that development before the Rules forbid it.

Once the mariner finds himself in this most difficult situation his best option is probably a reduction in speed at a very early stage in the encounter, and if he is to reduce speed that reduction should be to the lowest practical level so that the situation is resolved as quickly as possible. That reduction need not be held long, as reduction from sea-speed to the lowest practical speed would in most cases lead to a decrease in average speed during the interval of at least 5 knots, which if held for twelve minutes would allow the other vessel to pass almost a mile ahead.

If sea room is available and the vessel is not hampered by other traffic to port a safe, simple and sure resolution of the problem is to make a turn of 90° to the left at some time before the distance between the two ships has closed to 1 mile. Even if that is followed immediately thereafter by a resumption of the original course the other vessel will clear ahead by a minimum distance of over half a mile where the course separation is as small as 1°,* and at correspondingly greater angles of course separation the distance of clearance will accordingly increase.

It will of course often be very difficult for the mariner to have a proper appreciation of the distance at which the Rules become applicable, and while the new Rule (17) governing the conduct of stand-on vessels allows them to "take action by [their] manoeuvre alone, as soon as it becomes apparent ... that the vessel required to keep out of the way is not taking appropriate action" one might be guilty of a statutory violation of the Rule if it had become operational. A statutory fault,[24] however, must contribute to a collision before it can be held to be a causative fault. In the United States the burden on the violator, following the principle laid down in *The Pennsylvania,* is to show that the infraction could in no way have contributed, and in most such cases that is extremely difficult.

Let us then consider the realities of the situation. For the fault to be causative it must increase the risk of collision. Certainly a turn to port away from the closing vessel could in no way be considered to increase the risk, nor could a reduction in speed allowing the ship two points abaft the starboard beam to draw ahead.[25] As these measures by themselves could not lead to collision no real objection to them can stand.

The position of the mariner on an overhauling vessel just under two points abaft the beam suffers from several additional handicaps. Where there is no clear view abaft the beam on the overhauled ship she may often be unaware of the approach of the overhauling vessel. If that vessel has the side and masthead lights of the other ship in view and regards herself as the stand-on vessel in a crossing situation she may approach very close before the port-hand vessel becomes aware of her presence. One of the most common misconceptions of mariners is to assume automatically that any vessel overhauling their ship is overtaking. In this case the conning officer of the overhauled vessel should, as advocated above, either slow materially or execute a "Z" manoeuvre to starboard in order to let the other vessel pass ahead.

Fortunately most overtaking situations are straight-forward with the ship to the rear having a clear view of the overtaken vessel's stern light by night, or by day, a plot or the other vessel's aspect distinctly indicates that she is being overtaken. The overtaking ship in such case simply makes such alteration as may be necessary to achieve a safe passing distance.

---

* We assume here a vessel of 600–700 feet in length with a normal tactical diameter of about 2,500 feet.

But how far should the procedure just discussed be carried? It is clearly most applicable where the angle of crossing or converging is most acute, begins to lose its validity as the angle broadens, becomes very questionable as the angle approaches 90°, and becomes inapplicable as it nears that point and passes beyond. Its outer limit of applicability in most cases could perhaps extend as far as 45° of separation between the courses.

In the cases just described we find within a period of little more than two years three collisions where all of the vessels involved seemed to suffer from a misconception as to what Rule applied in a converging overtaking/crossing situation. But aside from this several other mistakes and/ or oversights were common to these casualties. In all of them the collision could have been avoided had one of the vessels adopted the simple precaution of reducing speed for a brief period, but that step was apparently never considered until it was too late to be effective.

One reason for that was probably the common reluctance or refusal of many mariners to consider use of the engines as a manoeuvring option except *in extremis*. But in these cases it was simply an inadequate appreciation of the impending development of a close-quarters situation. There was first of all a poor lookout kept on all of the vessels. In spite of the fact that in all cases the collision took place during the hours of darkness in at least one instance there was no lookout posted.

Perhaps the most disturbing feature was that in no case was there an attempt to determine risk of collision by either the time honoured practice of checking the visual bearing of the approaching ship or by means of a radar plot. Indeed, while the radar was in use on all but one of the vessels (where it was on standby) no effort was made to monitor the movement of the other vessel let alone plot. The most basic precautions of collision avoidance were hence neglected and ignored on all of the vessels, which strongly indicates that the management of these ships was sadly defective, as the Liberian Board of Investigation concluded in the last case.

What would seem evident is that wherever two vessels come into collision in such circumstances neither will be able to avoid blame, and that is as it should be. Except under the most extraordinary conditions there can be no excuse for a collision on the open sea since there is no sufficient reason for either vessel to allow the development of close quarters, the avoidance of which precludes collision.

Notes   *   *   *   *   *   *   *   *

1 *L.L.R.*, 1976, Vol. 2, p. 692.
2 *Ibid.*, pp 687, 690.
3 *Ibid.*, 1977, Vol. 2, p. 95.
4 *Ibid.*
5 *Ibid.*
6 *Ibid.*, also cf. p. 98.
7 Page 98.
8 Page 96; also cf. *The Baines Hawkins-Moliere* (1893) as quoted in Cockcroft, pp. 95–6.
9 *Ibid.*
10 See R. G. Curtis, "An Analysis of the Dangers of Ships Overtaking", *Mathematical Aspects of Marine Traffic*; also Chapter Five.
11 Cf. J. W. Griffin, p. 180; also Marsden, p. 466.
12 There does seem to be some precedent for such a view, see Griffin, p. 163: "There is authority, under the Inland Rules, to the effect that the obligation of the overtaking vessel to keep out of the way exists at an earlier time than the obligation of the leading vessel to hold her course and speed . . . .".
13 *L.L.R.*, 1977, Vol. 1, p. 391.
14 *Ibid.*
15 Page 392.
16 *Ibid.*
17 Page 394.
18 Page 395.
19 *Ibid.*
20 Page 396.

21 *Report of the Liberian Board of Investigation*, p. 2.
22 *Ibid.*, p. 6. The pilot claimed he took a radar bearing at the time of sighting but that was contradicted by the testimony of the 2nd mate; no plotting was done.
23 The Board took the position that he had not been specifically ordered to assume the lookout and was hence a "mere volunteer," p. 7. That seems an unwarranted assumption. Lookouts may routinely take up their posts without specific instructions.
24 The doctrine of "statutory fault" seems to place an extremely onerous burden on a vessel so involved, and it was abolished in England in 1911 by the Maritime Conventions Act. Its practical effect has sometimes been alleviated by the "major–minor fault" rule whereby a minor fault by one vessel was overlooked when the other vessel was overwhelmingly to blame. Now that the U.S. courts have abandoned the divided damages doctrine the harshness of the "statutory fault" rule should be mitigated. Cf. Griffin, Ch. XV, and Gilmore & Black, pp. 404–08 for the doctrine of "statutory fault".
25 A speed reduction at this point could cause embarrassment if the starboard-hand vessel chose to turn at that time to the left to pass under the stern of the port-hand vessel, but only turning enough — say 30–40° — to pass narrowly astern at the port-hand ship's original speed. But such a manoeuvre would be grossly unseamanlike, and the port-hand ship's slowing could hardly be deemed caustic. Cf. Justice Brandon's observation in *The Auriga*, *L.L.R.*, 1977, Vol. 1, p. 295.

Appendix to Chapter Eleven

Explanation of author's conclusions of *Olympian's* manoeuvres

As sketch A shows there would have been no collision if the "facts" accepted by the courts were accurate. Notwithstanding this, the conclusions reached by them — reasoning from those "facts" — are not disturbed by this error, though it might have led the lower court to a different conclusion.

The courts rejected the claim of *Olympian* that she was on a course of 290° from the beginning to the end, and it was adequately shown that this could not have been so. The conclusion reached was that she was on a much more northerly heading of about 331°, and that she had been on that heading "since at least as early as 0245 and perhaps earlier" (*L.L.R.*, 1976, Vol. 2, p. 692). If that had been the case then *Olympian* would have had to have been on a bearing of over 30° abaft the beam of *Nowy Sacz* until only minutes before the collision when she would have started to draw ahead as the distance narrowed; if the bearings and times claimed by the 2nd mate of *Nowy Sacz* were accurate *Olympian* would have passed over half a mile ahead of *Nowy Sacz*. The most plausible supposition is that neither of the above were true (indeed could not have been) and *Olympian* was on a course of 290° when the vessels first came in sight of one another and then altered course to about 331° sometimes around 0330 (see sketch B).

There can be little doubt that *Olympian* was on a course of 290° (or very near to that) on her initial approach to Cape St. Vincent. Where then, and when, did she change to a more northerly heading? The master left instructions that he was to be called before the intended course change to 343° that he intended to steer from Cape St. Vincent. At about 0325 the 2nd mate was able to obtain a rough position showing that a course change to starboard was required in order to achieve the desired position off Cape St. Vincent. He allegedly called the master at around 0330 having quite likely laid down a course to take the vessel the same distance off Cape St. Vincent she would have passed had they made good the intended course. That course was probably about 331°. Perhaps he informed the master of this when he called him and was told to change course at that time, but if not then the course change was very likely made shortly after the master came to the bridge. But whether the course change was made shortly before 0330 or shortly after, the bearing of *Olympian* from *Nowy Sacz* was still more than two points abaft the beam of the latter (see sketch B).

After the course change the bearings steadied at about 122–123° relative and changed only very slowly until shortly before the collision at 0358. The bearing would only have begun to change noticeably some ten or twelve minutes before the accident (see sketch C). As the sketches show the bearing would have been approximately 110° at 0355, practically abeam at 0356, and about 80° on the bow at 0357 (see sketch D). Other than Justice Brandon's favourable impression of *Nowy Sacz*'s 2nd mate as a witness there was no good reason to place any great confidence in his credibility in this matter. It was rather unlikely that he paid any real attention to *Olympian* until she approached quite close. At the time she did change to an overtaking course she was more than two points abaft the beam (see sketch B) and he undoubtedly regarded her as an overtaking vessel obliged to keep out of the way, if he thought of her at all. He made no plot nor took no notes which would have lent any substance to his contention that *Olympian* was where he placed her at the times mentioned, and indeed she could not have been in any event. It may have seemed to him that she was abeam about half an hour before the collision, and that she was about 30° forward of the beam some fifteen minutes later, but our conception of time under such circumstances is notoriously unreliable.

What is certain is she was not where he claimed she was at the times indicated, and she was very likely quite close to where the sketches put her in the half hour or so leading up to the collision. She reached a position more than two points abaft the beam of *Nowy Sacz* before she changed to a collision course at about 0330. The situation was very similar to that between *Auriga* and *Manuel Campos*. Had there been no course change at around 0330 the vessels would have cleared, but the course chosen then by *Olympian* brought them straight into collision.

There was also dispute over the speed of *Olympian*. Her master maintained she was making only 13 knots, which the Court rejected and concluded she was instead making about 14.5 knots. She had a designed speed of between 15 and 16 knots and on the two days following the collision made 15.45 and 15.79 knots respectively.

During her approach to Gibraltar she made only 12.47 knots from noon until abeam Europa Point at 1430. From then until abeam Tarifa at 1600 the speed over the ground was 11.21 knots. That reduction in speed could be explained by the combination of the strong westerly wind often encountered in the Strait and the strong current set into the Med through the Strait. One can only reasonably assume that for the next hour she made the same approximate speed until course was changed to 290° at 1700. The position at that time would hence have been very close to 35°57.0′N. and 5°50.7′W. Assuming that *Olympian* reached a position of 36°33.6′N. 8°55.5′W. at 0330 (approximately 7 miles 151° from the point of collision accepted by the Court) she would have made 14.65 knots and a course of 283.8°. If she had been steering 341° since at least 0245 as the Court assumed she would have made good a course of 280.5°.

There was no suggestion or record of any substantial diversion from the course of 290° set at 1700. The normal currents experienced in the stretch from Trafalgar to Cape St. Vincent are not such as to account for a set of almost 10° to port, nor was any mention made of substantial wind from the north to account for it. These considerations, added to those already advanced, all argue for a course made good further to the right than 280.5° and a change from that course to about 341° at close to 0330 rather than 0245 or earlier.

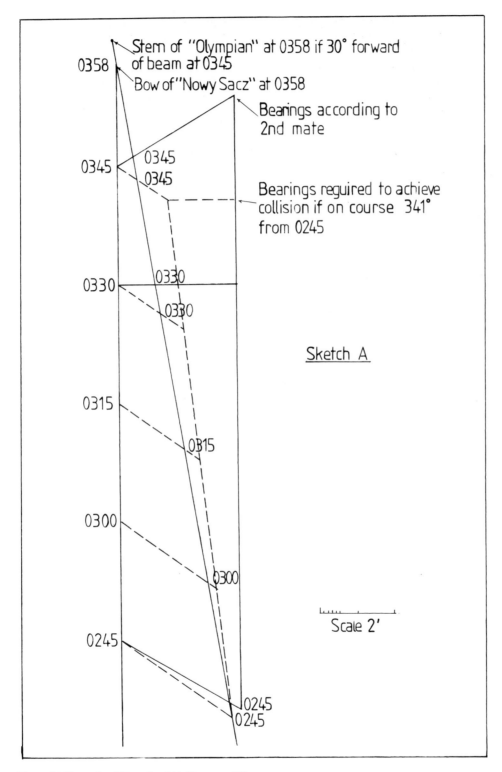

Figure 21 *Nowy Sacz/Olympian* (A) (See page 79)

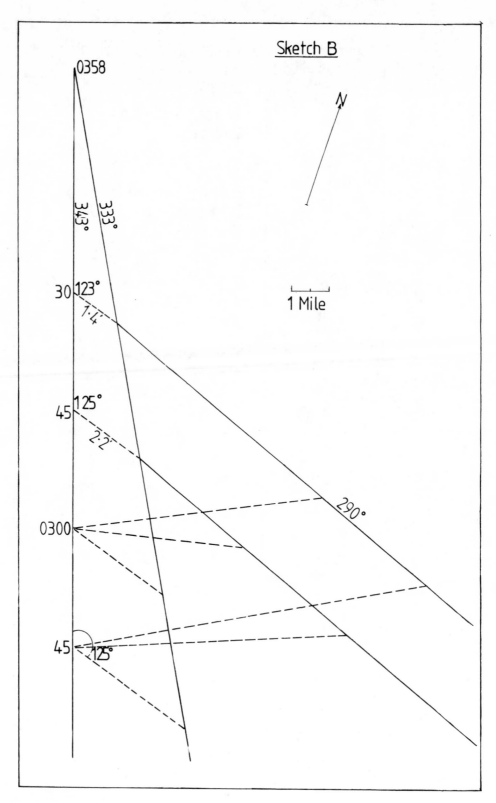

Figure 22 *Nowy Sacz/Olympian* (B)

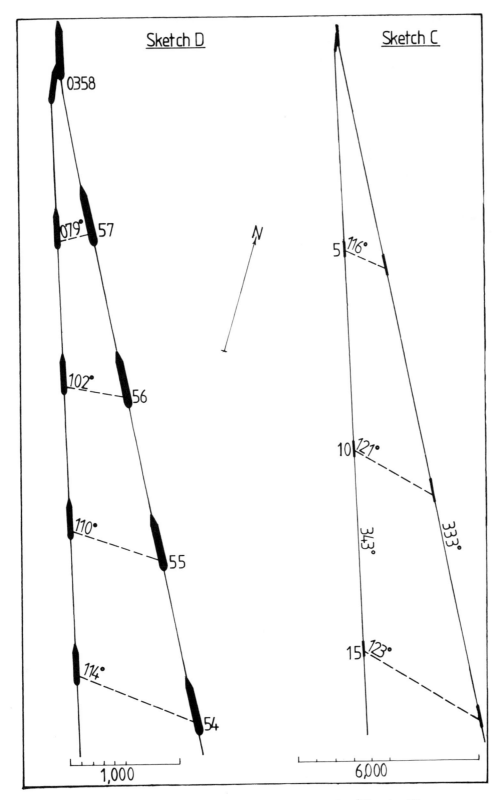

Figure 24 *Nowy Sacz/Olympian* (D)   Figure 23 *Nowy Sacz/Olympian* (C)

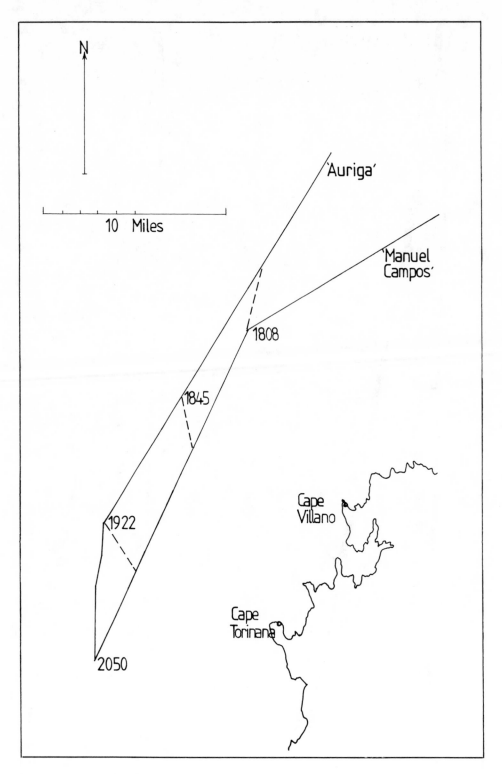

Figure 25 *Manuel Campos/Auriga* (See page 81)

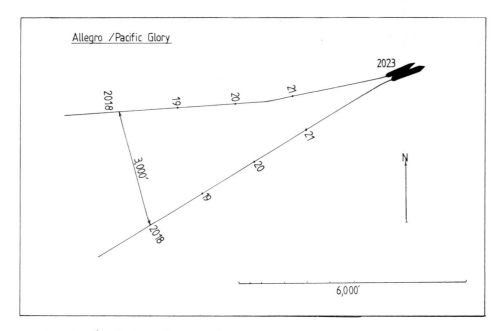

Figure 26 *Allegro/Pacific Glory* (See page 83)

Chapter Twelve

The Hazards of Close Overtaking

Up until fairly recently the typical collision casualty was between two meeting vessels. With the inception and subsequent widespread adoption of traffic separation schemes that situation has changed, or is changing, and the collision between overtaking vessels seems likely to become the most common, or at least a much more common, form of this casualty. If that is so then it might be well to look closely into collision cases between overtaking vessels to see what lessons they may hold. One that seems clearly to merit our attention occurred some years ago off Diamond Shoal between an American container ship and a Colombian general cargo vessel.

Transhawaii was a conventional C-4 cargo ship converted to a container vessel with a sea speed of about 17½ knots. At the time of the casualty, September 14th, 1972, she was en route from San Juan, Puerto Rico to Baltimore, Maryland. *Republica de Colombia** was a conventional freight vessel with a service speed of a little over 19 knots. She was bound from Jacksonville, Florida to the Virginia Capes.

Transhawaii had been steaming in fog for some six hours just prior to the collision and the master had been on the bridge for the whole of that time. The fog had lifted as the ship approached Diamond Shoal and *Republica de Colombia* (hereinafter referred to as *Colombia*) had overtaken her on the starboard side about half a mile off some minutes before.

The master of the American ship now decided to go below. It was the custom aboard that ship, as it is on many vessels, to fix her position at fifteen minute intervals when in such a situation near land or shoal water. The 2nd mate accordingly went to the port wing of the bridge to take a bearing of Diamond Shoal. The Colombian vessel at that time was probably little more than half a mile off broad on the starboard bow.

Colombia had been on course of 047° until about 1605 when course was slowly changed to 357°. *Transhawaii* must have been close to a mile off at the time, and as the Colombian ship was steadied on course the master saw that the two ships were on slightly converging courses. *Transhawaii* was steering 000° and maintained that course until immediately prior to the collision. At about 1622 *Colombia* altered course to the right to 005° to avoid passing the American vessel too close aboard, but about three minutes later changed to 000°.

Several minutes before the collision at 1644 the 1st officer of the Colombian ship, who was alone on the bridge — the helmsman was chipping paint on the deck below — noticed that the vessel's head had fallen off somewhat to port. Glancing at the rudder angle indicator he saw it showed left wheel of 10 to 15 degrees. He attempted to rectify that by switching from automatic to manual putting the wheel hard to starboard. The rudder not only failed to respond but went further to port. He then pushed a separate button on the steering stand that is

---

* *Transhawaii* was 611' long and 15,330 gross tons; *Republica de Colombia* was 512' in length and 11,656 gross tons.

supposed to direct the rudder to go in the direction ordered when held in the closed position. That too failed to have the desired effect and instead the rudder now went hard over to port. By now several minutes had elapsed as the mate fruitlessly attempted to restore steering.

He took a hurried look at *Transhawaii* closing on the port quarter and then repeated his attempt to restore steering from the console. He first tried the emergency push button, then the manual mode, and then once more the push button all to no avail. By now about three minutes had elapsed since he had first noticed the steering gear failure and up to now he had made no attempt to alert the master or summon the seaman on the deck below. It was now apparent that collision was imminent and he ran to the port wing and yelled to the master on the flying bridge. He then rushed back into the wheelhouse and sounded several short blasts on the whistle and rang "stop" on the engine telegraph.

The master, who must have been in a position to have a splendid view of the drama unfolding, apparently did not hear the mate's shout and continued to take in his laundry. A seaman, aloft in a bosun's chair painting a kingpost, was less oblivious, and seeing his ship swing across the bows of the American vessel shouted to the master. He scrambled down the ladder to the bridge wing just in time to see *Transhawaii* knife into his vessel's side just below the bridge.

On the American ship the 2nd mate had just finished taking the bearing of Diamond Shoal and turned to re-enter the wheelhouse when he saw *Colombia* swinging across the bow. He yelled to the able seaman at the wheel to put the helm hard left, but before that could take effect *Transhawaii* ploughed into the Colombian ship penetrating to her centre line.

There are numerous links in the chain of circumstances leading to this casualty, the absence of any one of which would have resulted in, at worst, a near miss. The first of these was the unnecessary closeness of passing. As has been shown in Chapter Five there is a period, and relative position, in any meeting or overtaking situation where a sudden and unexpected drastic course change by one vessel, such as may follow a steering gear failure, will make a collision inevitable. Once outside this "collision zone" careful attention to the movements of the other ship makes it possible by prompt action to avoid a collision, and the greater the initial passing distance the greater the "escape time". In all fairness it must be acknowledged that this sort of information has only recently become available, but common sense, which in this context is known as good seamanship, has always warned mariners of the dangers of unnecessarily close approaches.

The second mistake was the failure to have *Colombia* steered by hand as the overtaking situation developed. Steering-gear failures are not so infrequent that they can to all practical purposes be ignored. They are also much more common when the vessel is in the automatic-steering mode, so common prudence dictates that whenever another vessel approaches so close that a sudden steering failure or other aberration could put her across your bows (or vice versa) the vessel should be steered by hand.

The next error was the failure to sound a warning signal as soon as the situation began to develop. It might also be remarked that, although all this happened before VHF radios had become common, the value of establishing and maintaining contact by VHF during an overtaking or meeting situation could provide almost instantaneous intelligence of such a failure or difficulty.

The U.S. Coast Guard also cited the failure to back down in a timely manner, "which could conceivably have prevented or minimised the collision." In this particular instance the collision might have been narrowly avoided had the 1st officer of *Colombia* reversed the engines immediately after it became clear that the malfunction of the steering could not be rectified through the alternative modes available on the bridge. (When this case finally came to trial it was revealed that *Colombia* had suffered a recent similar steering failure and the 1st officer should have been aware of the futility of trying to rectify the fault from the bridge.)[1] To be realistic, however, it must be admitted that the first and natural reaction — and the proper one — would be to try to remedy the fault by switching to another steering mode. The manoeuvre of choice in almost any situation of developing close quarters is with the helm. To reverse the engines is the course of last resort, since if the vessel is making full way through the water the reversal of the engines would usually take so long to take effect as to have little positive result without some corresponding evasive action on the part of the other vessel involved.

In this particular case, had the engines been backed promptly, the collision might have been avoided, since the vessel's way would only have had to be reduced sufficiently to retard the vessel's movement through the water by less than a tenth of a mile for *Transhawaii* to have passed narrowly ahead.

The last and most important mistake was perhaps that made aboard *Transhawaii* by the failure to keep *Colombia* under constant close observation until *Transhawaii* was so far ahead as no longer to be an immediate threat.[2] *Transhawaii* had anyway the option of increasing the passing distance if she regarded it as uncomfortably close.

The responsibility for achieving a safe passing distance lay first of all with the Colombian vessel. Though most of the legal comment on the duty of the overtaking vessel to keep clear has been in an inland context, what applies in such restricted waters could certainly be deemed to hold with even more force where there is ample room to manoeuvre.

At least in the United States, the courts have taken a consistently clear position that the overtaking vessel in inland waters must pass at a safe distance. In some early decisions, yet to be successfully challenged, the courts were adamant that this was a duty the overtaking vessel could not avoid. In the case of the *Narraganset* the court stated: "True, it is not the duty of a faster boat to remain behind when she overtakes a slower one; but, if she takes upon herself the risk and hazard of passing, she must choose a *safe and sufficiently wide place* [emphasis supplied] where it may be done with safety to both. . . ."[3]

Justice Holland, in the case of the *Sif*, took the position that when *Sif* collided with *Murcia* while overtaking that vessel "it was her duty to pass at a safe distance and at a safe point."[4]

When the steamer *Gulftrade* collided with *Tarus* while overtaking, the United States Supreme Court held that, "There was ample room for the *Gulftrade* to pass. But if not, she should have slowed down and kept at a safe distance."[5]

Where such an unambiguous stance has been adopted in respect to a safe passing distance in inland waters, it would seem that logic would demand no less forceful a posture on the high seas.

In *A Guide to the Collision Avoidance Rules*, Cockcroft and Lameijer have summed the situation up succinctly where they say: "It would be good seamanship to move away, as far as it is safe and practicable, from the side of the fairway in which the overtaking vessel intends to pass, to allow a greater passing distance, and furthermore to reduce speed in order to decrease the period of running closely parallel to each other."[6]

While in the case under consideration here no blame was suggested on the part of *Transhawaii* for allowing the Colombian vessel to pass no more than half a mile off, it was incumbent upon her, if she chose to allow that to happen, to exercise the greatest diligence in keeping *Colombia* under observation until danger of collision was no longer an immediate hazard. That she failed to do.

There is, nonetheless, a limit to the closeness of approach that an overtaken vessel can allow and still escape at least partial responsibility for a collision, should one result. Griffin, in his comment on this point, says: "Even though the leading vessel has, in general, no duty save to hold her course and speed, still she must not do so stubbornly, and if, by a change, she can avoid an apparent danger, she must take it. Thus, where the courses are converging, so as to involve danger, and the leading vessel has ample room, she should swing off."[7]

As we saw in the preceding chapter where the case of the *Banshee* was cited it was held that "If the *Banshee* [the overtaking vessel] was, when the *Kildare* ported, so far astern that, with reasonable care, she could by altering her course have kept out of the way, then the *Kildare* was not to blame."[8] There was only a knot difference in their speeds and the distance separating them a bare 800 yards yet the Court held that the rule forbidding a course change was not applicable at that distance under the conditions obtaining at the time. If that be so, then in the case under discussion here an alteration to port by *Transhawaii* at any time up to the point of passing, and beyond, would have been both allowable and prudent.

While it may be debatable whether *Transhawaii* was in any way delinquent in not making some small alteration to port in order to allow more room for passing, it would seem quite clear that there was a lapse of judgment on the part of the 2nd mate in failing to keep *Colombia* under close observation until she was sufficiently far ahead to pose a threat no longer. Though the Rules clearly required the Colombian vessel to keep clear, even though she had passed, prudence would insist that the overtaken ship should remain alert to the possibility of some aberration or accident while the overtaking vessel was still so close.

One of the most common faults of otherwise competent watch-standers — as was noted in Chapter Five — is their assumption that, once it has been determined that another overtaking or meeting vessel will pass clear if course and speed are maintained, *the other vessel will in fact keep her course and speed.* Their experience may have lulled them into this belief and, unless they have learned the contrary by a very near miss or collision, they may have countless times passed quite close to another vessel under similar circumstances without any problem.

It is perhaps more common that not to find the watch officer taking a set of bearings, or in the chart room plotting them, with another vessel in just such a position as was *Colombia* when her steering gear failed. If his luck runs out at that point, as it did for the 2nd mate of *Transhawaii*, he will find that his diligence in fixing the ship's position, or other essential task associated with the navigation of the vessel, will almost certainly be taken as inexcusable lack of diligence in keeping a proper lookout.

If the navigation of the vessel, or such other necessary duty, is of such urgency that it cannot be delayed, when a passing ship is approaching and requires constant attention until clear, then that situation requires another officer on the bridge, since the keeping of a proper lookout can never be relegated to second place. The 2nd mate of *Transhawaii* learned that to his sorrow.

In apportioning the fault in this case the Court first of all considered the condition of the steering gear, the failure of which precipitated the collision. A month prior to this casualty a similar failure had occurred when the vessel was approaching Santa Maria, Colombia. The vessel was only able to complete her voyage on that occasion by recourse to the trick wheel on the stern.

The service man who was called in to correct the fault was unable to determine the cause of the failure but found two blown fuses, the replacement of which restored steering. While it should have been apparent to all concerned that the original fault that caused the failure had not been dealt with both the service man and the owner's representative seemed content to let the matter rest. The Court took a very grave view of this, holding that this lack of diligence rendered *Republica de Colombia* unseaworthy and she was hence unable to limit her liability in respect to the claims of cargo.[9] Taking this grave defect into account and the subsequent mistakes of the 1st officer following the failure of the steering system *Republica de Colombia* was held liable for 82½ per cent of the damages while the failure of the 2nd mate of *Transhawaii* to keep a proper lookout rendered her liable for the remaining 17½ per cent.

* * * * * * * *

Almost eight years earlier there had been a similar collision in the eastern Mediterranean on the 18th of September 1964. *Fogo*, a steam tanker registered in Lisbon, had departed Port Said on the morning of September 18th and was steering a course of 288°. At the time of the casualty she was steaming on only one boiler making about 11 knots through the water when she was overtaken by the British freighter *Trentbank** carrying a full cargo of a general nature from Australia to Liverpool. *Fogo* was likewise fully laden with a cargo of crude from the Persian Gulf to her home port.

Trentbank had been in the same convoy through the canal as the Portuguese vessel and at the time of overtaking was also steering a course of 288° making 14½ knots. The vessel was in automatic steering while the seacunny (Indian quartermaster), who would act as helmsman if need be, was painting on the deck below. The chief officer relieved the 2nd mate at 1555 and

---

* *Trentbank* was diesel powered, 487' long and 8,740 gross tons; *Fogo* was 629' in length and 17,557 gross tons.

during the normal routine of relieving, *Fogo* was pointed out 2 to 3 degrees on the starboard bow 2½ to 3 miles away on a similar course.

The mate was an officer of long experience and he could see at a glance that on the present course he would pass too close to the other vessel for comfort, and he later claimed that he accordingly altered first to 286° and then 284° intending to overtake the tanker at a distance of about a mile.

The testimony from the other side was quite different, and Mr. Justice Cairns (as he then was) found it more convincing. The 2nd officer of *Fogo* was on watch when *Trentbank* was first observed coming up from astern. She was originally on what appeared to be, and was, a parallel course and then altered a bit to port for a time before resuming her original course. He was relieved by the chief officer at about 1600 or perhaps a bit later, but he remained on the bridge until shortly after that time when *Trentbank* came abeam at a distance estimated at from 150 to 300 metres. *Fogo* was in automatic steering and the seaman on watch was on the port wing acting as lookout. He said he could see the name on the bow of the other ship and even hear her engines, and all the witnesses on both sides agreed that the names were distinguishable so it would appear that the distance between them was closer to *Fogo*'s estimation than *Trentbank*'s. [10]

The mate and the lookout on the Portuguese vessel both kept *Trentbank* under close observation, but the British mate seemed unconcerned with *Fogo* which he had now passed and he took up a position at a table in the wheelhouse where he proceeded to catch up on back entries in the deck log glancing up from time to time to look ahead. Some minutes later he heard a clattering of footsteps on the bridge wing ladder. They were those of the seacunny who had been painting on the deck below and had suddenly noticed his vessel's swing to starboard across the bow of *Fogo*. The chief officer looked up and saw *Fogo* through the wheelhouse window and his first thought was that the other vessel was swinging to port. He quickly realised that this was not the case and a hurried look at his compass confirmed that *Trentbank* was swinging to starboard.

While those on *Fogo* had been watching *Trentbank* draw ahead they understandably did not anticipate that she would swing across their bow. By the time it was realised that this was happening the British vessel was probably well into her turn. The mate and the lookout both noticed *Trentbank*'s swing at the same time and the former exclaimed "These people seem to be crazy" as he rushed to the wheel to put it hard right. [11] Before *Fogo* had time to respond to her helm her bow plunged into the starboard side of the British ship about midships flooding her engine room. She was later taken in tow by a passing vessel which brought her to anchor at Port Said where in worsening weather further flooding followed and she sank before she could be beached.

When the chief officer of *Trentbank* found she was swinging to starboard he hastily switched from automatic to telemotor and told the quartermaster (the seacunny) who had now taken the wheel to put it hard to port. He then tried to blow the whistle but no sound came from it. *Trentbank* was still swinging rapidly to starboard and as the mate rushed to the bridge wing to look at *Fogo* he saw her very close aboard heading directly for *Trentbank*. He dashed back to the wheelhouse and rang the general alarm just before *Fogo* struck her fatal blow.

Much of the evidence and testimony at the trial was devoted to the question of what went wrong with *Trentbank*'s steering. It was suggested that when the mate had made his last course adjustment on overtaking he had failed to re-engage the steering mechanism properly though he vigorously denied that. It also came out that the vessel had suffered several recent failures with its electric steering system. [12] In such case to leave the ship in that mode when approaching so close to another vessel was imprudent. No conclusion was reached as to what was the source of the steering failure in this instance, but we may recall that when the mate tried to blow the whistle on first noticing the failure nothing happened. If the whistle pull was electric as it almost undoubtedly was that would suggest that there was a failure of electricity to the bridge though that should have actuated some sort of alarm.*

---

* The gyro was not affected until power failed due to flooding of the engine room. A defective cable supplying both steering stand and whistle might explain it.

In any event the Court found the failure of *Trentbank* to keep a proper lookout with *Fogo* so close aboard so gross an error as to render her wholly to blame. The close distance of passing was not mentioned in the judgment but must have played a part in the forming of it. It was suggested by *Trentbank*'s counsel that *Fogo* was at fault for not reversing her engines, but in the seconds available for action that was not a realistic option and the Court dismissed it. Counsel also took the position that the Portuguese ship should have altered course herself to starboard to increase the passing distance when it became obvious that *Trentbank* was going to pass so close. That was a more attractive argument but the Court also refused to accept it (but see Griffin's comment on page 96).

While it might be unfair to blame *Fogo* for not taking action to correct *Trentbank*'s mistake (passing so close) the avoidance of close quarters must be a primary priority in every situation where vessels fall within the grasp of the Rules. The vessels were on the open sea with neither shoals nor other traffic to inhibit their movements, and while *Trentbank* was undoubtedly derelict in not hauling sufficiently to port to keep well clear of the vessel she was overtaking (relying here on the Court's assessment that the passing distance was no more than two cables)[13] there was nothing to prevent and certainly good reason to suggest that an alteration to starboard by *Fogo* would have been advisable. The failure of both vessels to have their ships steered by hand once they came into close quarters is also worth noting.

* * * * * * * *

A third very similar casualty took place in the Indian Ocean at the end of 1968 when the steering-gear of the Norwegian tanker *Frosta* jammed when she was overtaking the Liberian tanker *Fotini Carras*.* *Frosta* was steam powered with engines capable of propelling her at about 18 knots though it appears she was making about a knot less at this time. She was in ballast on a voyage from Japan to the Persian Gulf. *Fotini Carras* was diesel powered making about 16 knots, and she had sailed from Port Dickson in ballast also bound for the Persian Gulf. The wind was north-westerly force 3 to 4 and the weather was fine and clear. It was shortly after five o'clock in the morning about 15 miles off the coast of Travancore.

Fotini Carras was on a course of 312° on automatic pilot while *Frosta* was steering slightly to the right of that course and overtaking on the Liberian's port quarter. The master of *Frosta* had left orders for a course change to 327° at 0400 but the chief officer who came on watch at that time delayed execution of that order because of *Fotini Carras*' position on his starboard bow. As he gained on that vessel he altered first to 320° and about twenty minutes later to 325°, but as the bearing of the overhauled vessel did not change on that heading he came back to 315° after about five minutes.

Around 0515 he had reached a position just forward of *Fotini Carras*' beam. Though he later claimed that he was almost a mile off at that time and the chief officer of the Liberian ship thought the distance was about half a mile the testimony of expert witnesses convinced the Court that it was only about two cables. The mate of *Frosta* could tell that the courses were slightly converging and he accordingly told the helmsman (the ship was in hand steering) to steady on 310°. He then returned to the starboard wing to look at the other ship. He now heard the wing repeater start to click, and on looking at it saw that his ship was swinging to starboard.

He ran back into the wheelhouse and the helmsman told him the wheel had jammed. the rudder angle indicator showed 10° to starboard and he tried unsuccessfully together with the helmsman to move the wheel. He then switched to auto-steering but that made no difference so he put it back to manual and rang "stop" on the telegraph. No sooner had he done that then the quartermaster told him the helm was answering and he returned the telegraph to full ahead before running out to look at the ship close on his starboard side. Unfortunately the helm only moved a few degrees before jamming again. *Fotini Carras* was now about abeam due to *Forsta*'s swing and angling towards her. The mate now sounded a one blast signal on the whistle following with a second blast a moment later. He then rushed back into the wheelhouse and switched on the not-under-command lights but failed to extinguish the masthead lights. While

---

* *Fotini Carras* was 820' long and 44,646 gross tons; *Frosta* was 664' in length and 22,485 gross tons.

he was doing this the telephone rang. It was the watch engineer wanting to know what the stop bell had been for. The mate told him the rudder was jammed and they were about to collide; he then rang "full astern".

The chief officer of *Fotini Carras* had been watching *Forsta* closely during this time. The ship was in automatic steering with the helmsman acting as lookout. As *Frosta* drew ahead her side and masthead lights became obscured and the stern light came into view among the usual cluster of deck lights on the poop. As he watched her through the binoculars he thought she was steering more to the right than she had been on passing, and then the side and mast lights came back into view. He told the lookout to stand by the helm and looked again at *Frosta*. Her masthead and green sidelights were now showing brightly indicating that she was indeed turning towards him, and he went back into the wheelhouse and switched to manual steering telling the helmsman to steady on course.

He again turned his binoculars on *Frosta* and saw she was continuing to close. He blew the danger signal on the whistle and now ordered the helm put hard to starboard. He had heard no whistle signals from the other ship and it was later decided that his own signal had masked hers. He also failed to notice the two red lights of the not-under-command signal probably because the masthead lights were also burning. The hard right helm began to take effect and *Fotini Carras'* bow began to swing to starboard, but the swing of the other vessel was faster and she was getting very close. *Fotini Carras* now began to swing more rapidly, but there was not enough room. After she had swung twenty to thirty degrees the bows of the two vessels collided at a narrow angle of not more than 20°, and then collided again as their sterns swung together under the combined influence of imparted momentum and interaction.

At first *Frosta* tried to claim that she bore none of the blame as the jamming of the steering-gear was the result of inevitable accident, but her counsel soon abandoned that defence and sought instead to prove the involvement of *Fotini Carras*. The Court, however, would not accept that and found *Frosta* solely to blame. She was found remiss first of all for overtaking *Fotini Carras* at too close a distance as counsel for both sides accepted that ships of this size should not attempt passing at a distance of less than half a mile, a view with which the Elder Brethren concurred.[14] It was further found that *Frosta* was wrong in not stopping her engines and keeping them stopped as soon as it was found that her steering-gear had malfunctioned. She was also faulted for having a defect in her steering mechanism. The failure to extinguish her masthead lights on exhibiting not-under-command lights, though a fault, was not judged a causative one under the circumstances.

As regards the alleged faults of *Fotini Carras* the Court found that her chief officer "could not be fairly criticised for lateness in taking starboard wheel action."[15] Opposing counsel argued that the whistle signals sounded by *Frosta* and the exhibition of not-under-command lights should have warned the mate of *Fotini Carras* of the impending danger in time to have taken earlier action, and he agreed that had he either heard the whistle signals or seen the lights he would have given an earlier order to put his helm over. But he did not hear the signal or see the lights for the reasons previously explained and so was held blameless in these respects.[16] It was further suggested that he should have reversed his engines, but when the Elder Brethren were consulted they replied that "while the chief officer could reasonably anticipate the possibility of having to alter course a little if the *Frosta* came too close, he could not reasonably anticipate that he would need to manoeuvre with his engines."[17] Without having the engines on "standby" he could expect no prompt response to an engine order. But even had the engines been backed immediately at the same time as the wheel order was given the judge could see no reason to believe that the collision could thereby have been avoided.

Again as in the earlier case the Court would not countenance any suggestion that the overtaken vessel was open to any criticism for not having herself moved to starboard to increase the passing distance. That is probably as it should be since it would be very inconsistent if courts criticised even by implication stand-on vessels in such positions for failure to give-way before a position of *in extremis* had been reached. Nonetheless, we might note that the Elder Brethren suggested that such action might be desirable if the other vessel "came to close." We also have the authority of Marsden, previously noted, that an alteration made for greater safety when there is no risk of collision is not a fault. Indeed, the current Rules now provide that the stand-on vessel may "... take action to avoid collision by her manoeuvre alone, as soon as it becomes apparent to her that the vessel required to keep out of the way is not taking appropriate action in compliance with these Rules [17(a)(ii)]."

Where a vessel is being overtaken by another and it becomes obvious that the distance at passing will be inadequate the overtaken vessel could, and probably should, attempt to communicate with the overtaking ship so that a satisfactory agreement on passing can be reached. Where language is not a problem that can probably be done most easily by VHF radio. At night the initial contact can be made by a series of rapid flashes on the blinker or Aldis lamp; by day the vessel's name may be read off the bow as she approaches. If no response is forthcoming by the time the overtaking vessel is within a mile and she has made no course change to widen the passing distance it could be reasonably inferred that the "vessel required to keep out of the way is not taking appropriate action" and the stand-on (overtaken) vessel would be allowed on the grounds of good seamanship, if shoal water or other traffic do not interfere, to alter course so as to widen the separation between the two vessels. Indeed, it would be both prudent and practical to do so since with this new provision allowing such action a vessel involved in a collision such as these we have been investigating here might conceivably be held to share the blame for failure to haul off when there was nothing to prevent it.

* * * * * * * *

Notes

1 *A.M.C.*, 1979, p. 162.
2 Cf. *The Norwalk Victory*, 1949, *Farwell's Rules of the Nautical Road*, p. 442; also Marsden, *op. cit.*, p. 10.
3 Griffin, *op. cit.*, p. 171.
4 Page 172.
5 Page 175.
6 Page 77.
7 Page 180.
8 Page 174.
9 *A.M.C.*, 1979, pp. 176–88.
10 *L.L.R.*, 1967, Vol. 2, p. 215.
11 *Ibid.*
12 Pages 216–17.
13 Page 220.
14 *L.L.R.*, 1973, Vol. 2, p. 355. But cf. A. N. Cockcroft, *Safety at Sea International*, August 1974, pp. 32–34, where he disagreed with the Court's conclusion that the passing distance was no more than two cables. He found it unreasonable and unlikely that such an experienced officer would pass at such a distance when there was ample room to pass at a greater distance. He thought the distance to be between four and five cables.
15 *L.L.R.*, *ibid.*, p. 356.
16 Page 357.
17 *Ibid.*

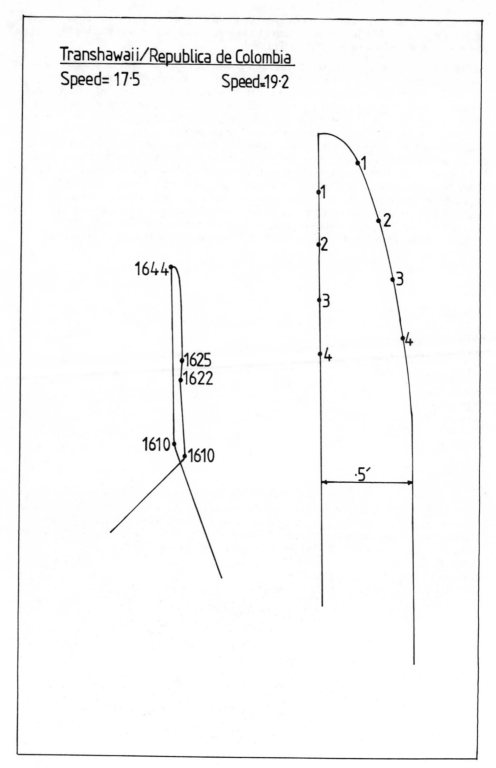

Figure 27 *Transhawaii/Republica de Colombia* (See page 94)

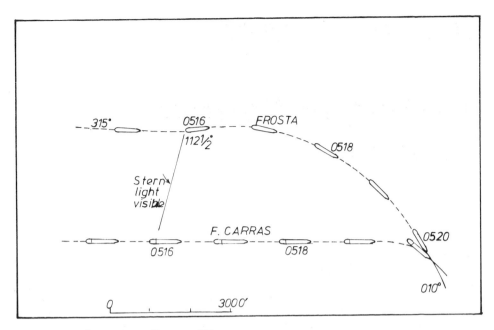

Figure 28 *Frosta/Fotini Carras* (See page 99)

Transhawaii locked into the *Republica de Colombia* after their collision 12 miles east of C. Hatteras. (U.S. Coast Guard photograph)

Chapter Thirteen

Meeting in Narrow Channels

During the mid-afternoon on February 25, 1963 the motor vessel *Abadesa* of London was bound down river in the Schelde Estuary on a voyage from Antwerp to Amsterdam. She had a full cargo of fuel oil with a maximum draft of about 32½ feet, the weather was overcast with visibility of 2 to 3 miles with a gentle to moderate easterly breeze, and the tide was flooding at about 1 to 2 knots. She had been proceeding at various speeds with her engines now at half ahead making about 5 knots through the water. She had a pilot aboard and had just rounded the bend at Bat after passing the No. 79 buoy when she sighted the Panamanian tanker *Miraflores** inward bound to Antwerp. That vessel was also conned by a pilot and had a deep draft of 34 feet.

The tides were at springs and it was about half an hour before high water at Bat. The Schelde River is one of the more difficult of the waterways serving a major port and the Bat Narrows is one of its more hazardous passages. Part of this is due to the fact that to the north of the main channel in this area lie a number of banks of varying heights with channels between them through which a considerable part of the water on a flood tide flows into the channel setting up what is known as the Zimmerman Polder cross-current.

The current varies substantially in strength over short distances making its effect difficult to anticipate and compensate for, and it was this strong and variable cross-current that played a significant part in the collision between these two vessels. So variable is the effect of this current that in the half hour or so before high water, especially on a spring tide, one vessel may experience a substantial effect while another following may feel little or none. Hence a vessel navigating within this stretch during that time must be prepared to counter the effects of the cross-current and to anticipate such effects on the navigation of vessels they meet or overtake in the vicinity. Under such circumstances the prudent thing is to try to avoid meeting or overtaking another vessel, if at all possible, in this particular part of the river.

Miraflores was during the early stages of this affair overtaking or had been overtaken by a coaster, *Johannes Schupp*. That vessel, probably by reason of her light draft,† was much more under the influence of the Zimmerman Polder cross-current, and contributed the first link in the chain of events that led to this casualty. *Miraflores* was about 5 to 6 cables below the N.v.B/S.v.B. buoy that marks the down-river end of the Bat Narrows when she saw the coaster — which was about half to three-quarters of a mile ahead at that time — suddenly sheer to starboard, then to port, and again back to starboard ultimately turning through 360° before she was able to extricate herself from the treacherous cross-current.

On observing the difficulties of *Johannes Schupp* the pilot of *Miraflores* immediately reduced

---

* *Miraflores* was 661′ long and 20,776 gross tons; *Abadesa* was 565′ in length and 13,750 gross tons; *George Livanos*, which grounded in trying to avoid these vessels, was 645′ long and 18,790 gross tons.

† The cross-current was a surface current running only to a depth of about 6 metres.

speed. The coaster having recovered passed on up river and caused no further difficulties, but the reduction of speed by *Miraflores* rendered her more liable to the effects of the cross-current and set in train her unfortunate reaction to it that resulted in the collision and the subsequent loss of the life of her master and chief officer.

When it became apparent that *Johannes Schupp* was back under control and would probably cause no further problem the pilot of *Miraflores* put the engines to either half or full ahead during the final two minutes before the collision. She was now just about off No. 71 buoy when she took a sudden sheer to starboard to a heading of between 80 and 90 degrees. To counter that the helm was put hard to port and as the starboard sheer was checked and the vessel began to swing back to port right wheel was applied to steady the ship. The cross-current coming out of the Zimmerman Polder, however, was too strong at this point and she continued to swing across channel into the path of the outbound *Abadesa* about half a mile or so up stream.

Ahead of that vessel, also outbound, was the 10,488 gross ton *Caltex Manila* which managed to squeeze by *Miraflores* before she crossed over to the northern side of the channel. *Miraflores* now put her engines full astern and attempted to let go both anchors, but only the starboard dropped. She also tried to signal her difficulties by blowing four short blasts — a local signal meaning: "You must keep out of my way, I cannot manoeuvre," but for some unexplained reason only two short blasts were blown.

Abadesa up to this point saw nothing to be concerned about. So blissful was her unawareness that she apparently did not even note the passage of *Johannes Schupp*, but more importantly no one aboard her saw *Miraflores* until *Abadesa* was almost abeam No. 77 buoy that marks the upper end of the entrance to the narrows.[1] *Miraflores* was now about half a mile away and angling across the channel.

Abadesa was also occupying the middle of the channel and kept there in spite of the obvious difficulties of *Miraflores* hoping no doubt that she would be able to extricate herself from her precarious predicament before *Abadesa* reached her position. Not only was she now entering a most dangerous stretch of a river whose navigation requires no little skill and attention, but a large tanker was clearly experiencing difficulty in the lower reaches of the narrow channel into which both vessels had to pass. Yet the British vessel was apparently not yet awake to the full hazard of her position and even delayed reducing speed until approximately two-and-a-half minutes before the collision.

On approaching the No. 77 buoy the engines had been briefly put to full ahead to assist her around the bend at that point. They were then worked ahead between slow and dead slow for the next two minutes, and then subsequently between dead slow and half ahead until she rounded the No. 75 buoy that marks the first leg of the Narrows. The heading was then about 240° which she held until the collision a few minutes later.

Shortly after *Abadesa* passed the No. 75 buoy *Miraflores*, which had hitherto been keeping well to her side of the channel, was now seen angled to port. The ships were then separated by perhaps half a mile, but *Abadesa* still kept to the middle of the channel hoping that the heading of *Miraflores* was only a temporary aberration that would be quickly corrected and so took no measures to take way off the vessel in the event that her hopes were not justified.[2]

When she heard the two blasts previously alluded to she belatedly realised that the difficulty being experienced by *Miraflores* was now assuming a decidedly dangerous aspect. She then stopped her engines and a minute later put them to emergency full astern, sounded three short blasts and let go her port anchor. This action came far too late and about a minute later still making almost 6 knots through the water her stem struck *Miraflores* at an angle between 60 and 70 degrees leading aft between her number four and five tanks igniting the oil that spilled out from her ruptured hull.

George Livanos, a deep loaded tanker also registered in Panama, had left her berth in Flushing shortly after 1300 not long after *Miraflores* had passed. *Livanos* was also bound up river and she followed *Miraflores* at a distance that while at first was between 2 and 3 miles gradually lessened to about one, and that interval was thereafter maintained with some difficulty because *Miraflores* was apparently trying to reach the entrance to the Bat Narrows at high water and had slowed accordingly.

As *Livanos* neared the N.v.B./S.v.N. buoy at the southern end of the Narrows the distance between the ships had decreased to around half a mile, which was about half the distance that was regarded as safe. *Abadesa* was then seen coming down river (as must also have been *Caltex Manila*) and she reduced speed to widen the distance between her and *Miraflores* so that when *Miraflores* took her sheer to port when abeam the No. 73 buoy *Livanos* was a mile or less astern.

What those aboard *Livanos* had apparently failed to notice was the preceding sheer to starboard after *Miraflores* had slowed because of the difficulties experienced by the coaster ahead of her. The pilot and master of *Livanos* were unaware of these facts and so unable to appreciate the dangerous situation developing. The pilot did mention seeing a slight motion to starboard by *Miraflores*, but so substantial a sheer should have been more readily noticed and its significance appreciated if *Miraflores* had been more closely watched during this critical time.

Had *Livanos* reacted more quickly to the developing disaster ahead she would not have shortly found herself in such serious difficulties, but presumably suffering from the same false optimism prevailing aboard *Abadesa* she kept on at half speed rather than stopping or reversing her engines as the Court decided she should have done at this point. She maintained her speed until she saw the collision, and perhaps even a minute or so longer when it finally became apparent that she might take a more direct part in the casualty she had just witnessed if more extreme measures were not quickly adopted.

The master of *Livanos* then took over from the pilot. He looked first at his radar to determine the distance off the unfortunate vessels ahead. He next reduced to slow from half ahead and followed that almost immediately by a double ring full astern at 1621, about a minute after the collision. The distance off was then some nine cables. He next ordered hard right rudder in an effort to turn the ship down river and passed word to let go the starboard anchor, which not surprisingly ran out to its bitter end and parted. The port anchor was then dropped and the vessel continued to swing under the influence of her starboard helm, but several minutes later she grounded on the south bank of the channel about a ship length up river of the No. 71 buoy on a heading of 135°. It took ten tugs to get her off the following day and their salvage claim was sought to be shared with those whose unfortunate collision had precipitated the action that led to the grounding.

In open waters the avoidance of close quarters is the obvious key to the prevention of collisions, and that is the primary objective of the Rules. Unfortunately in narrow channels and waterways pilots find close quarters so common an occurrence that they tend to overlook those measures that might limit their exposure to this hazard-fraught situation. Deep-sea sailors, whose every-day experience is of a different nature, habitually regard — or should regarded — the approach of close quarters as a development they should normally avoid and only accept with a keen appreciation of its dangers when rendered unavoidable by a necessary venture into confined waters.

It is hence incumbent upon ships masters and others in charge of navigation aboard ocean-going vessels that they guard against any unnecessary exposure to the close passage of other vessels in pilotage waters. One of the most important points in passage planning is to pin-point those parts of the passage, when the vessel is under the guidance of a pilot, where such things as current, dangerous confinement or configuration of the channel, or other hazards to navigation dictate the avoidance of an encounter with another vessel. It is normally both unnecessary and unwise to interfere and intrude upon the normal conduct of the pilot in the conning of the ship. It is conversely both necessary and prudent to make clear to the pilot as soon as convenient after boarding that he must take such steps as necessary so as to avoid passing other vessels at such points of hazard.[3] Fortunately in most of the world's ports today pilots habitually utilise VHF radio to monitor the traffic in their pilotage grounds and so can easily adjust speed to avoid situations such as led to the casualty just described.

The fact that this can easily be done does not necessarily mean that it will be done, and it is incumbent upon the master and his watch officers to see that it is done and to monitor such exchanges of information and intention. At the time that this disaster took place the use of VHF for such purposes was only beginning to be used in some places in the United States and Canada. Nonetheless, the common practice of seamen and the specific practices of the port warned against the meeting of vessels in such circumstances. Article 42(1) of the Rules of Navigation in Netherlands Inland Waters state:

> When vessels are meeting in a channel where a current is running, near a narrow passage, bridge, jetty or bend, the passage of which is so narrow that proceeding at the same time would be dangerous, the vessel proceeding against the current, will [hold back], until vessels proceeding with the current have passed the passage, bridge or bend, or have passed the jetty.[4]

As the Court pointed out, even without the specific regulation the principle embodied in it was a well established principle of good seamanship. Only a few weeks before a notice had been issued warning specifically about observation of this regulation, particularly in "the bend of the Bat."[5]

In arriving at a judgment Mr. Justice Hewson gave great weight to the failure of *Abadesa* to maintain a sufficient degree of diligence so as to discover the approach of the inbound vessels in sufficient time to abide by the relevant River Regulation requiring her to hold back and allow them unrestricted passage. She exacerbated her fault by keeping to the middle of the channel when the Rules required her to keep to the starboard side. She was also deemed at fault for proceeding at such a high rate of speed under the circumstances that she was unable to hold back when *Miraflores* took a sheer across her path.

While the fault of *Abadesa* was held to be great and grave the conduct of *Miraflores* was not considered blameless. She not only for some never determined reason failed to sound the required four blast warning signal but improvidently delayed in attempting to give it. She was also criticised for failing to back down and drop her anchor when she lost control of her movements so that she might swing upriver under the influence of the tide and so clear the channel for other vessels to pass. Her fault, however, was seen as nowhere so extreme as *Abadesa*'s and so was assigned only one-third of the blame compared to the two-thirds given to the outbound vessel.

The claim of *George Livanos* was next to be considered. While her own misfortune stemmed directly from the faults that led to the collision, she had not exercised that degree of prudence that would allow her to avoid all censure. She kept on a minute or so after observing the collision before stopping and reversing, and the Court held that had she taken action earlier her way would have been so reduced that her anchors might have held allowing her to swing clear without grounding. Though she was found "the author of her own subsequent misfortune" the negligence of all three was seen to be so entwined as to make it unfair that she bear the sole burden of her mishap. She was accordingly held only 50 per cent responsible for her damages and the other two shared the balance in the same proportion as in the first instance.

* * * * * * * *

On New Year's night of 1971 the Danish coaster *Thuroklint* collided with the Harwich/Hook of Holland ferry *Koningen Juliana** in such circumstances wherein the former's failure to abide by the provisions of the "narrow channel" rule was seen as dominant in respect to a series of faults by the latter.

The coaster was inbound on a voyage from Trollhatten in Sweden carrying a cargo of chemicals in drums bound for Ipswich. The weather was fine and clear with a light west–north-westerly wind and flood tide of half a knot or less. *Thuroklint* was under the con of a pilot embarked at the Sunk lightvessel, who in the moments preceding this affair disembarked about a cable length north-west of the North Shelf buoy where he was relieved by an Ipswich district pilot. At the time of the change of pilots the engines were on dead slow and the ship's head was about 314° from where she could proceed directly up the River Orwell to Ipswich.

With the change of pilots about 2212 *Koningen Juliana* (hereinafter referred to as *Juliana*) was pointed out to the new pilot by the master showing her masthead and green sidelight on the

---

* MV *Thuroklint* was of 300 gross tons and 150′ in length; the Dutch motor vessel *Koningen Juliana* was 6,682 tons gross and 431′ long with two variable pitch propellers, a bow thruster, and wheelhouse control of her engines.

port bow. The master who had been steering turned the wheel over to the pilot who assumed the con, and as soon as the pilot launch was clear the engines were put to full ahead which would give a speed of around 9 knots within a few minutes. Course was also altered slightly to starboard so as to put Orwell No. 1 buoy fine on the starboard bow with the Walton buoy just to the right of it.

The Dutch ferry had just left her berth at Parkstone Quay and was approaching the Guard buoy on a course of 085°. In keeping with her normal manoeuvring procedure she had only two of her four engines in use at the time and was working up to a speed of 8½ knots. Her speed was reduced momentarily as she approached the Navy Yard Wharf and her course changed slightly to port to 080°. At about this time *Thuroklint* was seen by the master on the ferry's true-motion radar between one and one-and-a-half cables to the north-west of the North Shelf buoy proceeding very slowly on a north-westerly heading. Both the master and the pilot of the ferry saw her visually well on the starboard bow showing a red sidelight with her masthead lights slightly open. The pilot thought she was almost dead in the water as the master had unfortunately not mentioned the movement he had observed on the radar.

It was the normal practice on the ferry to change course at the Guard buoy to 115° if traffic conditions permitted, and it was the assumption of the pilot on the coaster that she would do so. As *Juliana* came abeam of the buoy at about 2215 the pilot accordingly told the helmsman to come right easy to 115°, but as the ferry swung he amended his order telling the helmsman to steady on 109° as believing the coaster dead in the water he felt she might interfere with him taking a course that far to the right. He informed the master of his decision to pass *Thuroklint* starboard to starboard, and perhaps not realising the pilot was not aware of the coaster's movement the master said nothing about it. The small Danish vessel was then 7 to 8 degrees on the starboard bow. On making his course change the pilot sounded two whistles rather than one as an invitation to the coaster to accept a green-to-green passage, and he repeated the signal shortly thereafter.

Those aboard *Thuroklint* heard neither of the whistle signals, which was perhaps just as well as they were more likely to confuse than inform. While it was agreed that *Thuroklint* was guilty of a defective aural lookout in failing to hear these signals the Court concluded that it could hardly have contributed to the collision that shortly followed. The pilot of the coaster, fully expecting the ferry to change course at the Guard buoy so as to pass port to port, was puzzled when he observed no change since *Juliana* did not change enough to show her red light. He accordingly altered about a point more to the right in order to allow more room for the ferry to haul to starboard as he expected her to do. He neglected, however, to signal his alteration on the whistle.

When the coaster did not answer *Juliana*'s whistle signal both the master and the pilot became apprehensive, particularly as they both now realised that the coaster had increased her speed and was altering to starboard. The master took over at this point ordering the helm to port and both engines backed full. He followed this by ordering both anchors dropped and blew three blasts on the whistle. The starboard anchor went almost immediately but before the port could be released the bow of the ferry struck the port side of the coaster flooding her single hold.

Meanwhile *Thuroklint*, still expecting the ferry to haul to starboard but disappointed in that expectation, put the helm hard-a-starboard in an attempt to come round on a parallel heading with *Juliana*. Though she was capable of turning very sharply she could not turn quick enough to avoid the collision, and with her single hold flooding rapidly she was in imminent danger of foundering. Luckily she was not far from shallow water and by continuing on at full speed she was able to reach a position of relative safety before the last of her buoyancy was lost.

Though there were a number of questions before the Court the main point to be settled was the position of the collision so that the issue of whether the coaster was on the proper side of the channel could be resolved. The faults of *Juliana* were dealt with first, however, but not before some time was wasted in consideration of the flawed claim of counsel for *Thuroklint* that the limits of the channel, and hence its mid-point, were defined by the boundaries of the navigable water available to the vessels rather than the line defined by the buoyed channel. If that claim were carried to its ultimate absurdity one vessel could be guided by one set of limits and another by a different set.

The ferry was first of all found at fault for failure to appreciate the movement of the coaster through the water through the information available, i.e., the true motion radar, and to navigate *Juliana* accordingly. Her second fault was in attempting to effect a starboard-to-starboard passing by failing to haul sufficiently to the right on passing the Guard buoy. That stemmed from the first fault in not realising that *Thuroklint* was underway, but even so the ferry could have safely come to a heading of 120° or even 125° if necessary so as to show the coaster a red light and forestall confusion. The final mistake was in once having decided to take an unorthodox course and try to pass green to green the pilot should have stopped or even backed the engines so as to prevent the development of close quarters until it was clear whether the coaster would accede to this proposed departure from normal practice.

On the part of *Thuroklint* the Court held that she had first erred in changing pilots on the port side of the channel. She knew that the ferry would be leaving her berth at this time, and she should have kept well to the starboard side of the channel so as to preclude the sort of confusion that did in fact arise. But having once fallen into this error she could have quickly righted it by hauling boldly to the right so as to get "into her own water as quickly as possible."[6] She was next faulted for failing to hear the two whistle signals as noted earlier, but that was dismissed as of no consequence. Her action in coming hard-a-starboard just prior to the collision next came under fire, and relying on the advice of the Elder Brethren it was decided she should instead have gone full astern. Her final mistake was failure to signal her alterations to starboard with the required whistle signals. In fact the pilot of *Juliana* declared that had he heard a one blast signal he would have immediately backed his engines. With such a clear preponderance of faults against the Danish ship it was held that she should be held responsible for two-thirds of the damages. On appeal both were held equally to blame, but when the case reached the House of Lords the original decision of Mr. Justice Brandon was affirmed.

* * * * * * * *

The last of our narrow channel investigations concerns an incident that took place not on pilotage grounds where such accidents usually occur but in the narrow passage known as the Irako Suido where the Bay of Nagoya enters on to the open sea.

On the evening of March 11, 1972 the Pakistani motor vessel *Moenjodaro* was outbound from Nagoya when she encountered the inbound British motor ship *Glenfalloch** on her way to Nagoya from Shimizu. Both were conventional dry cargo vessels, modern and well equipped. The British ship had, among other things, two true motion radars but curiously no course recorder. She had a sea speed of 21 knots compared with 18–19 knots for *Moenjodaro*. The Pakistani vessel, however, was inhibited in her ability to manoeuvre by the fact that on departure about an hour earlier a switch from diesel oil to heavy fuel oil had been made which rendered her unable to respond readily to any sudden order for a reduction in speed. This is an apparently common though questionable practice in the circumstances.

Though it was dark the visibility was excellent and there was a southerly current of about $1\frac{1}{2}$ knots setting out of the large bay in which Nagoya is situated. The entrance to this bay is through the Irako Suido (channel), which has a navigable width of little more than a mile and-a-half at its narrowest part. There are numerous rocks and shoals in the vicinity but there are ample navigational marks and aids. A flashing red buoy lights the pinnacle of rock called Ashai Sho on the north-east side of the fairway and two flashing green buoys mark two rocky patches on the south-west.

The axis of the channel is defined by two flashing white buoys one of which is situated about 4 miles to seaward of the narrowest part of the channel; the other lays about a mile inside. The distance between them is approximately 5 miles and the courses along the axis of the fairway are 133/313 degrees.

Glenfalloch was approaching the Irako Suido on a course of 268° when the 3rd officer came on watch at 2000. The master was on the bridge but had not yet assumed the con. Though the

---

* *Glenfalloch* was 550′ long with a gross tonnage of 9,640; *Moenjodaro* was 506′ in length and 8,917 gross tons.

vessel was still on sea speed the master had prudently given instructions at 1943 for the engine room to be ready to go on standby in about forty-five minutes time if that seemed desirable. The chief officer was also on the bridge to assist if necessary. The vessel was in hand steering and there was a lookout on the bridge wing.

At 2020 the 3rd mate obtained a position that placed the ship a mile or so east and slightly north of the No. 1 buoy that marked the southern extremity of the Irako channel. The master now assumed the con and at 2023 with the vessel about 2 cables off with the buoy bearing 187° course was altered to 313°. After this course change two outward bound ships were observed on the port bow. The closest was showing a red light and passed half a mile off to port around 2030. The furthest one off, however, was showing green fine on the port bow of *Glenfalloch*, which indicated a narrow angle crossing if both vessels continued on.

The Irako Suido can present some nasty problems if one encounters an approaching vessel in such a position. Though the navigation of the channel presents no particular difficulty it does require strict attention or one can quickly find oneself in trouble. There are frequently numerous fishing boats in the area to hamper freedom of manoeuvre, and it is relatively rare to effect a passage without encountering traffic. The master of the British ship hence probably felt some apprehension in the situation in which he found himself, and at 2025 he had the engines placed on standby and ordered revolutions reduced from 112 to 95, which would give a speed of approximately 18½ knots after way was run off.

On *Moenjodaro* the master was also at the con as was to be expected in approaching a narrow channel. He was assisted by a 3rd officer and apprentice, and while the vessel was being steered by hand there was no mention of a lookout. At the trial considerable confusion arose over the navigation of the Pakistani ship in the moments leading up to the collision, and Mr. Justice Brandon who heard the case was convinced that alterations had been made to the chart in use after the event in order to present a more favourable view of *Moenjodaro*'s navigation.[7]

What was not in dispute, however, was that *Moenjodaro* was steering a course of 123°, a full 10° to the left of the axis of the channel, and at the time of the collision was well to the east of the axis and in the inbound fairway. In fact so gross was her fault that *Moenjodaro* accepted 60 per cent of the blame at the outset and only sought to limit her liability to that figure.

During the approach to the Irako Suido *Moenjodaro* was on a course of 133° according to her deck log, but the course recorder shows her heading to have been between 131 and 132 degrees during that time. It would appear, however, that she had set some distance to the west of her charted track, and at 2005 when the ship must have been in a position approximately 8.6 miles 302° from the No. 2 buoy that marks the northern extremity of the channel course was changed to 123°, and except for minor deviations she remained on that heading until shortly before the collision at 2036½.

No reasonable explanation of why the master of *Moenjodaro* chose to take this dangerous course was offered at the trial, which leads one to surmise that he lacked a proper appreciation of the peril of his venture and was perhaps in ignorance of the applicability of the narrow channel rule in the prevailing circumstances. In any event both the master and the 3rd officer claimed to have first become aware of the approach of *Glenfalloch* as they passed about half a cable to the east of the No. 2 buoy at 2031.[8] *Glenfalloch* would have been about 2½ miles off at that time, which indicates that a very poor lookout indeed was being kept on *Moenjodaro*.

With the British ship fine on the starboard bow showing a red light and an imminent meeting in the middle of the Irako channel there was only one possible sane course open to the master of *Moenjodaro*: an alteration of course to starboard of at least 10° so as to pass the stand-on vessel port to port. Yet nothing was done, perhaps in the foolhardy hope that *Moenjodaro* would narrowly cross ahead or in the almost equally foolish and hazardous expectation that the inbound vessel would herself give way.

At about the same time that *Moenjodaro* became aware of the approach of *Glenfalloch* that vessel was just passing the first outbound ship and a position obtained by the 3rd mate showed her to be 2.4 miles from the Kami Shima lighthouse bearing 338°, though she was probably a bit to the west of that position. The master of *Glenfalloch* regarded the outbound ship as crossing and burdened, and expected her to giveway to starboard.[9] As the outbound vessel continued to stand on with the distance closing rapidly the British master become increasingly concerned at the failure of the approaching ship to give way, and he ordered the chief officer to sound the danger signal on the ship's whistle and told the 3rd mate to try to contact her on the Aldis lamp; but *Moenjodaro* continued to stand on.

At that point, with the vessels about three-quarters of a mile apart,[10] the master of *Glenfalloch* ordered hard right rudder and half ahead on the engines while the chief officer sounded one blast on the whistle. As these orders were being executed, the other ship was heard to sound two short blasts and was seen swinging to port. *Glenfalloch*'s master responded to this by ordering full-ahead with a double ring in order to increase the rapidity of his swing — but to no avail. With *Glenfalloch* now swinging rapidly to starboard and *Moenjodaro* swinging to port the vessels collided with the bow of the British vessel striking the Pakistani ship in the way of number one hold at an angle of nearly 45° to the left of the other vessel's heading.

While admitting her fault in being on the wrong side of the channel *Moenjodaro* attempted to limit her liability by claiming that she had in fact crossed narrowly ahead of *Glenfalloch* at the time that vessel altered to starboard, thereby bringing about a collision that would otherwise have been barely avoided. The Court found the testimony of *Moenjodaro*'s master singularly unimpressive on this point and totally contradicted by the confident and convincing testimony on the other side.

Nonetheless, in spite of the fault on the part of the master of *Moenjodaro* Mr. Justice Brandon reached the reluctant conclusion that *Glenfalloch* was not entirely free from blame. There was first of all some question as to which of the Rules governed, viz., whether it was a case of the narrow channel Rule (25a), or the applicable Steering and Sailing Rules pertaining to crossing situations. The Judge felt that it made little difference as far as *Moenjodaro* was concerned since she was at fault in either case. With *Glenfalloch*, however, the question assumed some significance since, if the crossing rule applied, the question arose of whether she had held her course and speed long enough under the circumstances. He concluded, however, that ". . . where one ship is proceeding along a narrow channel in the other direction, even though their courses are crossing so as to involve risk of collision, the narrow channel rule governs the case, and not the crossing rules." He then went on to say: "If one of the ships is not proceeding along a narrow channel at all, but crossing more or less directly from one side of it to the other, then the crossing rules may apply . . . ."[11] He found the former to be the case here, and so held *Glenfalloch* was free to take such action in accordance with the principles of good seamanship as would best avoid a collision.

He found *Moenjodaro* at fault in four respects. Firstly, she was in violation of Rule 25(a) by being on the wrong side of a narrow channel; secondly, that she was guilty of not keeping a proper lookout; thirdly, for her failure to take avoiding action in good time; fourthly, for putting her wheel to port rather than to starboard when she did take action. All of these faults he found, "while to some extent interlinked, were causative of the collision."[12]

When he turned to *Glenfalloch* he took a difficult but not uncommon view that in spite of the flagrant disregard of the Rules and all principles of good seamanship on the part of *Moenjodaro*, *Glenfalloch* could not be absolved from all blame herself; the master of the British vessel should have recognised early in the development of the situation that all was not as it should be. Once an approaching ship gives an indication that she is ignoring the Rules the prudent mariner must assume that she may continue to do so. *Moenjodaro* was first seen shortly after *Glenfalloch* had made the turn to enter the Irako Suido about thirteen minutes before the collision when the vessels were some 8 miles apart. It should have been immediately apparent that she was trying to cut a corner or was being navigated in an unseamanlike manner. If the former one could assume that if a competent and prudent mariner were at the con[12] he would soon realise the hazard of his venture and haul to the right to show a red light, but if that did not happen by the time the distance of discovery had been halved, i.e., about 4 miles, one should be drawn to the conclusion that the latter was in fact the case. Once that conclusion was drawn measures to prevent the development of close quarters should be put in hand.

In this case shoals and rocks to the south and west of the Irako Misaki lighthouse prevented *Glenfalloch* steering much more to the right than she was on first sighting *Moenjodaro*. She could of course have turned around and gone back out to sea at this juncture, but the level of anxiety had hardly risen to such a pitch at this point as to have evoked so radical a response to the developing threat, and the master cannot be justly criticised for not taking that step. Nonetheless, some action was required unless he was to suffer a very close approach by a vessel conned by what appeared to be a seaman of questionable judgment. Since a substantial alteration of course to starboard was precluded if he was to continue on through the Irako Suido the only alternative open was a marked reduction in speed. The master of *Glenfalloch* had obviously anticipated such a necessity when he ordered the earlier reduction when the engines were placed on standby at 2025 soon after sighting *Moenjodaro*. It would hence have been a simple matter to have ordered a reduction to slow at this time thereby reducing the speed of closing and allowing the oncoming vessel to pass ahead if she persisted in her wrongful course. Only minutes would have been lost by such an easy and prudent measure yet so great is the reluctance of mariners to manoeuvre with the engines at sea that this otherwise skillful and prudent seaman hesitated, and for that hesitation he was held at fault.

Justice Brandon considered that at the very latest a substantial reduction in speed should have been made no later than 2033 when the ships were slightly less than 2 miles apart. He sought confirmation from the Elder Brethren in this matter based upon the assumptions that: the other vessel was approaching fine on the port bow on a more or less constant bearing showing a green light; that she combined speed of approach was 36–37 knots; that *Glenfalloch* was not under constraint of Rule 21 and free to manoeuvre as she saw fit.

The questions posed based upon these assumptions were: What was the latest stage at which *Glenfalloch* should have taken action, and what action should she have taken? The answers given by the Elder Brethren were: to stop or at least to reduce to slow speed at a distance of not less than 2 miles. *Glenfalloch* was accordingly held to be responsible for one-fifth of the damages.

If fairness alone were to rule in such cases an assessment of one-fifth of the blame would seem a very harsh penalty indeed. The fault of *Moenjodaro* was monstrous compared to that of *Glenfalloch*, but if a fair assessment of fault was allowed to be the sole criterion in determination of damages there might be less inclination to take the misguided actions of others into account in such predicaments.

* * * * * * * *

Notes

1 *L.L.R.*, Vol. 2, 1965, p. 264.
2 *Ibid.*, p. 273.
3 See Marsden, pp. 220–23 on relationship of pilot/master; also Griffin, pp. 439–40, and Gilmore & Black, *The Law of Admiralty*, pp. 429–30.
4 *L.L.R.*, Vol. 2, 1965, p. 264. Also cf. Cockcroft, p. 80, *Trevethick/Talabot*.
5 *Ibid.*
6 *L.L.R.*, Vol. 2, 1973, p. 315.
7 *L.L.R.*, Vol. 1, 1979, pp. 253–54.
8 The claimed they passed 2 cables to the west, but that was not accepted by the Court. *Ibid.*, p. 253.
9 Unfortunately the master of *Glenfalloch* died before the case came to trial so his testimony was not available. If he did in fact regard *Moenjodaro* as a crossing vessel that would explain his failure to reduce speed earlier.
10 *Ibid.*, p. 251.
11 *Ibid.*, p. 255, but see Appendix for the apparent conflict with *The Genimar*.
12 *Ibid.*
13 Whether a mariner who chose to cut a corner in passing through such a place as the Irako Suido could properly be called prudent is questionable. What seems likely in this case is that the master simply was guilty of ignorance and poor judgment. His vessel had been set to the right in approaching Irako Suido and when he discovered this he may have simply set a course from the position he found himself in through Irako Suido without any thought or realisation of the applicability of the narrow channel rule, or the dictates of good seamanship.
   In extenuation the master of *Glenfalloch* seemed to believe that he was governed by the crossing rule also.

Appendix to Chapter Thirteen

Steering and Sailing or Narrow Channel Rule

A Traffic Separation Scheme is now in effect in the Irako Suido, and in *The Genimar* Mr. Justice Brandon some six months later held that in the collision between *Genimar* and *Larry L* in the TSS in the Dover Strait the Steering and Sailing Rules held when the two vessels met. In spite of the fact that the stand-on vessel in this case was the offending ship as regards the TSS the vessel following the TSS (*Larry L*) was held at fault for violation of Rule 22 (now 16). Now it cannot be disputed that the Narrow Channel Rule has precisely the same object as the rule pertaining to traffic separation schemes, i.e., to divide the traffic going one way from that going in the opposite direction. In the case in question (*Moenjodaro/Glenfalloch*) *Moenjodaro* was held to be in violation of the Narrow Channel Rule, but had this taken place several years later when the location of the casualty had been embraced by a TSS would *Glenfalloch*, following the decision in *The Genimar*, have been held a stand-on vessel?

The Irako Suido had not been changed physically one whit by the implementation of the TSS. If it was a "narrow channel" when *Moenjodaro* and *Glenfalloch* collided it is surely still a narrow channel today when it is also covered by a TSS. Surely logical consistency would dictate that a vessel proceeding up a TSS in the wrong direction should be held to be in violation of the Narrow Channel Rule rather than, as in the case of *The Genimar*, momentarily "privileged" forcing the "burdened vessel into a potentially very awkward predicament (as was *Larry L*) when she happened to have other vessels pursuing their legitimate courses in such a position as to hamper her ability to get out of the way of the "privileged" rogue.

Admittedly the TSS in the Dover Strait is of such width that a vessel (if not hampered with another vessel to starboard as was *Larry L*) meeting another could easily alter to starboard in order to avoid the oncoming vessel. A vessel in a narrow channel could do the same though the width would necessarily limit its ability to do so without stranding.

There is no question but that a vessel pursuing its legitimate course in a TSS encountering another taking an illegitimate course against the traffic flow should, nonetheless, follow the Steering and Sailing Rules in attempting to avoid collision. But if a collision does ensue simple justice should demand that the fault of the vessel wrongfully proceeding against the traffic flow should weigh heaviest in the scales.

In this case the present Rules that specifically require vessels to follow IMO recognised TSSs were not in effect when The *Genimar* and *Larry L* collided. Had they been perhaps more weight would have been given to The *Genimar*'s fault in being where she had no right to be and placing *Larry L* in such an awkward position.

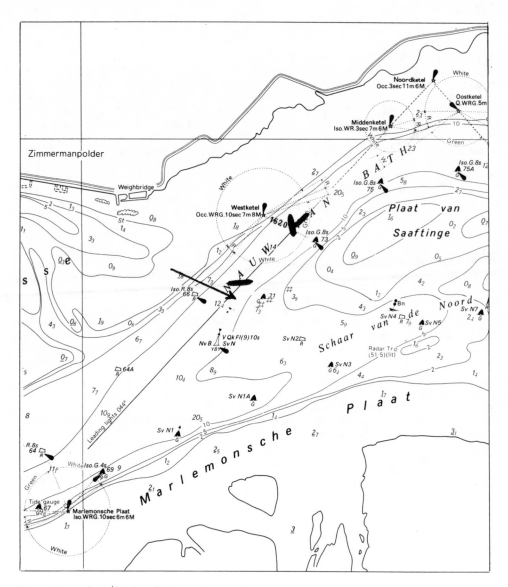

Figure 29 *Miraflores/Abedesa* (British Admiralty Chart) (See page 105)
(Produced from portion of BA chart No 139, former BA chart 1491, with the sanction of the Controller, H.M. Stationary Office and of the Hydrographer of the Navy)

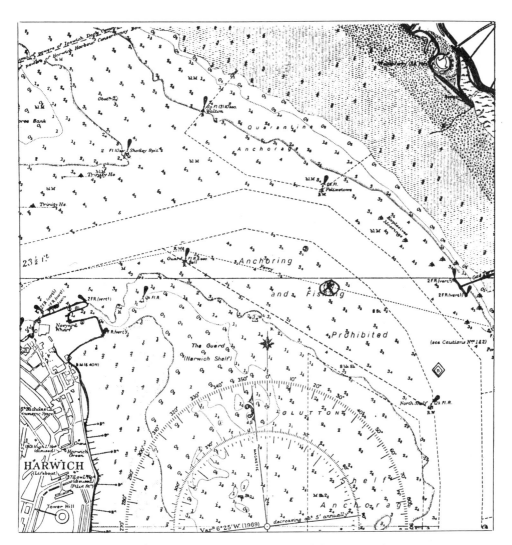

Figure 30 *Koningen Juliana/Thuroklint* (British Admiralty Chart) (See page 108)

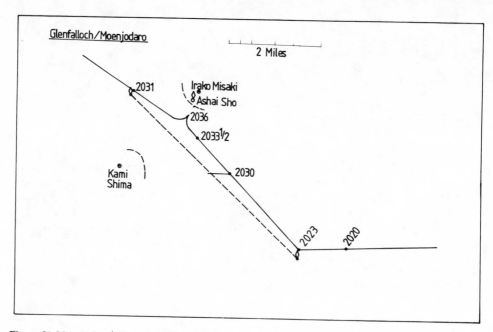

Figure 31 *Moenjodaro/Glenfalloch* (See page 110)

Chapter Fourteen

Interaction

Though the forces of interaction between vessels have long been recognised they have only been studied in detail in recent years.[1] We have seen in some earlier chapters how they have been a factor in some of the collisions studied, but they are usually associated with encounters in narrow channels. While the collisions thus resulting are ordinarily between the ships interacting in two of the cases examined here there was a different result; one hit a pier and the other stranded.

The River Schelde has been the scene of many casualties as its twisting course, narrow channels and treacherous currents, not to mention the heavy traffic in and out of its major port of Antwerp and the numerous fogs and other impediments of weather, combine to make it one of the most difficult and dangerous waterways — as we noted earlier.

On the 25th of August 1968 the Liberian steam tanker *Olympic Torch* loaded with a full cargo of crude oil was bound for Antwerp from Ras Tanura. She was on an even keel with a draft of 38½ feet. The *Ore Chief** was a twin screw ore carrier also registered in Monrovia carrying a cargo of iron ore from Puerto Ordaz in Venezuela to Antwerp drawing 39 feet. Both ships were under the dirction of licensed pilots and were able to communicate by VHF radio. *Ore Chief* was the faster of the two vessels having a speed of about 15 knots compared to 13 for *Olympic Torch*. The former was thus overtaking the latter when the casualty occurred.

Both vessels had anchored at Flushing to await the tide due to their deep drafts. High water at Flushing was 1504, 1539 at Terneuzen where the incident took place, and 1640 at Antwerp. *Olympic Torch* had left at 1355 and *Ore Chief* at 1404. A third ship, *Norbella*, faster than both the others left soon after *Ore Chief* and passed both before *Ore Chief*'s ill-fated attempt to pass *Olympic Torch*. Their order of departure was probably based upon their time of arrival at the roadstead. Safe traffic management would seem to indicate an order of departure based upon speed so that unnecessary overtaking would be avoided. That might mean, however, that the slowest ship would miss high water. Alternatively faster vessels could adjust speed so that they would overtake slower ones at a prearranged and safe place.

The tide was necessarily on the flood at a rate determined to be about 1½ knots at the place in question. *Olympic Torch*'s full manoeuvring speed was 9½ to 10 knots while that of *Ore Chief* was about 11. It soon became obvious that *Ore Chief* would overtake *Olympic Torch* within about an hour of departure from Flushing and the pilot of the former contacted the pilot of the latter on VHF informing him of the intention to overtake. Unfortunately he did not say when or where nor was any agreement arrived at, which had fateful consequences. Almost immediately thereafter revolutions on *Ore Chief* were brought up to about 14 knots. That vessel was then a couple of miles below Terneuzen and about a mile astern of *Olympic Torch*.

After leaving Flushing a ship follows a buoyed deep water channel for something over 10 miles on an easterly to south-easterly direction. Above Terneuzen the channel bends gradually to port over a distance of about 3 miles from a heading of about 90° off Terneuzen to about 67°

---

* *Ore Chief* was 794′ long and 20,910 gross tons; *Olympic Torch* was 705′ in length and 24,689 gross tons.

between buoys Nos 26 and 28. Above the latter buoy the channel divides into two with the main channel turning sharply to the north into a reach called Middel Gat. The course up Middel Gat is indicated by leading marks on a heading of 101° and marked by port hand buoys Nos 30, 30A, MG and 32.

Beginning at buoy No. 28 the channel turns sharply to port until it reaches the division referred to above. The split in the channel is occasioned by a sandbank called the Rug Van Baarland, the southern tip of which is marked by the MG-PvB buoy where the channel narrows to about 400 metres. There is also a ridge or bar here that markedly reduces the depth of water available, and it was in this vicinity that *Ore Chief* happened to overtake *Olympic Torch*.

A more unpropitious locale for overtaking would be hard to find though the tortuous Schelde offers many choices. The spot was not chosen for overtaking but rather it happened to occur there determined by the relative speeds of the two ships. Neither pilot understandably wanted to lose any time since they needed to make high water at Antwerp in order to lock in, but time was not so tight that a safer spot for passing could not have been chosen. Even had it meant missing the tide there was no justification for overtaking at a place that can justly be described as one of the main obstacles to be overcome in safely transiting the Schelde.

At 1502 *Ore Chief* passed Terneuzen with *Olympic Torch* about three-quarters of a mile ahead. Shortly thereafter the pilot of *Ore Chief* again called *Olympic Torch* on the VHF repeating his intention to overtake but no agreement was sought or offered on the proposal. The pilot on the tanker simply reiterated that his maximum speed was 9½ knots. She had meanwhile reached the vicinity of buoy No. 28 and commenced her turn by stages to a northerly heading which she reached shortly before coming abeam of buoy No. 30 just below the MG-PvB buoy. That heading was taken to counter the effects of the tidal current setting across the entrance to the Middel Gat and to avoid getting too close to the starboard side of the channel under such circumstances.

Ore Chief was meanwhile coming up fast on the port quarter turning onto a course of 010° as she came almost abreast of *Olympic Torch* just above buoy No. 30. The tanker then altered 10° to the right onto a parallel course with the ore carrier separated by a distance estimated to be about 75 metres. As *Ore Chief* moved ahead of the other ship to a position where her stern was approximately amidships of *Olympic Torch* interaction between the two vessels began to take effect and the bow of the tanker began to fall off rapidly to starboard. The helmsman put the wheel hard to port in an attempt to counteract the sheer but to no avail. She continued to swing right until her heading reached about 035° at which point the master ordered the port anchor let go, but before that could check her swing she fetched up on the bank between buoys Nos 30 and 30A.[2]

In arriving at a judgment in this case Mr. Justice Brandon turned first to the local Dutch Regulations governing navigation in the Schelde, which provides for the overtaken vessel not only keeping as far over to the starboard side of the channel as practicable and safe but also specifies that speed be reduced in passing if necessary and describes the sound signals to be used in such a manoeuvre.

He next addressed himself to the question of whether *Ore Chief* was negligent in overtaking where she did asking advice of the Elder Brethren. They not surprisingly agreed that it was not seamanlike to overtake at the point.

He then went on to consider the use of VHF radio in lieu of whistle signals as a means of reaching agreement for passing. He took the rather narrow view, and amply contradicted by long experience of mariners and pilots in American waters and elsewhere, that the misunderstanding that arose between the pilots here "illustrates the undesirability of substituting imprecise exchanges on VHF for precise exchanges by whistle signals as laid down in art. 40 [Dutch Regulations].[3]

Whistle signals of course can be precise, but as a means of conveying information they are severely limited. The use of VHF here did not demonstrate its inadequacy but rather the failure of those using it to use it properly. Had the pilot of *Ore Chief* not merely confined himself to expressing his intention to overtake *Olympic Torch*, but also asked for and received an agreement to his proposal together with an agreement on the place of passing (which could not have been achieved by whistle signals) it is reasonable to expect that the pilot of *Olympic Torch* would have refused to countenance a passing in the narrow entrance to the Middel Gat and insisted that it be delayed until a wider and safer place for passing was reached. The pilot of *Ore Chief* should also have asked the other pilot to slow materially at the time of passing to reduce the possibility of interaction and also expedite the manoeuvre. The masters of both these vessels should have insisted that such a procedure be carried out. But without direct discussion of the details of passing by VHF no such agreement could have been reached. In any event *Ore Chief* was held solely to blame.

*   *   *   *   *   *   *   *

Probably the most catastrophic collision resulting from the effects of interaction and/or bank effect was that which took place in the River Plate on the 11th of May 1972 between the British steamship *Royston Grange* and the Liberian motor tanker *Tien Chee*.*

Royston Grange was outbound from Buenos Aires with a crew of sixty-three and ten passengers. The vessel was fitted for the carriage of refrigerated cargoes and had loaded 2,813 tons consisting mostly of frozen meat, and was due to call at Montevideo and Santos before returning to the United Kingdom. Her draft on sailing was a little over 22½ feet forward and a foot more aft, though at the time of collision it was somewhat less as the vessel was then in salt water.

Tien Chee was inbound from Rosales to La Plata with very nearly a full cargo of crude oil. She had a crew of forty-two though she was a considerably larger vessel. Her draft was just under 29 feet forward and a few inches over 30 feet aft. She had arrived at the pilot station at about 0230 that morning having lost several hours because the master had taken a course further offshore than at first planned due to her deep draft. He expected to anchor in the vicinity of Recalada for several hours so as to go up the river on a flood tide, but the pilot did not fancy a delay and claiming that there was almost 2½ feet more water in the river than that shown for low water convinced the master that this was sufficient to proceed without waiting. Having already lost about three hours and somewhat concerned about the attitude of his time-charterers to this delay the master was inclined to be persuaded, which proved to be a disastrous mistake.

Tien Chee accordingly proceeded without further delay up the Punta Indio Channel at full manoeuvring speed which should have given a bit over 12 knots. With the amount of water under the keel it was later calculated she would squat almost 3 feet.

The River Plate suffers from the navigational disability of forming part of the border between Uruguay and Argentina, and while the latter country has assumed responsibility for maintenance of the channel part of it appears to lie within the territorial waters of Uruguay. The Liberian Board of Investigation convened to look into the collision remarked that they had "looked in vain for any concerted and planned effort to maintain the channel."[4]

The channel is marked in the conventional manner by pairs of buoys with a width of between four and five-hundred metres. The bottom is very irregular and it appears that at the time most of the dredging being carried out was done by the passage of the vessels through the silt that would otherwise build up along the bottom. The channel is also roughly dish shaped so that its effective width is substantially less than that shown on the chart. Mariners are warned in the Argentine Pilot Book that the centre line of the channel does not necessarily coincide with its deepest part. It is hence imperative that vessels whose draft approaches the limits imposed by the river's depth must pay the strictest attention to the state of the tide and any meteorological factors affecting water levels.

This is important for vessels of deep draft as the range is comparatively modest, usually being less than 1 metre. The water level is also affected by the wind, with a northerly wind diminishing the level and a southerly wind increasing it. It so happened that the tide was very near low water as *Tien Chee* began her passage up the river and it was in fact low water when the two vessels approached each other between number 15 and 16 buoys. The Liberian ship must have been very near the bottom as she made her way up the river and was at times probably engaged

---

* *Tien Chee* was 580' long and had a deadweight tonnage of 19,700 tons: *Royston Grange* was 489' in length with a gross tonnage of 10,262.

in a bit of unintentional dredging through the soft mud. She should have been making about 12½ knots but in fact only made about 11 between the first set of buoys and the point of collision.

The course to make good was 272° but it was necessary to steer 274° because of a southerly cross current. Due to the deep draft, however, it was necessary to favour the port side of the channel. The supplement to the British "South American Pilot" current at the time states: "Between Nos. 1 and 20 light buoys the deepest part of the channel lies southward of the centre line, and deep-draught vessels usually keep towards the southern side."[5]

Not long after 0500, when *Tien Chee* reached the vicinity of the No. 12 buoy, the lights of *Royston Grange* were seen ahead at a distance of about 9 miles bearing slightly on the port bow. As she approached her green sidelight came into view indicating she was sheering a bit to the north to counter the effect of the south-going current. The pilot now attempted to contact the outbound vessel via VHF radio, but due to a defect in either one set or both communication was not established. The pilot then gave a series of quick flashes on a red light on the signal mast of *Tien Chee*, which was a local signal to indicate that the vessel is a tanker of deep draft.

As the vessels closed to within a mile *Royston Grange* was seen to alter course slightly to starboard closing her green light and showing her red so as to pass port to port. *Tien Chee*, which was now steering 276° altered 2° more to starboard to facilitate the passing. It appeared that they would pass perhaps 100 metres off though the master later said he estimated the distance to be somewhat less, and possibly as little as half that. Nonetheless, neither the master or the pilot felt any anxiety as yet and there seemed to be no reason to believe that things were not as they should be. It apparently did not occur to them that a substantial reduction in speed should be made by one or both vessels in order to minimise the effects of interaction and bank suction.

When the bows of *Royston Grange* and *Tien Chee* came abreast of one another the bow of the former suddenly sheered sharply to port, and seconds later her stem struck *Tien Chee* at an angle of about 40° in the way of her No. 7 cargo tank just forward of midships tearing a large gash in her side which was extended into the three tanks aft as *Royston Grange* surged ahead. When the British vessel took her sheer the helm on *Tien Chee* was put hard-a-port, but that had no effect. After the initial contact the vessels swung together and became locked in a fatal embrace.

The engines of *Tien Chee* were left working ahead, however, and partly due to the effect of the position of her helm coupled to the force of the impact *Tien Chee* swung rapidly to port with *Royston Grange* alongside and took the ground on the far bank on a southerly heading.

What happened aboard *Royston Grange* could only be surmised since all aboard her apparently perished almost instantaneously as she was swept by a fire storm following the ignition of the gas vapour released with the oil gushing from the ruptured tanks of *Tien Chee*. The charred remains of her bridge personnel were found at their stations in the wheelhouse. The rudder was found to be hard right and the bridge telegraph on full astern though there had been no time for the engine room to respond.

Due to the northerly wind the "fire-ball" that came hard on the heels of the collision and enveloped *Royston Grange* only touched *Tien Chee* and she was spared the immediate horrific scene transpiring on her partner in disaster. The British vessel was gutted and charred to her waterline. Apparently some of those within the ship were able to make a few frantic but futile movements towards the direction of escape before perishing in the holocaust, but none survived. On *Tien Chee* eight of the total complement of forty-two lost their lives, though these fatalities came in the aftermath of the disaster rather than as a direct result. The master, who survived, played a heroic role in aiding his surviving crew to escape.

In the formal investigation held a year later in New York City two veteran fire officers were called to offer testimony. The Board concluded that a cloud of inflammable vapour was released at the moment of collision when the oil first spilled from *Tien Chee*'s ruptured side. The numerous sparks from the grinding steel ignited the cloud causing the "fire-ball" or "flash-fire" that enveloped *Royston Grange*. It was estimated that temperatures of at least 1,000 degrees Fahrenheit were generated within seconds. The 800 tons or so of oil that escaped from the tanks of *Tien Chee* was ignited to burn in a more normal fashion and complete the destruction of the two vessels. So fierce did the fire rage that the refrigeration insulation in the holds of *Royston Grange* was ignited causing the complete destruction of the cargo in her holds.

When the experts assembled to consider why the collision occurred it was concluded that *Tien Chee* was almost certainly "ploughing through the mud on the bottom of the channel."[6] A survey of the bottom conducted after the disaster showed that probably unknown to the pilots there was a bank of mud extending from the south side of the channel nearly to its centre. The northerly wind would also have worked to lower the level of water to be expected in the channel. The place of passing was, moreover, one of the shallowest in the river. The British vessel, though lighter in draft, was probably skimming over the top of the bank on the southern side with her starboard bilge-keel probably in contact with it. Pressure would hence be built up on the starboard bow with a corresponding degree of suction drawing her stern towards the bank.[7] That would have produced a sheer to port towards the deeper water to the north. The sheer may also have been accentuated by helm action initiated to counteract it, though that is only speculation.

What this casualty demonstrates most forcefully is the need for passage planning in the area in which it is most apt to be neglected, i.e. when a pilot is aboard. While the master may be forced to rely to a certain extent upon the pilot for recent and specific information about depths of water and obstructions or shoaling in the channel, he should, nonetheless, make a careful study of the waters through which the pilot will take him so as to acquaint himself with those points where the navigation of the vessel will be most difficult and where meeting or overtaking other vessels should be avoided. That will enable him to discuss with the pilot on boarding the general plan of passage and reach agreement on such points as the handling of the vessel in specific localities and situations. To delay such discussion until confronted with the situation is to risk confusion and distraction of the pilot at the very moment when his concentration on the conning of the vessel should not be disturbed (see also p. 106).

The Board of Investigation in this case reprimanded the master of *Tien Chee* for not waiting for more favourable conditions of tide to take his vessel up the Punta Indio Channel and for faulty navigation of his vessel leading to this casualty, *viz.*, failure to slow his vessel materially on meeting *Royston Grange* and allowing the meeting to occur in such a narrow place.[8]

*   *   *   *   *   *   *   *

The last case we will consider here has none of the preceding one's drama but it is a clear example of how two highly experienced ship-handlers well aware of the dangers of interaction and bank effect could, nonetheless, fall victim to these hazards. *Liquilassie* was a small highly manoeuvrable tanker trading regularly between Montreal and Great Lakes ports. She was down to her marks and had just left the Côte St. Catherine lock in the Welland Canal on her way up the St. Lawrence Seaway when she encountered the deep loaded and much larger *Nipigon Bay*,* a large diesel propelled bulk carrier. It was late afternoon on a clear calm day on July 20, 1973 with only a slight current.

Nipigon Bay had been lying almost dead in the water for some time waiting to enter the lock. When the master of *Nipigon Bay* saw *Liquilassie* emerge he put his engines to ten revolutions ahead which would give a speed of about a knot. The Canal at that point is about 300 feet wide though its navigable width is somewhat less. *Nipigon Bay* was almost in the middle of it as she moved to meet *Liquilassie* port to port. The latter vessel had moved slightly to port as she left the lock towards the middle of the channel when she saw the bulk carrier, whereupon the master blew one whistle and moved back to starboard. The master of *Nipigon Bay* did not hear the signal nor did he respond by moving to starboard himself, but kept on his course down the middle of the Canal. He saw it as a normal port-to-port meeting and perhaps felt his larger size justified taking a larger share of the channel. *Liquilassie*'s estimated speed was about 2 knots

---

* *Nipigon Bay* was 692′ long and 13,274 tons gross; *Liquilassie* was 366′ in length and 4,207 gross tons. She had twin-screws.

as she approached the larger vessel though the Court concluded it was a knot or so faster. It was not, however, judged an unsafe speed.

Nipigon Bay's position forced *Liquilassie* farther over towards the bank than she would normally have gone leaving her in crowded circumstances as *Nipigon Bay* met her. The tanker's master estimated that the vessels were only about 10 feet apart though the master of another vessel following thought it was perhaps twice as much. In any event as the vessels approached the stern of *Liquilassie* smelt the bank and her bow began to sheer to port. The master was alert to that possibility, however, and he counteracted the suction by putting his port engine full ahead and reversing his starboard. This also had the effect of reducing his headway, and as his stern approached the stern of the other vessel she gave her engines a kick of half ahead to counteract the effect of interaction due to the closeness of *Liquilassie*. The wash of the engine action pushed the stern of the smaller vessel to starboard causing her bow to slew around across the channel towards a dock on the other side.

The master of *Liquilassie* was unable to overcome the force of this push by either helm or engine action, and in an attempt to check the way on his vessel he ordered the starboard anchor dropped. The bottom unfortunately was rock and it would not hold. Her bow struck the dock causing damage to both.

The Court found that the initial sheer that set in train the sequence of events culminating with *Liquilassie* striking the dock was caused by *Nipigon Bay* forcing her to navigate too close to the bank. The tanker's subsequent efforts to counteract that sheer rendered her vulnerable to the push on her stern by the kick ahead on *Nipigon Bay*'s engine as their sterns drew abreast, which then resulted in *Liquilassie* striking the dock. For these faults *Nipigon Bay* was apportioned 80 per cent of the blame. *Liquilassie*'s faults for which she was held 20 per cent responsible for the casualty were her failure to signal her difficulty occasioned by *Nipigon Bay*'s crowding, which should have alerted her to the need to move over, her failure to then stop and wait for the larger vessel to move over, and failing that for not slowing down to such a speed as to eliminate or diminish the effect of bank suction.[9]

*   *   *   *   *   *   *   *

Notes

1 Cf. E. C. B. Cortlett, "Studies on Interaction at Sea", *Journal* of the Royal Institute of Navigation, May 1979. Also, J. P. Hooft, "Manoeuvring Large Ships in Shallow Water, I and II *Journal,* April & July 1973; and I. W. Dand & P. J. V. Paget, *Ibid.,* "Interaction at Sea", September 1979; P. F. Willerton, *Basic Shiphandling for Masters, Mates & Pilots,* pp. 138–41.

2 *L.L.R.,* 1974, Vol. 2, p. 431.

3 *Ibid.,* p. 433.

4 "Report of the Marine Board of Investigation and Decision of the Commissioner of Maritime Affairs", April 25, 1973, Monrovia, Liberia, p. R7.

5 *Ibid.,* p. R8.

6 *Ibid.,* p. R15.

7 Cf. Cortlett, *ibid.,* p. 219; Dr. Cortlett was also consulted in this casualty.

8 "Report", p. R18.

9 *L.L.R.,* Vol. 2, 1975, pp. 87–8.

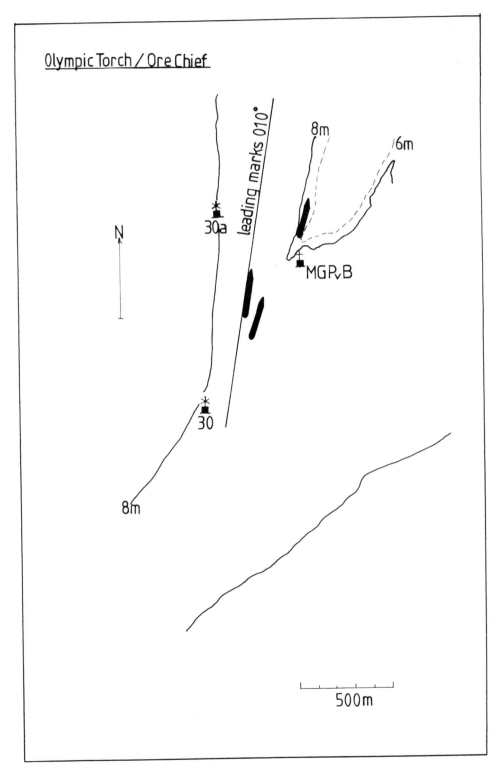

Figure 32 *Olympic Torch/Ore Chief* (See page 118)

Chapter Fifteen

Collisions Getting Underway

While encounters between vessels on the high seas may occasionally lead to collision due to confusion over the applicable Rule, as we have seen in a number of incidents here, they are usually on clearly defined courses making recognition of the relevant Rule a somewhat straightforward affair. A more fertile breeding ground for confusion, however, is when vessels are in the process of beginning or ending their voyages such as getting underway at anchor, coming to anchor, leaving a berth or picking up or disembarking a pilot. We will direct our attention in this and the following chapter to such cases.

On May 24, 1970 the Italian steam tanker *Savina* had loaded a part cargo of crude oil while lying at South Pier at the Saudi Arabian oil terminal at Ras Tanura. Shortly before 2200 on that day she prepared to get underway to shift to an anchorage before returning to her berth to complete loading.

The Dutch motor tanker *Forest Hill** had gone to anchor after loading a full cargo of crude for Karachi and she was preparing to pick up her anchor and commence her voyage at about the same time *Savina* left her berth. The Dutch vessel's anchor was aweigh at 2148 and after about ten minutes of backing and filling she had swung from an original heading of 235° to 340°, at which time the engines were put dead slow ahead as she began to move out of the anchorage into the channel. Seven minutes later engines were put to half ahead and she steadied on a course of 350°. At 2212 speed was increased to full and half a minute later to full sea speed.

Several minutes before increasing to half ahead *Savina* was seen to be leaving her berth and was on a heading of about 080° showing a green sidelight with masthead lights well open almost broad on the port bow of *Forest Hill*. The master thereupon directed the chief officer to contact the other ship on VHF to advise her of *Forest Hill*'s intentions. The radio officer of *Savina* responded and was told that *Forest Hill* was steadying on a course of 350° and was increasing speed from dead slow to full ahead. The conversation was in English which was not the native tongue of either participant, and *Savina*'s radio operator maintained later that he understood *Forest Hill* was going full ahead on a course of 307°, which was obviously wrong as it would have meant she was heading straight for *Savina*. It was never suggested that the master of *Savina* was misled by that misunderstanding and he appreciated that *Forest Hill* was increasing to full ahead.

Savina had left her berth at about the same time *Forest Hill* had weighed anchor and had swung to a heading of 340°. She had been assisted by a tug, which cast off at 2159 with *Savina* on a heading of 080° and the engines were put on slow ahead. At about this time the first VHF exchange was made followed shortly by a request from *Forest Hill* that *Savina* stop her engine which she did. A final request some five or six minutes before the collision at 2013 was made by *Forest Hill* that *Savina* reverse her engines though *Savina*'s radio officer claims he called

---

* *Forest Hill* was 12,718 gross tons and 559′ in length; *Savina* was 21,080 gross tons and 679′ long.

124

Forest Hill advising her that *Savina*'s engines were working full speed astern. The engine movement book of *Savina* shows that this was done at 2208. There is some difficulty in reconciling the evidence here as the speed of *Savina* was estimated at 2 knots at the time of collision yet her engines had been backing emergency full astern for five to six minutes before the collision.[1]

In any event the judge held that the Collision Regulations had taken effect at about 2205 when *Forest Hill* had steadied on a course of 350°. The vessels were then in a crossing situation at that time with their courses 90° apart and *Savina* obliged to keep out of the way as a give-way vessel. Nonetheless, both the lower court and the appeals court found each vessel guilty of bad lookout at the beginning for failing to become aware of the movement of the other vessel and gain a proper appreciation of the situation in time to avoid the development of a close-quarters situation. *Savina* was also found guilty of not taking avoiding action earlier. The lower court considered that three to four minutes after putting the engines on slow ahead after dropping the pilot at 2159 the master of *Savina* should have realised that a close-quarters situation was imminent and he should have stopped the engines then five minutes before he actually did so. Assuming that he shortly thereafter put his engines to full astern a collision would almost certainly have been avoided.

Mr. Justice Brandon who heard the case held, on the advice of the Elder Brethren, that the increase of speed from dead slow to half ahead at 2205 was in effect calculated to increase the difficulty of *Savina* in keeping out of the way. Lord Justice Cairns who presided at the appeal did not, after consulting with his Assessors, see it that way, holding that this would not have embarrassed *Savina* if she had taken off her way at an earlier time, which he considered should have been done some three to four minutes earlier. It was also suggested by his Assessors, and he concurred, that alternatively she could have proceeded very slowly under starboard helm so as to pass under the stern of *Forest Hill*. The Lord Justice accordingly reversed the apportionment of fault found by the lower court where *Forest Hill* was held 60 per cent to blame and *Savina* 40 per cent.

* * * * * * * *

In a somewhat similar case about six years earlier the motor tanker *Naess Tern* laden with a cargo of fuel oil was bound down the Mersey River on the evening of January 13, 1964 with visibility restricted by sleet and snow showers to about 1 mile. The tide was flooding at nearly 2 knots and there was no wind to speak of.

*Santander** had come to anchor on the western side of the river about 2.7 cables west of the Pluckington Bank Buoy earlier that morning. A fire had broken out in one of her after holds during the day and though it had been brought under control she was brightly illuminated making it somewhat difficult to pick out her anchor lights. As *Naess Tern* approached *Santander* was in the process of weighing anchor to enter the Brunswick Dock. Both vessels were conned by pilots and *Santander* had tugs alongside.

Naess Tern was making about 11 knots through the water against the tide when the pilot discovered *Santander* at anchor about a mile away dead ahead. At that time he altered course 10° to starboard, and after reaching that heading another 10° more to steady on a course of 345° which would take him down the starboard side of the channel close to the Pluckington Bank buoy. *Santander* was then about two points on the port bow and shortly thereafter he noticed an alteration in the lights of *Santander*, which now appeared to be moving, though a number of bright lights were still burning on deck making it difficult to distinguish what navigation lights she was showing.[2] He accordingly reduced to slow ahead, which was recorded as 2139. Soon thereafter he saw the green sidelight.

It was now "tide time" at the Brunswick Dock entrance, which was precisely why *Santander* was picking up her anchor and a period in which increased movement of traffic within the river

---

* *Santander* was a motor vessel of 8,550 gross tons and 466′ long; *Naess Tern* was 12,302 tons gross and 559′ in length.

could be expected. The alteration in the lights of *Santander* noticed by the outbound pilot was no doubt due to the forward deck lights being switched off as the vessel prepared to pick up the anchor. The afterdeck lights, which it was later alleged interfered with the view of her navigation lights, were probably left on to enable activities to continue associated with the fire they had been fighting. The movement observed by the pilot was probably due to a slow ahead bell at 2138 to ease the weight on the anchor cable as it was being picked up. The anchor was observed to be aweigh at 2142 at which time half ahead was rung on the engines, the helm put to starboard, and one short blast sounded on the whistle. Shortly before this, however, an echo was seen on the radar about a mile away which was no doubt *Naess Tern*.

After *Santander* had put the engines half ahead *Naess Tern* was seen about 5 or 6 cables away fine on the starboard quarter showing two masthead lights nearly in line but only the port sidelight. The pilot of *Santander* said that in this situation it was a recognised practice between pilots for the outward bound vessel to port her helm and pass under the stern of the ship manoeuvring to enter the Brunswick Dock, and he confidently expected *Naess Tern* to do so. He was disappointed in his expectation and it led him into collision.

Santander's pilot had commenced an operation described as "edging over" where the combination of the effect of the tide and the engines working at half ahead with starboard helm would carry him over into a position to enter the Brunswick Dock. It soon became evident to him, however, that this operation was not going to succeed as *Naess Tern* had not ported as expected and was instead shaping up to pass ahead. The engines were hastily put full astern and the wheel to port but *Santander* had unfortunately gathered too much headway and continued to move forward into the path of *Naess Tern*.

After seeing the green sidelight of *Santander* upon reducing to slow ahead, the pilot of *Naess Tern* concluded rightly that the other vessel was attempting to cross ahead and he stopped the engines and ordered hard right while blowing one blast on the whistle. The vessels were closing rapidly by this time and it soon became evident that more would need to be done if collision were to be avoided. At 2142 (there seemed to be a discrepancy of a minute or two between the times of the two vessels) the engines were put full astern, three short blasts were sounded, and the helm either reversed or put midships. There was some disagreement as to how long after that the collision occurred; the time given is 2146 but whose time it was was not noted. In any event *Naess Tern* was still making substantial headway when the ships collided.

The Court first looked at the assertion of *Santander*'s pilot pertaining to the alleged practice of down bound vessels porting to pass astern of ships crossing the river. The other pilot made it abundantly clear that he had no intention of embarking on such a manoeuvre, and the Judge made it equally clear that whether or not it was an accepted practice it was a most unseamanlike one. The main question, however, was the wisdom of the *Santander*'s pilot to make the attempt in the first place, and once that question was posed it was obvious that the lookout kept from the vessel was defective.

Good seamanship would dictate that before commencing this manoeuvre those on *Santander* should look to see if it was safe to do so. Every child is cautioned to look before he crosses the street. The visibility was, moreover, restricted to about a mile. The 2nd mate was on the stern at docking stations in a position more favourably situated to see than from the bridge, yet he was not asked to keep a lookout and indeed did not see *Naess Tern* until just before the collision.

That vessel had seen *Santander* at a mile so if those on the latter ship had been properly alert they should have also seen *Naess Tern* at that distance. Indeed, in such visibility it was incumbent upon the vessel at anchor to determine by careful inspection of the radar scope *before* picking up the anchor that there were no vessels underway in the river that might interfere with her movement to cross it. *Santander* was plainly guilty of gross negligence in failing to keep a proper lookout.

But aside from the bad lookout there was ample time after discovery of *Naess Tern*, especially with the aid of tugs, to have turned to stem the stream until *Naess Tern* was safely past. Even if the dubious practice earlier alluded to of the outbound vessel giving way to the crossing one was commonly accepted, the position of *Naess Tern* was too far advanced to make it practical or safe in this case, and *Santander's* pilot was held guilty of a grave error of judgment in assuming that his colleagues would be a party to such a hazardous undertaking.

Santander was further criticised for showing lights that interfered with recognition of her navigation lights though that was not seen to contribute to the collision. It was further pointed out that these bright lights could have interfered with her own lookout.

Naess Tern, however, did not escape all censure. She was deemed guilty to a certain extent for an inadequate lookout, but on somewhat scant evidence. As she approached there was nothing to indicate that *Santander* was on the point of picking up her anchor, though it was tide time and it should not have been unexpected. The pilot noticed the alteration of her lights that preceded her anchor breaking free and shortly thereafter her sidelight. Perhaps he might have discovered these changes slightly sooner had he concentrated his attention on the other vessel, but to hold him guilty of a bad lookout seems to be a trifle harsh.

There was another matter, however, of a less questionable nature. The visibility was no more than a mile. *Naess Tern* was approaching the entrance to the Brunswick Dock at a time when it was reasonable to expect vessels would be attempting to enter or leave. The ship was on full manoeuvring speed making about 11 knots through the water and she was deep loaded. If under those conditions *Naess Tern* unexpectedly encountered another vessel underway she would have only the helm to rely on to avoid her, and shoal water restricted that capability. It would hence have been prudent to have substantially slowed before approaching this area, but her pilot ignored that hazard and so cannot escape blame in the collision following his unexpected encounter with *Santander*. The Court so held, and *Santander* was not surprisingly assigned two-thirds of the blame with the balance of fault falling on *Naess Tern*.

* * * * * * * *

Another case with somewhat similar features and a similar result took place a few months earlier under more favourable circumstances but no more favourable a conclusion.

Forest Lake was almost identical in size and horsepower with *Naess Tern,* and she was in fact a sister ship of *Forest Hill* which we encountered at the beginning of this chapter. She had loaded a cargo of Qatar crude in the Persian Gulf and was on her way to Montreal via the Suez Canal. She had arrived there early in the afternoon of August 23, 1963 and after embarking a pilot proceeded into Suez Bay to anchor there while waiting to join the northbound convoy the next morning. The weather was perfect: unlimited visibility, no wind and negligible tidal current, nor was there any sign of movement within the Bay; hardly the scenario for a casualty.

Janet Quinn* was an American Liberty ship carrying a full cargo of wheat for Bhavnagar, India. She had transited the Canal a day or so earlier and had gone to anchor in the Bay to effect some repairs. She also had a pilot aboard and her repairs completed was preparing to get underway. *Forest Lake* was plainly visible making her way up the channel past the Newport Rock Beacon and heading for her designated anchorage just to the north of where *Janet Quinn* rode to her anchor. The pilot was also no doubt well aware of the movements of the Dutch vessel and her designated anchorage — or should have been.

A few moments more delay could not have made any appreciable difference to *Janet Quinn,* but having already experienced an unforeseen and annoying detention her master was most likely impatient to resume his voyage, and he allowed his impatience to interfere with his judgment. What the pilot's attitude was in this sorry affair was not revealed but suffice to say the decision to pick up the anchor without further delay was made, and what should have been a simple and safe manoeuvre was turned into a tricky and hazardous undertaking with costly results.

Janet Quinn was anchored in berth 2A which is in the eastern part of Suez Bay about 8 cables south–south-east of Green Island.† As *Forest Lake* proceeded past Newport Rock the American

---

* *Forest Lake* was 12,718 gross tons and 559′ long; *Janet Quinn* was 7,233 gross tons and 441′ in length.

† *Janet Quinn* was using an out-of-date chart that gave an incorrect position for the beacon. She was apparently some 200–300 yards further west.

vessel was riding to her anchor on a roughly north-easterly heading. *Forest Lake* was bound for her designated anchorage 3A just to the north-west of *Janet Quinn*. Anchored to the north-east of her was a tanker *Harpula* some 3 to 4 cables away whose chief officer was watching *Forest Lake* approach and was later to give important testimony relating to the incident.

The Dutch vessel had come up the channel at manoeuvring full head, which gave her a speed of about 8½ to 9 knots and was quite proper under the circumstances. When abeam Newport Rock speed was cut to half ahead and she shortly thereafter altered to port to a heading of 322° to take her to a position between *Janet Quinn* and *Harpula* now a point or so on the port bow. Not long thereafter speed was reduced further to slow ahead. *Janet Quinn* was still showing her anchor ball at this time and apparently at anchor. She was in fact underway having just hoisted her anchor.

Janet Quinn denied this claiming that the anchor ball had been dropped as soon as the anchor was aweigh while *Forest Lake* insisted that the American ship was observed moving ahead with the anchor ball aloft just before she began backing her engines. The dispute was resolved to the satisfaction of the Court by the testimony of the chief mate of *Harpula* who had closely watched the whole affair. The ball was dropped, in his words, "momentarily before the three short blasts sounded by *Forest Lake*."[3]

Janet Quinn having weighed her anchor, went slow ahead to make her way out of her berth and then intended to turn to the right and go down the channel *Forest Lake* had just left. Her triple expansion steam engines accelerated very slowly so she gathered way accordingly. As she began to move from her berth those aboard her now noticed what they should have seen before they chose to get underway: *Forest Lake* approaching on the starboard bow now less than 2 cable lengths away.

Forest Lake had meanwhile slowed further to dead slow ahead shortly after the reduction to slow ahead. Very soon after this those on the Dutch vessel saw the anchor ball of *Janet Quinn* come down and water streaming from her hawse pipe. She was little more than a cable length away at this time and about a point on the port bow. The engines of *Forest Lake* were immediately stopped and a prolonged blast was given on her whistle to attract the attention of the other vessel. That was followed by emergency full astern on the engines.

The whistle signal of *Forest Lake* seemed to cause some confusion on *Janet Quinn*, the master seeming to believe that a prolonged blast was of ten seconds duration rather than four to six.* In any event it was too late to make any difference. While the Dutch ship had powerful diesel engines that responded quite readily so that way was substantially reduced, the distance was too close. *Forest Lake* hit the American vessel just abaft her house at close to a right angle opening her number four hatch to the sea. She was subsequently beached to prevent her settling on the bottom in the anchorage.

Judgment was decided by Mr. Justice Karminski who asked first if *Janet Quinn* was right in attempting to get underway when she did. The Elder Brethren confirmed his own opinion that a prudent seaman would have waited until *Forest Lake* was safely anchored. Logically it is hard to fault her for *that* mistake since those on *Janet Quinn* seemed to be oblivious to all that was going on around them and did not discover *Forest Lake* until they were already underway and separated by less than two ship lengths.

The main cause of the collision, however, would appear to be the failure of the American vessel to drop her anchor ball once the anchor was off the bottom. Those on *Forest Lake*, who *were* keeping a proper lookout, were thus denied the opportunity to discover the movement of *Janet Quinn* while there was still time to avoid her. There was an attempt on the part of counsel for the American ship to fault *Forest Lake* for failing to discover she was underway, but the Court, after first consulting with the Elder Brethren, rejected that claim. Her movement through the water was so slow as to make it difficult to detect had there been suspicion she was underway, but with her anchor ball still aloft *Forest Lake* could hardly be faulted for failing to notice the bare headway of *Janet Quinn*.

---

* The Rules of Navigation for the Suez Canal under the heading "Sound Signals in Canal Waters"[3] specify that "One prolonged blast: calls attention." A note also defines that as from 4 to 6 seconds duration.

The Court also found the two vessels in a crossing situation wherein the American vessel was the give-way ship and the Dutch vessel obliged to stand on. That seems a rather academic observation since the vessels were *in extremis* before they had an inkling of the situation facing them. As Mr. Justice Karaminski remarked on passing judgment, this was one of those rare cases of collision where one vessel, *Janet Quinn*, was held entirely at fault. Several years later the same judge had occasion to hear a somewhat similar case where a corresponding balance of blame was found.

* * * * * * * *

In the early evening of June 11, 1965 the Norwegian ship *Nidareid* was approaching Panama Bay where she intended to anchor awaiting transit the next morning. She was fully laden with a cargo of iron on her way from San Nicolas, Peru to Ymuiden in Holland. The Cuban ship *Aracelio Iglesias** (hereinafter referred to as *Aracelio*) was also fully loaded and had just finished her transit of the Canal having dropped her pilot and was preparing to resume her voyage from Cuba to Asaka, Japan with just over 10,000 tons of raw sugar.

The moon was three-quarters full as *Nidareid* eased down from her sea-speed of 13½ knots on approaching the anchorage area on a course of true north. The master of the Norwegian vessel testified that just before 1900 he saw *Aracelio* coming out of the Canal showing a green sidelight and range lights that indicated a course of about 140°, a normal one for a vessel leaving the Canal. He ordered engines placed on standby and instructed the chief officer to go forward with the carpenter to prepare the ground tackle for anchoring. At 1902 the engines were placed on slow ahead and stopped at 1905. He planned to hold his northerly heading until about a half mile east of the fairway buoy from whence he would make his way into the anchorage. That allowed him about 3 miles to run off his way. *Aracelio* was about 20° on his port bow and he expected her to alter to starboard under his stern.

Aracelio was a new ship built in Poland about two years before. She was somewhat smaller than the Norwegian but slightly faster having a sea-speed of 14½ knots and powered by diesel engines. The pilot had been dropped about five to ten minutes before seven. This was the Cuban master's first time through the Canal and he consulted with the pilot on the courses to steer on departure. He was told to pass the sea buoy close aboard on a course of 137°, and he understood he must hold that course until the light of Taboguilla Island broke clear.† *Nidareid* was observed about this time around 3½ miles off bearing about broad on the starboard bow. It was a clear cut crossing situation with the Norwegian ship the stand-on vessel and the Cuban the give-way one, and so the master of *Nidareid* understood it. Not so the Cuban master.

He took a somewhat singular view of the Rules as being subordinate to navigational exigiencies even though they posed no great difficulty for a seaman of ordinary competence. In a written statement he attempted to explain his reasons as follows:

> The anchorage was close to my port side and she must have seen me going out to the Sea buoy so that I fully expected I would be well clear of the buoy when she reached it. I was a ship leaving port and *under the circumstances I did not consider the position such that I should act as the give way ship* under the crossing rule . . . . [emphasis supplied][4]

The chief officer of *Aracelio* offered an equally amazing statement:

> I believe we had the right of way out to the Sea buoy and that *Nidareid* should have acted accordingly. If she had reduced speed *or altered to port* [emphasis added] there would have been no collision. I was surprised that she continued to come on. . . .[5]

These were not off the cuff observations but written statements offered as evidence. It is hardly surprising that a collision resulted with both vessels considering that they were in a stand-on position.

---

* *Aracelio* was 508′ in length and 9,732 gross tons; *Nidareid* was 631′ long and 19,746 gross tons.

† That would have happened while the Cuban ship was still over a mile from the sea buoy allowing ample room for a turn to starboard.

Aracelio on dropping the pilot had shortly thereafter gone up to sea-speed. She was deep loaded, however, and it was the opinion of the Court that she had only worked up to about 9 knots at the time of collision. The master of the Cuban ship continued his remarkable summation:

> When she was about half a mile distant, we had got a little less than one of our lengths from the buoy. *Nidareid* was still about the same bearing, but I have the impression that her lights are a little more open. I could not then starboard and get under her stern, for there was not enough room and I had the tide with me, nor could I go to port because the buoy was close off my port bow, also if I had taken way off either by stopping or reversing I would have run into her port side. If I had starboarded as she ported there would have been a head on collision and I still thought she could clear my vessel by porting, so I still kept my speed as the best thing to do in the circumstances.

As the distance closed to half a mile it became apparent to the master of *Nidareid* that the oncoming vessel for whatever reason was not giving way and he went hard right and blew one blast. With still no response from *Aracelio* he put the engines full astern and blew three blasts. He followed that with a double ring. The bow now started to slowly fall off to starboard with the engines now reversed. In spite of the fact that the engines had been stopped for almost ten minutes before the astern bell it was estimated that due to her heaviness she was still making about 7 knots as her bow sliced into the starboard side of the Cuban vessel.

There was no question of the gross and glaring faults of *Aracelio*, but before judgment was passed it was necessary to dispose of the charges brought by counsel for the Cuban ship against the Norwegian vessel. It was first of all maintained that *Nidareid* had as a stand-on ship failed to hold her speed. The Court turned here to the classic case of *The Roanoke* where that vessel, which was privileged, was slowing down to pick up a pilot and came into collision with *Windsor*. Lord Alverstone in his opinion held that the burdened vessel should have been aware of what *Roanoke* was doing. Griffin in commenting on that case said: "It was held that, when the holding on vessel was evidently about to slow down to take a pilot, the giving-way vessel should not act on the assumption that the holding-on vessel would keep her speed unchanged."[6]

Justice Karaminski applied these principles to the case before him and found that it should have been perfectly obvious to the Cuban master that the Norwegian ship was going to anchor and it was hence necessary for her to reduce speed if she was to carry out that operation.

He next turned to the question as to whether *Nidareid* had put the helm over too early. Here he relied on *The Otranto* where it was noted that while the duty of the stand-on vessel is of the utmost consequence the Court cannot and should not expect the mariner to be able to determine that time and place (of reaching *in extremis*) with mathematical precision, but he must observe the other vessel carefully "endeavouring to do his best to act at the right moment, [if so] he will not be held to blame, though it afterwards appears that he waited too long or acted too soon."[7] He concluded that this described the actions of the Norwegian master and attributed the whole of the blame to the Cuban.

* * * * * * * *

In the early evening of November 15, 1956 the Italian steamer *Clelia Campanella* (hereinafter referred to as *Campanella*) and the British twin-screw steamship *Corfu** had anchored in the Outer Roads of the port of Dakar to await a pilot to take them to their berths. It was a fine clear night with a gentle north–north-westerly breeze and little or no current. *Corfu* was lying into the wind with three shackles in the water. She was partially loaded and had only been anchored a short while. The same was true of the Italian vessel, which had anchored about 500 yards off on the port beam of *Corfu*.

The pilot boat came out shortly before 1900 and the understanding was *Corfu* would weigh anchor first and *Campanella* would follow her in. The British vessel had commenced heaving at about 1840 and eight minutes later the anchor was aweigh. The helm was then put to port and her starboard engine slow ahead. About two minutes later the port engine was put half

---

* *Corfu* was a combination freight and passenger ship of 14,280 gross tons and 543′ in length; *Clelia Campanella* was 437′ long and 6,934 gross tons.

astern. The vessel was thus turned to port to angle across the bow of the Italian ship towards the harbour entrance. At 1857 both engines were put slow ahead and half ahead two minutes later with the vessel steadied on a course of about 303°. The master estimated that *Corfu* would clear the bow of *Campanella* by about 100 feet though in the failing light an accurate estimate would have been difficult. The Court thought the estimate was probably optimistic.[8] It certainly allowed little margin for error.

Campanella had four shots on the windlass when the pilot boarded about five minutes before the collision and the chief officer was instructed to commence heaving. When the mate reached the bow he found the cable leading slightly forward a bit on the starboard bow, and about three and a half minutes before the collision they commenced heaving away slowly. *Corfu* was seen to be making her way across the bow of *Campanella* towards the harbour entrance. After about two minutes it was realised by both the master and the pilot of the Italian ship that *Corfu* was going to pass dangerously close and in fact would not make it cross *Campanella*'s bow.

The master quickly ordered the chief mate to cease heaving and let the cable run free. There was an ordinary seaman in the chain locker and it was not feasible to do this so the mate ordered the seaman out of the locker, reversed the windlass, and ordered the focsle vacated as collision appeared inevitable.

Heaving on the anchor had given *Campanella* some slight headway and that coupled with the meagre distance at which *Corfu* had chosen to pass ahead defeated the venture. The pilot on the British vessel on realising the hazard of his position stopped the engines at 1901 and ordered hard right helm. The speed at this time was about 3 to 4 knots. *Campanella* was now very close probably no more than about 50 feet off. While the helm threw the bow to starboard it naturally canted the stern to port without imparting any lateral movement to the vessel during the moments remaining. The helm action had in fact worsened the situation. That was soon realised and the port engine was put full astern, the starboard full ahead and the helm reversed. These actions had barely begun to check the vessel's swing to starboard when the stem of *Campanella* passed a scant 6 feet or so off under the bridge of *Corfu* and seconds later the bow of the former struck the port side of the latter. The port engine was then stopped and the starboard put to slow ahead.

As the chief officer of *Campanella* ordered the focsle head cleared the master rang full astern on the engines with a double ring. The collision occurred about a minute later. In this short space of time the backing of the engines could have had little effect and the Court concluded that the Italian vessel was still moving ahead under bare headway when her stem collided with the side of *Corfu* just abaft her accommodation ladder about 150 from the stern.

Counsel for *Campanella* maintained that those aboard that vessel could not reasonably expect *Corfu* to pass so close ahead that the shortening up of the anchor cable on the Italian vessel would be significant. Mr. Justice Hewson after discussing this with the Elder Brethren concluded that there was no excuse for *Corfu* to attempt to pass so close ahead, which would allow such a scant margin for the unforeseen. While thus agreeing with *Campanella*'s counsel he found that when she decided to begin to heave on her anchor it became incumbent upon her to keep a very vigilant lookout, as in the case of *Janet Quinn*.[9] Had the movements of *Corfu* been closely observed it would have been apparent that she would pass closely ahead, and the prudent thing would be to allow her to clear before heaving on the anchor. It was unseamanlike to do so and *Campanella* was consequently held at fault. The Judge found each equally to blame and decided they should share the damages.

* * * * * * * *

When preparing to leave one's berth either alongside a dock or at anchor the first precaution to be taken is to determine if other vessels in the vicinity are engaged in a similar activity. The same applies to vessels entering a pilotage or anchorage area and neglect of that elementary principle had the gravest consequences for the vessels involved in these collisions. This stage in a vessel's journey is one where close quarters is the norm, and hence where hazard is at its highest. Only by paying the strictest attention to the movements of other vessels within the area can one minimise the dangers of such meetings.

As vessels encountered under such circumstances will ordinarily be changing their heading and speed in carrying out their manoeuvres one must be careful not to put more way on one's vessel than circumstances allow. The mariner should always remember the obvious fact that it is easier to increase one's speed than take it off, and that once it becomes necessary to back down control over the vessel is compromised and may be lost altogether. The effects of wind and current must also be carefully considered. On ships where the entire superstructure is aft even a modest amount of wind may require more headway for manoeuvring than is safe within a crowded anchorage. Without a bow thruster or the aid of tugs an operation which a more traditionally constructed vessel might accomplish with relative ease may be too dangerous for vessels of this newer design to attempt.

The use of whistle signals to indicate one's manoeuvres is a must, though communication of intentions by VHF has become the method preferred in many places today and in American waters is required by law. VHF communication, however, is no substitute in law for whistle signals[10], but from a practical standpoint whistle signals cannot be as effective as an unambiguous VHF exchange.

The question of local regulations, that takes precedence over COLREGS, is one that is commonly neglected. The gap in such knowledge is usually filled by the local pilot, but it behooves the shipmaster to acquaint himself with any points of variance between local regulations and COLREGS so that he is not vulnerable to unpleasant surprises and the vagaries of a pilot's memory or interpretation. This information may not be readily obtainable in a published form and the ship owner should instruct his agents to procure this information as a matter of routine for such of his vessels as call at their ports.

* * * * * * * *

Notes

1 *L.L.R.*, Vol. 2, 1975, p. 144.
2 *Ibid.*, Vol. 2, 1966, pp. 80, 81.
3 *Ibid.*, Vol. 1, 1967, p. 177.
4 *Ibid.*, Vol. 1, 1968, p. 136.
5 *Ibid.*
6 Griffin, p. 137. Also cf. Cockcroft & Lameijer, pp. 117–18. It was mentioned in the case that the *Roanoke* was flying the International code signal for a pilot, hence *Windsor* who collided with her should have known her intentions. It would follow from this that failure to display the appropriate signal could be held to be a fault.
7 *L.L.R.*, Vol. 1, 1968, p. 139.
8 *Ibid.*, Vol. 2, 1963, p. 413.
9 Justice Hewson had been the original presiding judge in the case of the *Janet Quinn* but had been forced to retire before it was decided due to ill health.
10 Except in U.S. waters.

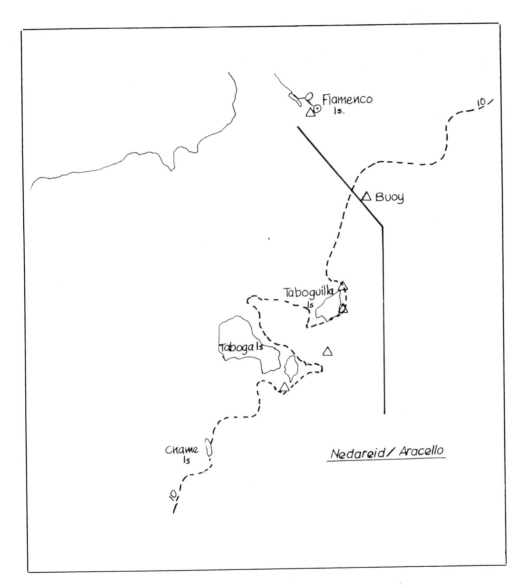

Figure 33 *Nedareid/Aracello* (See page 129)

Chapter Sixteen

Collisions on Pilot Stations

Pilot stations or boarding areas are well known as breeding grounds for collision. Far too often one observes vessels engaged in a foolhardy race for the pilot, but even where such recklessness does not cloud the scene, pilot stations are places where vessels must unavoidably "congregate" with all the hazards that this entails. Hence the highest degree of prudence and alertness should be maintained when embarking or discharging a pilot. Failure to abide by these precepts led to the collisions considered here.

On the evening of October 1, 1963 *Lucille Bloomfield* left Le Havre passing through the breakwater just before ten o'clock at about the same time as the inbound ship *Ronda** passed just south of the Le Havre lightship. Both were headed for the pilot cutter, the former to discharge her pilot and the latter to embark one. The visibility was moderate with rain squalls attended by strong westerly winds, but the weather was not an active element in the collision that followed.

After passing the lightvessel the master of *Ronda* set a course of 109° and went below for a short while to rest his leg which he had injured on a previous voyage. About a quarter of an hour later, or less than ten minutes before the collision, he returned to the bridge when he heard the telegraph ring, which was a slow ahead bell. The watch officer had just altered course a bit to the right to 114° and the master assumed the con. He steered no set course thereafter but adjusted the ship's head to keep the pilot cutter 10 to 15 degrees on the starboard bow. He noticed at the time an outbound vessel (*Lucille Bloomfield*) about a point and a half on the starboard bow and opening. On the course she was then steering she would pass well clear to the south. He assumed she would alter to port a bit to make for the lightship. It did not seem to occur to him that the outbound ship would probably have a pilot aboard and so in the process of disembarking him might haul up to the north. In any event he thought she posed no threat and so ignored her.

As *Lucille Bloomfield* neared the pilot station the cutter was observed cruising on a northerly heading in her usual spot to the eastward of the L.H.2 buoy. She was then just about dead ahead, and as the American vessel neared she ported a bit to pass under the pilot cutter's stern before coming up on a northerly heading to bring her abeam the cutter. Speed was reduced from manouvring full ahead at 2216 to slow ahead, and the engines were stopped a minute later so as to run off her way before the pilot disembarked.

As the ship came on to a northerly heading the pilot later testified that he saw *Ronda* about a mile off four points on the port bow showing a green light. The master also claimed that he saw *Ronda* at this time, but Mr. Justice Karminski who heard the case in the lower court found the master's evidence, on this point at least, unreliable, as did the several judges of the appeal court who considered his testimony and rejected his claim. [1]

The launch from the pilot cutter was making her way over into the lee of the American ship

---

* The Norwegian vessel *Ronda* was 4,608 gross tons and 428' long while the American ship *Lucille Bloomfield* was 463' in length and 6,103 gross tons.

134

and the pilot left the bridge to disembark. This was about 2219 but he did not actually go over the side until around three minutes later. All during this period it appears that the master's attention was directed solely to seeing the pilot safely off his vessel. Neither he nor anyone else aboard took any notice of, nor indeed was aware of, the vessel approaching close on the port bow during this critical interval.

As soon as the pilot was away the master gave the order for full ahead. He then tardily lifted his eyes to the horizon to discover to his horror *Ronda* very close on the port bow crossing from port to starboard. He immediately ordered hard right rudder though there is some doubt as to whether the engine order was given before or after he saw *Ronda*. It would seem plausible that he discovered the vessel after giving the engine order but before giving the helm order.

As we had learned earlier the master of *Ronda* was equally oblivious or unconcerned with the presence of *Lucille Bloomfield*, and with the American ship seemingly passing clear on his starboard side he gave his vessel a kick ahead as he prepared to come to port to make a lee for the pilot boat. He only held that speed for a moment before he again reduced to slow followed at 2219 by dead slow and stop at 2220. The vessel from that moment until the collision some three minutes later was slowly turning to port as she ran down her speed to about 3 knots.

The lookout had meanwhile been sent back to help rig the pilot ladder while on the bridge all attention was concentrated on the pilot boat and none on *Lucille Bloomfield*. That situation was not long in being rectified as the American ship was now approaching so close she could not easily be ignored. It was suddenly realised on *Ronda* that *Lucille Bloomfield* was now showing not a green light but a red, and was little more than a ship length off broad on the starboard bow. A signal of one short blast was heard as the wheel of the American ship was put to starboard. *Ronda* responded with hard left rudder signalled by two blasts, and followed at 2222 by full astern on the engines. The vessels, both making close to 3 knots, collided a minute later, with the bow of *Lucille Bloomfield* penetrating the side of *Ronda* in the way of number two hatch at almost a right angle. The latter vessel made it into port, but subsequently capsized and sank alongside the dock when the bulkhead between one and two hatches collapsed.

The pleas of the opposing counsels was not lacking in ingenuity, and Lord Justice Willmer who presided at the appeal considered but rejected them on the overwhelming evidence of bad lookout on both sides, dismissing the appeal and confirming the decision of the lower court that both ships were equally to blame.

Counsel for *Lucille Bloomfield* had contended that as she arrived first at the pilot station it was the duty of *Ronda* to keep out of her way. The Court accepted that plausible argument, but then they attempted to pursue their advantage by claiming that as the American vessel was in a privileged position and was under no obligation to act until a "late moment" the fact that she was keeping a bad lookout was irrelevant. The argument ran that even if *Lucille Bloomfield* had been keeping a perfect lookout there was no way she could discover that *Ronda* was not. She could hence assume that the Norwegian ship would keep out of her way. Lastly, she could not foresee that *Ronda* would port her helm at the last moment without signalling, so that under the circumstances *Lucille Bloomfield*, being obliged to do nothing until a late moment, could not be held at fault for an action taken *in extremis* that was unsuccessful. The Judge found that a very attractive and persuasive argument, but counsel for *Ronda* soon demolished it.

They maintained that the master of *Lucille Bloomfield* did the worst possible thing by putting the engines full ahead at that time. Not only is the speed of closing quickened but the amount of damage increased if a collision results. It was not a case here where the privileged vessel watched the burdened ship approach with apprehension and agony before taking action at the last moment based upon a considered and careful appraisal of the facts. The action she took was founded upon no previous assessment of the facts since she remained unaware of them. Had she been keeping a careful lookout she would have had a growing awareness of the disturbing and unseamanlike behaviour of *Ronda*. [3] When the pilot disembarked there was still time to avoid collision by backing down instead of going full ahead.

After careful study of the facts Mr. Justice Karminski was unable to distinguish different degrees of fault between the two vessels and so held them equally to blame. On appeal that decision was affirmed.

* * * * * * * *

On August 30, 1971 the motor vessel *Shavit* of Haifa was on her way from Yokahama to Nagoya. Her agents there had instructed her to arrive at the pilot station off the entrance to the port at 0700, and she had accordingly reduced speed at about 0330 in order to arrive at the pilot station at the scheduled time. The weather was overcast but the visibility was good, there was a light breeze from the south-west, and the tide was flooding in a northerly direction at a half knot or less.

Shavit had apparently not been recently to Nagoya as she was using an old chart which did not show some recent changes consisting of a second fairway and an extension of the old one almost a mile farther south. Working from this chart had seemingly created some confusion in the mind of the master of *Shavit*, which led him to make an erroneous assumption and serious mistake as to the course the outgoing vessel, *Troll River*,* would steer on her departure.[4]

Troll River, a motor ship registered in London, had loaded a cargo of motor cars for New Orleans and was now outbound with the pilot who was scheduled to take *Shavit* to her berth. After casting off she proceeded down channel at full manoeuvring speed of approximately 12.5 knots. Her course was 212½°, which she steered, except for some minor alteration to pass an inbound vessel, until moments before the collision. As she continued down the fairway and approached the No. 1 buoy (where the pilot was due to leave) the pilot pointed out *Shavit*, bearing about a point on *Troll River*'s starboard bow and about a mile and a half off, saying that this was the vessel he would board on leaving *Troll River*.

That vessel was to the west of the fairway and appeared to the master of the British ship to be on an easterly heading and lying dead in the water or nearly so. There was nothing unusual about the situation and he understandably paid no particular attention to her. The engines were first put on half and then dead slow ahead as the pilot prepared to disembark. He informed the master before leaving the bridge that he should proceed past the number one buoy leaving *Shavit* on his starboard hand, and after clearing the fairway buoy he could come to the right.

The 2nd officer, who was on watch, went with the pilot to see him off and the master strolled to the starboard bridge wing to observe the pilot's departure. The chief officer was in the wheelhouse. They were now passing the No. 1 buoy close to starboard and the pilot boat was coming up on the starboard quarter to take the pilot off. As the master looked up he saw to his surprise and dismay *Shavit* underway making to cross his bow from starboard to port. He immediately shouted to the helmsman to put the wheel hard right. He ran to the wheelhouse and paused for a moment to allow the right wheel to take effect before putting the engines full astern. The bow of *Troll River* began to swing slowly to starboard, but *Shavit* was too close aboard and the stem of the British vessel struck her abaft No. 5 hatch at an angle of 55° leading aft. The force of the blow almost severed the afterbody of *Shavit* from the rest of the vessel leaving it hanging only by the starboard shell plating.

At around 0700 those aboard *Shavit* saw *Troll River* pass through the breakwater and continue down the fairway at a brisk rate of speed. *Shavit* had been slowly approaching the pilot station varying the engines between dead slow and stop just sufficient to give her steerage way. She was on a course of 023° which was altered gradually to starboard until she was on a heading of 045° at about the time *Troll River* was first seen coming down the channel. *Shavit*'s head continued to swing slowly to the right and at 0710, some four minutes before the collision, she had reached a heading of almost 048° and was still swinging slowly to the right. Some two and a half minutes before the collision she had reached a heading of almost 055°, and at that time her helm was put 15 to 20 degrees to starboard, the engines to slow ahead, and one blast was sounded on the whistle. Less than a minute later the wheel was put further to starboard and

---

* *Shavit* was 451′ long and 4,896 gross tons; *Troll River* was 601′ in length and of 22,159 gross tons.

the engines to half ahead followed by another single blast on the whistle. That was followed a half minute later by hard right rudder and full ahead. It was now becoming rapidly apparent that *Troll River* was not behaving as expected and the vessels were in danger of collision. The helm was reversed and emergency full ahead rang on the engines in a frantic attempt to swing the stern clear. Before this last manoeuvre had time to take effect the vessels collided.

The master of *Shavit* had evidently expected *Troll River* to slow substantially before she reached the No. 1 buoy and on coming abeam to alter course sharply to starboard. It was upon those expectations that he began *Shavit*'s swing to starboard in order to pass port to port. He had no grounds upon which to base those expectations other than supposition, and for jumping to these conclusions he paid a heavy price.

There was no question of the fault of *Shavit* in undertaking the unseamanlike manoeuvre that brought about the collision. The trial judge first cited the general principle "that a ship which is outside the fairway should not enter it at such time or place as will cause danger or difficulty to other ships already in the fairway and proceeding up and down it." He saw this as the main cause of the collision and went on to say that it was the view of the Court that the master of *Shavit* (who did not appear before the Court) had been led to embark upon his disastrous endeavour because he was "misled about the extent of the fairway by having an out-of-date chart, and, because of that he formed an erroneous view about what the *Troll River* was likely to do."[5]

While admitting his client's fault counsel suggested that *Troll River* was also to blame in maintaining an excessive speed under the circumstances and keeping a bad lookout. It was likewise suggested that she was further guilty of failing to react promptly enough when *in extremis*.

The Judge consulted the Elder Brethren on these points and they responded that there was no reason for *Troll River* not to proceed at the speed she did since she could not be expected to anticipate difficulty as the only vessel in the vicinity in a position to cause trouble was outside the fairway and could reasonably be expected to remain so until *Troll River* was clear. She was thus behaving in a normal and seamanlike manner in pursuing her voyage with dispatch with no expectation that any reasonable movements of *Shavit* would hamper her.

In the matter of the lookout it was conceded that the aural lookout of *Troll River* was indeed defective in respect to the failure of anyone on the bridge to hear the one blast signals made by *Shavit* that might have alerted them to her unseamanlike and dangerous manoeuvre. The last of the two one blast signals were heard by both the bow lookout and the 2nd mate at the pilot ladder, but no report was made to the bridge. While the Elder Brethren advised the Court that these signals should have been heard on the bridge or been reported, and the Court accepted that advice, it was evidently not deemed a causative fault as *Shavit* was found solely to blame.

Shavit's fault was undeniably extreme and it is hard from the standpoint of justice to quarrel with the decision. Still, from the standpoint of law and logic, it is difficult to see how the failure of those on the bridge of *Troll River* to discover the dangerous manoeuvre on which *Shavit* was embarked, so that *Troll River*'s way could have been reduced sufficiently to avoid collision, did not contribute to the collision.

There would first of all seem to be the question of whether the bow lookout was an adequate lookout. It is a settled principle that a lookout must have sufficient experience to be able to carry out his duties.[6] If the man is an able seaman then that would ordinarily constitute *prima facie* evidence that he has adequate experience. If not, and particularly if the man has very little experience on deck, the question of whether he has been adequately instructed in the duties of a lookout would become germain. Lookouts, even experienced ones, should also be given special instructions from time to time where special circumstances supervene. This may be because of particular conditions obtaining at the time or unusual conditions pertaining to the ship. An experienced lookout should know that the sounding of whistle signals by approaching vessels is a fact that requires reporting to the bridge, "and it has been said that a lookout who hears a signal without reporting it might just as well not be there."[7]

Troll River's bridge was located almost a cable length from the bow. She had diesel engines which are notoriously noisy and can interfere with the aural lookout on the bridge. It would be prudent of the master on such a vessel to see that his watch officers impressed upon their seamen the importance of reporting whistle signals to the bridge since it was quite likely that some signals audible from the bow would not be from the bridge.

When Mr. Justice Brandon solicited advice from the Elder Brethren as to the adequacy of the visual lookout on *Troll River* he was advised that under the prevailing circumstances "there was no need for those on board *Troll River* to pay any particular attention to [*Shavit*], because they could reasonably assume that she would remain outside the fairway until *Troll River* had passed."[8] While there can be no quarrel with the reasonableness of the assumption it would seem advisable that any vessel approaching another at such a distance that if she does something unexpected serious consequences could ensue would as a matter of routine keep her under observation. That would be the normal function of the watch officer, and as he had gone to see the pilot off we can assume that he had been temporarily relieved by the chief officer. Under such conditions the watch officer would normally be on the alert for manoeuvring instructions of the master as the pilot was in the process of disembarking, but he should also be keeping an eye on the movements of *Shavit* as a matter of routine. Whenever there is another vessel in a position to do you harm you watch her, and if you do not you may well be found negligent if she does you harm or you do harm to her, no matter how gross her fault.

* * * * * * * *

In a more recent case two Liberian flag vessels came into collision at the pilot station in the Gulf of Thailand in the approaches to the port of Bangkok in circumstances that on the face of it seem roughly similar to those in the above case. The inbound vessel, which was expecting to embark a pilot, turned across the path of the outbound ship which had sometime earlier disembarked hers, yet here the former was found free from guilt and the latter solely to blame.

Thomaseverett had departed Bangkok on the evening of May 6, 1972 on a voyage to Hong Kong laden with some five thousand tons of latex, jute and general cargo. The weather was fine with a south-westerly wind force 3–4, excellent visibility, and the tide setting in a northerly direction at about 1 knot. She had just emerged from the Mae Nam Chao Phraya River where she had dropped her pilot and was proceeding at slow speed on a course of 155° as she approached the lightship, which also served as a pilot boat, anchored to the south-west of the mouth of the river.

At 2038 she was on the aforesaid course just under half a mile due south of the pilot/lightship. South of this vessel and about a mile off she observed the MV *Esso Chittagong** which had earlier been lying at anchor awaiting a pilot and had got underway to approach the pilot boat. She was on a heading of 350° and had bare headway. Both vessels had the other under observation and visual and radar sightings made by the watch officer on *Thomaseverett* showed that *Esso Chittagong* was about 30° on the starboard bow nearly a mile distant. She was also aware of the heading of the inbound ship and that she was moving very slowly in order to pick up a pilot.

Soon after this *Thomaseverett* increased her speed to half ahead and changed course to the right to 180°, but she neglected to signal that alteration by a whistle signal. Some three to four minutes later at 2312 she passed to the west of the pilot/lightship about a cable off making a speed now of close to 7 knots. *Esso Chittagong* had meanwhile slowly changed heading to about 342° and was dead in the water. Those on board that vessel, however, had not seen the altered heading of *Thomaseverett* which was still showing a green light. Not long after passing abeam of the pilot/lightship she had come right to 190°,† again sounding no whistle signal, so that when she reached that heading she was showing both her sidelights to *Esso Chittagong*.

---

* *Esso Chittagong* was a fully loaded tanker of 13,154 gross tons and 572′ in length; *Thomaseverett* was 449′ long and 5,853 gross tons.

† It was claimed by her counsel that this was inadvertent when the helmsman allowed the ship to swing off course. If so the master was negligent in not keeping a closer check on the course being steered.

138

The master of that vessel observed that change and realised the danger it put him in; he responded by ordering hard right helm and put the engines, which had been stopped, to slow ahead. It was now 2212½ and he signalled his manoeuvre with one blast of the whistle.

Thomaseverett now belatedly realised the developing danger and changed course to the left, and in continuing stubborn disregard of the Rules failed again to blow her whistle. She had meanwhile gone to full manoeuvring speed several minutes before passing abeam the pilot/lightship and now slowed first to half and then slow ahead in an attempt to take some way off her progress into what had suddenly become an alarming situation. At about the same time that *Thomaseverett* had begun her swing back to port *Esso Chittagong* increased to half in an effort to pass ahead of *Thomaseverett* and repeated her one blast signal. *Thomaseverett*, which was now rapidly closing on the port bow of *Esso Chittagong*, put her helm hard to starboard and belatedly first stopped and then rang full astern on her engine. Now that it was too late to give the other any helpful signal by which she could govern her manoeuvres *Thomaseverett* tardily blew one short blast followed by three. Less than a minute later when *Esso Chittagong* had swung to a heading of about 040° and *Thomaseverett* had swung right to 190° the port bow of the latter struck *Esso Chittagong* on her port side forward igniting the cargo of aviation gasoline she was carrying, which caused her great damage before it was finally brought under control.

In the original action brought before Mr. Justice Parker *Thomaseverett* was held solely to blame. In the appeal before Judge (now Lord Justice) Brandon the decision was upheld without dissent though some issue was taken with peripheral findings of the lower court.

Counsel for *Thomaseverett*, while not denying the fault of that vessel, sought to prove subsequent error in the navigation of *Esso Chittagong* claiming that her putting her helm hard to starboard and increasing speed to first slow and shortly thereafter to half even when she saw the alteration back to port of *Thomaseverett* was a contributory fault. Counsel contended that the initial action of the master of *Esso Chittagong* was precipitate, and on seeing the alteration of course to starboard by *Thomaseverett* so that both her sidelights were showing less than a point on the port bow he should have waited to see if that was a prelude to a further alteration to starboard that would take her clear across his bow. It was further claimed that having made his alteration to starboard under hard right wheel and an increase in speed to slow (to give effect to his helm action) he made a further mistake in increasing to half ahead in spite of the fact that *Thomaseverett* had by then closed her red and opened her green. Counsel also suggested that *Esso Chittagong* had made an earlier error in failing to note the previous alteration of *Thomaseverett* from 155° to 180° and that this led to the later mistaken actions.

Lord Justice Brandon referred these allegations to his Assessors and they advised him that the master of *Esso Chittagong* had reacted properly in putting his helm hard to starboard and increasing to slow ahead on seeing the alteration of *Thomaseverett* to starboard so as to show both sidelights, and that it was also proper and in accord with good seamanship to increase to half ahead when he observed the erratic behaviour of the other vessel in swinging back to port shortly thereafter.[9] The initial failure of *Esso Chittagong* to note the first course change of the other vessel was seemingly not regarded as significant.

Advice from the Assessors had earlier been sought on defining the faults of *Thomaseverett*, and they found that she laid the basis for the development of the close-quarters situation that precipitated the later mistakes causing the collision by setting an improper course at 2038 when she changed from 155° to 180. The seamanlike thing to do was to keep well clear of the pilot boarding area into which it was obvious *Esso Chittagong* would enter to embark a pilot. She could have done that either by passing well to the east of the pilot boarding area, which the Sailing Directions define as "being within an area of three cables from the pilot light vessel," or by passing to the westward of *Esso Chittagong*.

Having made her initial error in setting an improper course they found she compounded it by imprudently increasing her speed as she passed through the pilot boarding area where she could expect to encounter the other vessel. They argued that she should have been making no more than 4 knots at that juncture.

They were next invited to comment on her action in altering from 180° to 190 and her subsequent return to the former course on hearing *Esso Chittagong*'s one blast signal and seeing her turn to starboard. They replied that having once swung to the right of the 180° course, for whatever cause, it was bad seamanship on the part of *Thomaseverett* to attempt to resume it, and that once *Esso Chittagong* signalled her turn to starboard the seamanlike thing to do was to respond by putting the helm hard right and the engines full astern, which action would have reduced her way and swung her bow to starboard. The Lord Justice accepted that advice and denied the appeal.

It might seem that there was an inconsistency here in holding *Thomaseverett* at fault for increasing her speed after having gained the open sea and her pilot was away when *Troll River* was held blameless for doing the same. *Troll River*, however, had no reason to believe, and every reason to expect, that the inbound vessel waiting to embark the pilot would keep well clear and do nothing to embarrass her. Had *Thomaseverett* set a proper course at the outset so as to avoid the pilot area the question of her speed would never have arisen. But she chose to enter an area which *Esso Chittagong* not only had every right to enter but had to enter to pick up her pilot, and which every consideration of seamanship warned against the entry of *Thomaseverett*. Once she adopted that course, of proceeding through the pilot boarding area, her primary obligation was to keep clear of vessels navigating legitimately within its confines, and that she failed to do.

* * * * * * *

The collision between *Guam Bear* and *Esso Seattle** in the entrance to Apra Harbour in Guam is yet another instance where the operation of disembarking a pilot and the approach to the pilot station so consumed the attention of those involved that they had little left to devote to the other vessel, with deplorable results.

Guam Bear was on a voyage from San Francisco to Apra while *Esso Seattle* had just discharged a cargo of aviation gasoline and was returning to the west coast of the United States. It was not long after sunrise on January 13, 1967 with excellent visibility and little or no wind or current to affect the navigation of the vessels. The Port Regulations for Apra Harbour required inbound vessels to wait outside when a vessel was departing until such time as that vessel was clear. However, it became obvious during the court proceedings that the regulations regarding priority of movement applied only to those within the harbour limits, and indeed a copy of the book containing such regulations could not be retained upon said vessel on its departure. The regulation was also unknown to the pilot involved and to both masters, and the U.S. Government's attempt to claim that *Guam Bear* was unseaworthy because of her failure to know of this supposed restriction was given short shrift by the Court. Nonetheless, *Guam Bear* had an unimpeded view of the harbour and its entrance, and as in the case of *Shavit/Troll River* the outbound vessel, *Esso Seattle*, was in a narrow channel bound for the open sea so it was the duty of *Guam Bear* which was approaching from the open sea to allow the outbound ship to discharge her pilot and gain the open sea before attempting herself to enter.

She could see *Esso Seattle* moving in the harbour making for the entrance long before she was committed to entering. Moreover, *Guam Bear* approached the harbour entrance on a diagonal course from the north-west thereby adding to the difficulty of the meeting by creating a crossing situation where good seamanship required that she first line up on the ranges before attempting to approach. The master of *Guam Bear*, probably intent upon promoting the quick despatch of his vessel, chose to ignore or did not consider the risk his haste entailed. It should have been obvious that it would be a near thing whether he could enter the harbour before *Esso Seattle* reached the entrance, but he seemingly felt he could and chose to press on, and having jumped to that false conclusion he made no effort to check his assumption. *Esso Seattle* was disregarded until her proximity made it impossible to ignore her any longer.

Had *Guam Bear* taken the elementary precaution of checking the bearing of *Esso Seattle* she would have realised the error of her assumption. The Court referred to the *Federal Insurance Co. vs. SS Royalton* wherein it was stated that: "It is well settled that if a steamer be approaching another vessel . . . whose position or movements are uncertain, she is bound to stop until the

---

* *Guam Bear* was 8,197 gross tons and 463′ in length; *Esso Seattle* was 19,291 gross tons and 666′ long.

course and *intentions* [emphasis added] of the other vessel be ascertained with certainty."[10]
That is an injunction every vessel approaching a pilot station should religiously observe.

A much earlier decision, *The New York* (1899) was then quoted:

> The lesson that steam vessels must stop their engines in the presence of danger, or even anticipated danger, is a hard one to learn, but the failure to do so has been the cause of the condemnation of so many vessels that it would seem that these repeated admonitions must likely have some effect. . . .

While it was agreed that *Guam Bear* "had hopelessly misjudged and miscalculated the entire situation" the Court held that this was an equally apt description of the conduct of *Esso Seattle*.[11] Although she could clearly see *Guam Bear* continuing to stand on for a period of five minutes while the pilot was debarking there was no lookout kept by anyone on board and no attention was given to *Esso Seattle*'s progress. Only after the pilot was away was the master rudely awakened to the fact that it was the apparent intention of *Guam Bear* to enter the harbour before *Esso Seattle* had left.

Guam Bear was now seen close ahead less than a point on the starboard bow trying to cross from right to left. The entrance to Apra Harbour is a narrow channel, and it allows little more room for manoeuvre in any direction than the direction defined by the channel. Seamanship and the common sense on which it relies, not to mention the Rule that requires it, dictated that *Esso Seattle* remain as close to the starboard side of that channel as safe navigation permitted. Yet for some inexplicable reason she chose to alter course to the left after blowing a two blast signal to indicate her intention.

A peculiar feature of this case was that *Guam Bear* was in international waters while *Esso Seattle* was quite obviously to everyone concerned still within the precincts of the Inland Rules. Under the former a whistle signal is an announcement of execution but under the latter it is a signal of intent, and must be answered before the proposed action is taken.[12] Had *Esso Seattle* followed that Rule, as she was bound to do, she might have been saved the collision in which she shortly found herself. By her action she made the collision inevitable.

Guam Bear, perhaps relying on a mistaken assumption that *Esso Seattle* being obliged by the Inland Rules to refrain from taking the action she proposed until it was answered, continued on in what was now a hopeless effort to get across the bow of the oncoming tanker. The attempt was doomed to failure as *Esso Seattle* ported her helm as she repeated her two blast signal. Moments later her bow penetrated the side of *Guam Bear*, which sank in the middle of the channel blocking the harbour. Both vessels were held jointly and severally liable for the loss and damages as well as the expense of raising the wreck and sinking it at sea.

It may have been noticed that in none of the cases presented here has there been any reference to the Steering and Sailing Rules as governing, nor for that matter, to special circumstances. While it has long been accepted that there is a limit beyond which the Rules do not apply there must be a natural corollary to this that there is also an inward as well as an outward limit to these Rules, and the former is the province of special circumstances and good seamanship.

That is not to say that the Steering and Sailing Rules do not apply to vessels approaching one another in a pilot boarding area. Indeed, British courts have consistently held that they do, but in a special way. Griffin remarks:

> When two vessels, in crossing situations, are approaching a pilot station, where both will slow and stop for the purpose of taking or discharging a pilot, the question has arisen whether their relations to one another are governed by the crossing rules or by the special circumstances rule. In England, at least, it is settled that the crossing rules apply, since the giving way vessel knows what the holding-on vessel is going to do, and the slowing and stopping of the latter is merely what her obvious intentions require. . . .[13]

And in another place he observes that a holding-on vessel was ". . . entitled to reduce her speed in order to take a pilot on board, when that manoeuvre was perfectly visible to a ship whose duty it was to keep out of her way."[14]

Nevertheless, in the cases examined here reference to the Crossing Rule was strictly avoided and the emphasis placed on the principles of good seamanship in handling vessels in such circumstances. To invoke the Steering and Sailing Rules at a point where the vessels involved are in or very near to close quarters would tend to freeze their options at the very point that flexibility is required. As the stand-on vessel approaches the pilot boarding area she is of course bound by her duty to maintain course and speed, but once within that area good seamanship demands that she proceed with the utmost caution, which requires that she reduce headway early in her approach to obviate the necessity for backing down should she close another vessel as she manoeuvres to embark or discharge a pilot.

* * * * * * * *

Notes

1 *L.L.R.*, Vol. 1, 1967, pp. 346, 348; 1966, Vol. 2, p. 244.
2 The case was tried in both London and New York. In the American court the testimony of the master of *Lucille Bloomfield* that he was aware of the approach of *Ronda* during the disembarkation of the pilot was accepted (see A.M.C., 1969, pp. 2208–09). A contrary view, however, was taken in the English court, *L.L.R.*, Vol. 1, 1967, p. 348; Vol. 2, 1966, p. 244.
3 *L.L.R.*, 1967, Vol. 1, p. 349.
4 *Ibid.*, 1974, Vol. 2, p. 184.
5 Page 187.
6 See Griffin, p. 271; also Farwell, p. 418.
7 Marsden, p. 605.
8 *L.L.R.*, 1974, Vol. 2, p. 187.
9 *Ibid.*, 1981, Vol. 1, pp. 7–8.
10 *A.M.C.*, 1970, p. 1602.
11 *Ibid.*, p. 1603.
12 Cf. Griffin, p. 210.
13 *Ibid.*, p. 115.
14 Page 144.

Esso Chittagong burned out after her collison with *Thomaseverett*

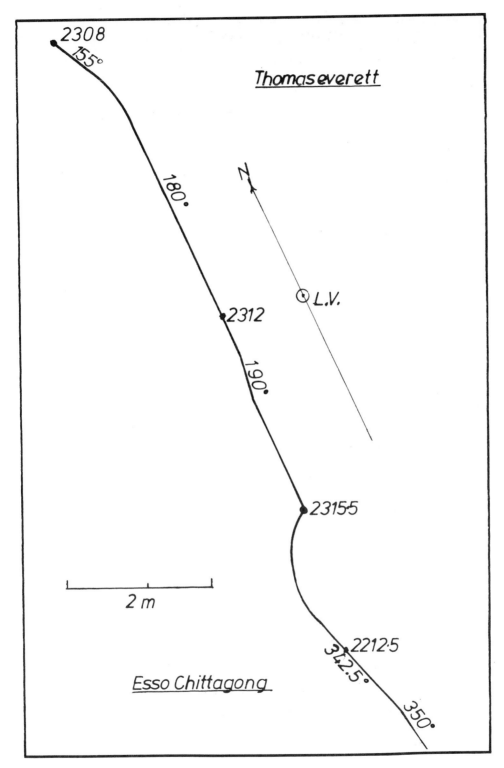

Figure 34 *Esso Chittagong/Thomaseverett* (See page 138)

Chapter Seventeen

Collisions at Anchor

When a vessel is safely riding to her anchor another colliding with her is all but certain to be held to blame in ordinary circumstances, and this case forms the exception to the general rule that when two vessels collide both will almost inevitably be held to contribute though not necessarily in equal shares. Yet there are exceptions to every rule,[1] and we will find some here.

On the morning of April 3, 1964 a gale was blowing in New York harbour where the transport USNS *Buckner* was preparing to sail for Bremerhaven with her usual complement of military personnel and their dependents. The wind was blowing from the south-west at 30 to 40 knots with higher gusts. The weather, however, was clear as the transport lying bow in at Pier No. 4 at the Brooklyn Army Terminal began to undock at 1400. She backed clear with the aid of tugs and turned to starboard to make her way down the Bay Ridge channel towards the Narrows and the open sea beyond. As the docking master debarked and left with the tugs the Sandy Hook pilot, who assumed the con, noticed along with the ship's master and other officers on the bridge a vessel riding to her starboard anchor athwart the Bay Ridge channel stern towards the Brooklyn shore almost a cable length north of the sewage disposal plant. It was the Liberian flag freighter *Japonica** which had dragged her anchor on several occasions during the morning from her original anchorage on the Bay Ridge flats.

She was light, drawing only 5 feet forward and 19 aft, and with only three shackles of chain out it was not surprising that her anchor was not holding in the notoriously poor holding ground in the flats. Her master was ashore and her chief mate was now on the bridge with the 3rd officer preparing to try to get *Japonica* back into her anchorage.

Their own problems somewhat understandably claimed the bulk of their attention and they seemingly paid scant heed to *Buckner* backing out of her berth. They probably felt that being at anchor it was up to the transport to keep out of their way, and the fact that they were in the way of where *Buckner* would normally attempt to go was apparently ignored, as were *Buckner*'s manoeuvres in general.

It was immediately apparent from the transport's bridge that to try to squeeze in between the stern of the freighter and the Brooklyn shore would be too risky an undertaking on such a boisterous afternoon, and the pilot with the master's approval wisely chose to pass to the west of *Japonica* and over the Bay Ridge flats. It was a simple enough manoeuvre and could have been executed without difficulty had those on *Japonica* not chosen at that time to move their vessel back into the anchorage across the bow of *Buckner*.

At around 1415 with *Buckner* now on her chosen heading of roughly south-west the transport commenced to pass *Japonica* as planned. That vessel was about 1,000 yards to the south and appeared to be lying normally to her starboard anchor. As *Buckner* gained way, however, the pilot was surprised to see the freighter's propeller, which was half out of the water at her light

---

* *Buckner* was 609′ long with a gross tonnage of 16,039; *Japonica* was 480′ in length with a gross tonnage of 10,401.

draft, to be turning ahead. The transport was now just off the No. 3 buoy and coming into anchorage No. 21B at a speed of 3 to 4 knots with the wind almost ahead. *Japonica* had swung to an approximately westerly heading by now and was some three to five hundred yards on the port bow.

While there had been adequate room for *Buckner* to pass to the west of *Japonica* in her original position athwart Bay Ridge channel the tide was at low water and the transport was restricted on her starboard hand by the shoaler water of the flats. The pilot blew one blast to indicate his intention to pass ahead of *Japonica* as he had every right to do. He waited for a few moments for the freighter to answer and when she did not he blew another whistle. Again no answer and though *Japonica* had her anchor ball up and her anchor down she was seen to be moving slowly ahead.

The pilot, now thoroughly alarmed, blew the danger signal with again no response from the vessel now underway with her anchor down, who was now in effect the give-way vessel in a crossing situation. He repeated the danger signal and then noticed that *Japonica*'s screw had stopped turning and her bow was swinging to starboard.

Japonica had belatedly become aware of the peril of her predicament and begun to back her engines. With the strain off her chain due to her ahead movement the bow fell off to the right, and the wind that had been ahead came on to her port bow's sail area and she began to swing rapidly toward *Buckner*. At about 1418 in an apparent effort to check her swing *Japonica* dropped her port anchor but she continued her swing to starboard. The distance between the two ships was now very close and the effect of her swing to the right was to narrow that distance.

Buckner's pilot ordered first hard right rudder in an attempt to swing away from *Japonica*, but that canted the stern of the transport towards the swinging bow of the freighter and he ordered the helm reversed to try to swing the stern clear. These manoeuvres were unfortunately to no avail, and at approximately 1420 *Japonica*'s bow struck *Buckner*'s port side at almost a right angle in the way of the No. 12 lifeboat.

The manoeuvres of *Buckner* to avoid *Japonica* now placed her in difficulties with a Yugoslav vessel anchored in No. 21B, and she was only narrowly avoided by the skillful handling of the pilot. *Japonica*'s escapade, however, was not over. After colliding with *Buckner* with both anchors down and broadside to the wind she ran over the No. 3 buoy continuing her uncontrolled clockwise swing and wind induced north-easterly course finally striking Pier 2 of the Army Terminal before the completion of her sad saga.

The Court found no fault with the conduct of *Buckner* but criticised *Japonica* severely holding her completely to blame.[2] Though she had dragged her anchor into the Bay Ridge channel where she had no right to be she had lain there for an hour refusing the assistance of a passing tug and leading those on *Buckner* to believe that she would remain where she was for the few moments needed for the transport to get by. Having gotten up steam she then proceeded to come ahead on her engines and towards *Buckner*. In spite of that vessel's protestations on the whistle she continued her dangerous exercise when she should have stopped and dropped her port anchor until *Buckner*, who was now the privileged vessel with *Japonica* underway, was safely by.

* * * * * * * *

Aghios Gerassimos (hereinafter referred to as *Aghios*) was lying quietly at anchor on the afternoon of November 6, 1975 in the Shatt al Arab off Khorramshahr waiting for an Iraqi pilot to take her down river to Abadan. There was a moderate north-westerly breeze with good visibility and an ebb current of 1½–2 knots. She was lying on a heading of around 300° which to the eye of anyone upriver from her would appear to be substantially across the course of the stream. So she appeared to the master and pilot of the Iranian motor vessel *Arya Rokh** which was outbound down the river.

---

* *Aghios Gerassimos* was 8,309 gross tons and 472' long; *Arya Rokh* was 8,408 gross tons and 476' long. Both were light.

The Greek vessel had left her berth that morning and gone to anchor to await her pilot. The position in which she had anchored was afterwards established to be clearly within an area wherein anchoring was prohibited because of submarine cables. Counsel for *Arya Rokh* contended that the position in which *Aghios* was anchored and the angle at which she rode to her anchor so blocked the channel as made it dangerous to pass.[3] The harbour master himself had acted as pilot when *Aghios* went to anchor so the Greek master had some reason to expect that he was in a proper anchorage though a set of anchor bearings should have told him otherwise. Nonetheless, when the Elder Brethren were questioned on this point they replied that while a vessel passing would need to take care as the Greek's position made navigation awkward it was not so difficult that it could not be done safely, and there was hence no reason for *Aghios* to shift her berth particularly when she expected to remain there only briefly.

Arya Rokh had left her berth early that afternoon and though she had experienced some difficulty in turning down river she had subsequently passed an Indian vessel at anchor without trouble. She was making a speed of some 5 knots through the water on a heading of around 130° when she approached the Greek ship and that course would have taken her clear to starboard. The engines were put to dead slow ahead as an added precaution as the Iranian vessel prepared to pass the anchored ship. *Arya Rokh* unfortunately did not steer well at such slow speed, but the pilot was unaware of that. When the ship came abeam the Customs House he decided he would leave *Aghios* to port instead and ordered 5° right wheel to effect that. When the vessel did not answer he rapidly increased the helm order to 10 and then 15 degrees, but still the ship did not respond. The master who had a better appreciation of his vessel's handling characteristics then took over and ordered hard right wheel whereupon the ship's head swung about 10° to starboard before her stem struck *Aghios* on her starboard bow.

The Court found *Arya Rokh* solely to blame due to indecision and wrong action. The master admitted that had the helm action been supplemented by a kick from dead slow to slow ahead the vessel would probably have responded in time to clear the anchored vessel. Here is a clear case of the master failing to monitor the actions of the pilot closely enough and to use his superior knowledge of his vessel's handling characteristics to advise the pilot in the performance of his duties.

* * * * * * * *

The collision in the Antwerp docks between the Belgian steam tanker *Esso Brussels* and the French tanker *Aldebaran** during the early hours of July 7, 1968 was of a different sort. Both vessels had been lying in the Zandvlied lock waiting to proceed to their berths by way of a canal. The weather was clear at the time and *Aldebaran* was first out going slowly down the canal towards the Lille Bridge about a mile or so straight ahead, but she soon ran into thick fog and anchored about half a mile above there. *Esso Brussels* left the dock about twenty minutes later and encountered the same fog.

Both vessels were assisted by tugs and had pilots aboard who were in communication by way of VHF radio. One tug was fast forward as *Esso Brussels* left the lock. A second was made fast aft as she proceeded out when the first wisps of fog were encountered. The engines were put slow ahead and fog signals sounded from thence on. At 0323½ speed was reduced to dead slow and when the fog closed in they were stopped at 0326 and the stern tug ordered to pull astern. At 0330 the engines were backed full and the port anchor dropped. A half minute later the lights and stern tug of *Aldebaran* were seen and another jingle full astern was given, but *Esso Brussels* still had too much headway and at 0333 holding one and a half shots on the port anchor the bow of *Esso Brussels* struck the stern of *Aldebaran*.

The principal dispute in this casualty concerned the sounding of signals by *Aldebaran* after she anchored. The applicable rules were the Antwerp Port Regulations, and they provided for, among other things, the ringing of the ship's bell rapidly for about five seconds at intervals of not more than one minute for vessels in fog. They also require the sounding an "Attention signal" which may be sounded "in any particular circumstances to attract attention to avoid

---

* *Aldebaran* was 787′ long and 56,604 gross tons; *Esso Brussels* was 699′ in length and 29,850 gross tons.

accidents."[4] Where any conflict between the International Collision Regulations and the local rules existed it was the latter that would prevail, and the former "could apply only to fill in gaps in the local regulations and not to contradict them."[5]

On first anchoring *Aldebaran*, at the request of the pilot, had blown the attention signal, which consists of a sustained blast of about ten seconds duration, at around 0328, or some five minutes before the collision.[6] It was also agreed that those on *Esso Brussels* should have heard that signal, and indeed the helmsman did but did not report it. When the case was originally heard before Mr. Justice Brandon *Aldebaran* was held to be partially at fault for failing to sound an earlier signal which might have alerted those on *Esso Brussels* in time to have averted the collision. When the case went to appeal it was not only held that this view was wrong since the later signal went unheard except by the helmsman, but that the regulations regarding the attention signal applied only to vessels underway. *Aldebaran* was hence not only under no obligation to blow such a signal but was prohibited from sounding it. She was only allowed to sound the signal provided for in the rules for vessels at anchor, viz., the ringing of the ship's bell and no other. The fact that the signal might be inadequate under the circumstances, it was observed by the Court, might be a powerful argument for amending the rules, "but it could be no grounds for sounding a signal which would be contrary to the regulations."[7] The judgment of the lower court was hence reversed and all blame assigned to *Esso Brussels*.

This case spotlights a little heeded but potentially important point; conflict between local rules — that are more often than not unknown to the master — and the International Regulations (see Chapter Fifteen, p. 132). Such divergencies between local rules and the International Regulations can, of course, have potentially serious consequences. The master will ordinarily tend to rely on the pilot for such knowledge since the information may not be readily available elsewhere. The pilot should, of course, know the local regulations under which he works, but that does not guarantee that he may not have a faulty appreciation of portions of them, as was apparently the case here.

* * * * * * * *

On the evening of August 10, 1977 the Greek twin screw motor tanker *Neil Armstrong* had just completed a southbound transit of the Suez Canal on a voyage in ballast from Alexandria to Wadi Feiran some 60 miles to the south of Suez. The night was dark but clear and she had dropped her pilot just north of the Newport Rock before turning into the dredged channel leading out of Suez Bay. The master claimed he cleared that channel at 2010 at which time the engines were put to full ahead manoeuvring, which the Court later determined would have given her a speed of about 11½ knots. Mr. Justice Sheen, who heard the case, also expressed considerable scepticism about the time, as he did of several other features of the case, believing that it was somewhat later than that claimed; the reason being that one of the charges made against *Neil Armstrong* was excessive speed, and Mr. Justice Sheen stated quite unequivocally that the evidence had been doctored to counter that charge.[8]

The southern approaches to the Suez Canal are not inherently difficult of themselves, but the absence of any usable fixed navigational aids, the dearth of readily distinguishable radar targets, and the haphazard anchoring of a large number of vessels in the approaches combine to create a navigational challenge of substantial complexity and no little hazard.

During daylight this presents no great problem for a reasonably competent navigator if he exercises sufficient caution and proceeds at a speed commensurate with the paucity of options for fixing his position. But at night he can be faced with challenges to his skill that he would normally eschew if given the choice, and among the problems he faces is that many of the vessels he may encounter underway and at anchor are of a nondescript nature and manned accordingly. It was one such vessel that lay in the path of *Neil Armstrong* as she attempted to work her way to seaward.

Coral I* was a Liberian flag steam tanker waiting at anchor for repairs before embarking on the last leg of her final voyage to a wrecker's yard in Kaohsiung, Taiwan. She had been anchored

---

* *Neil Armstrong* was 703' in length and 25,471 gross tons; *Coral I* was 813' long and 40,467 gross tons.

a little over 2 miles west of south of the dredged channel from which *Neil Armstrong* had just emerged. She lay there to her starboard anchor at the end of seven shots of chain in the path of the main stream of traffic of vessels departing Suez and the Canal.

Vessels waiting to be broken up are often given only the barest minimum of attention, and *Coral I* was no exception. The chief officer was the only deck officer aboard, and it was hardly to be expected that he would or could keep an alert round-the-clock anchor watch. The engine room was abandoned, and four days before fuel for the emergency generator had been exhausted so since that time the vessel had relied on oil lamps for light. Two oil lanterns had apparently been supplied to provide the lights required by the Rules for ships at anchor. Mr. Justice Sheen came to the conclusion that the standard of vigilance obtaining aboard *Coral I* left something to be desired,[9] and in spite of the argument of her counsel that she could be expected to pay particular attention to these lights simply as a matter of "self preservation" the Court declined to agree and found that such lights were in fact not displayed.

On clearing the dredged channel the master of the Greek vessel set a course of 195° which would take her down to the beginning of the southbound zone of the traffic separation scheme for the Gulf of Suez. As previously noted the engines were put to manoeuvring full ahead at that time. *Neil Armstrong* passed several vessels at anchor but did not have to alter course to do so even though at least one was passed quite close aboard.

The master claimed that the 2nd mate, who was on watch, had been instructed to keep a visual lookout with binoculars, which was the excuse given for failure to notice *Coral I* on the radar dead ahead. The master was evidently using the radar to fix the ship's position, but the major obstacle to getting safely out of the approaches to Suez Bay, especially at night, are the numerous vessels at anchor and the ships and small craft moving among them. When outbound the danger posed by Conry Rock, to which a vessel approaching from the south must give so much attention, is minimal as the course required to make the TSS will take one well clear of that danger.

While one cannot, of course, neglect the position fixing aspects of the vessel's management during this interval it is the hazard posed by other vessels that is the chief concern, so that while a very strict visual lookout must be kept an equally strict watch must be kept on the radar, and it was that neglect that led *Neil Armstrong* into grief.

Coral I was riding to her anchor on a heading of about 020°, which meant that she was almost bow-on to the southbound Greek vessel, but had she been showing an oil light from her foremast it seems highly unlikely that her presence would have remained undetected until she was a scant 50 metres off, as was the case; and that led the judge to conclude that she was in fact blacked out. She was, however, a very large vessel and she was light so that even though the night was dark a vigilant lookout with binoculars should have discovered her bulk in time to avoid her. But whether one will agree with that conclusion or not one cannot dispute that she would have shown as a very substantial target on the radar scope, but she was not seen until too late to avoid her and *Neil Armstrong* struck her head on.

In seeking the advice of the Trinity Masters on this matter Mr. Justice Sheen asked them first, given the conditions obtaining, what would have been a "safe speed" for *Neil Armstrong* and could she be excused for failing to discover *Coral I* on her radar? To the first question they answered that a safe speed was half speed. To the second question they answered that the Greek ship was required by the Collision Regulations to maintain an efficient radar lookout while proceeding through such a congested area, and that the radar should have been used on the 6-mile scale "with frequent scanning" on the 3-mile one.[10] In spite of the fact that Mr. Justice Sheen found *Neil Armstrong* at fault for excessive speed and failure to maintain an effective lookout he assigned the major portion of the blame to *Coral I* for failing to exhibit anchor lights holding her responsible for 60 per cent of the damages.

*　*　*　*　*　*　*　*

Where a vessel is properly anchored in a recognised anchorage exhibiting and/or sounding, as the case may be, the regulation signals another vessel underway which collides with her will almost certainly be found wholly to blame under ordinary circumstances. But where the anchored vessel is anchored in a fairway or waters frequently traversed by ships and not a recognised anchorage, and is subsequently struck by a vessel underway at night or in a fog then any defect in her observance of the Rules as they pertain to anchored vessels are almost certain to come under close scrutiny and may well undermine her position of privilege as an anchored vessel.[11]

Where a ship is anchored in a position where anchored vessels are not normally found, and she can offer no reason other than convenience to justify her presence in such an exposed position she would ordinarily be held to a higher standard of vigilance then normally expected of a vessel at anchor. She should be prepared to give a sheer with her helm, use her engines, pay out more chain or any other way possible to assist other vessels in clearing her where such action might be advisable, but she must "beware of acting too soon."[12]

Nonetheless, vessels underway must take every reasonable precaution to avoid another vessel at anchor. It was said on high authority many years ago that "It is the bounden duty of a vessel underway, whether the vessel at anchor be properly or improperly anchored, to avoid, if it be possible with safety to herself, any collision whatever."[13] That is an injunction that neither the passage of time nor changing circumstances have altered in any way.

* * * * * * * *

Notes

1 The contention that when two vessels collide both will almost inevitably be held at fault to some degree might seem to be contradicted by several of the cases in the two preceding chapters. That is explained by the fact that in these cases close quarters was inherent in the operation. Where that is not the case a vessel must be able to justify her venture into close quarters, and that is an almost impossible task.
2 *A.M.C.*, 1970, pp. 707–08.
3 *L.L.R.*, 1980, Vol. 1, p. 70.
4 *Ibid.*, 1973, Vol. 2, p. 77.
5 *Ibid.*
6 *Ibid.*, p. 79.
7 *Ibid.*, p. 78. Had *Esso Brussels* heard the signal and been misled by it the decision of the Appeals Court could have been quite different.
8 *Ibid.*, 1982, Vol. 1, p. 445.
9 *Ibid.*, pp. 444, 445. A vessel at anchor ordinarily will also have burning powerful deck lights all round the vessel, and indeed Rule 30(c) requires that "a vessel of 100 metres and more in length shall, also use the available working or equivalent lights to illuminate her decks." These lights will normally serve to indicate that she is at anchor more readily and vividly than the two lights specifically provided for by the Rules. Those lights may in fact be somewhat difficult to distinguish at first surrounded by the blaze of the others.
It has become a common practice in some ports such as Suez — Piraeus is perhaps the worst offender in this respect — to put old or derelict ships such as *Coral I* which are idle or laid up in the anchorage without any electrical power, hoisting oil lights as their sole means of identification at night. These lights, even if given close attention, easily go out, and it is not uncommon (particularly at Piraeus) to find vessels completely blacked out.
A vessel moving through an anchorage at night will not expect to encounter an anchored vessel of substantial size to be so abysmally illuminated, and economic expediency is not a sufficient excuse to allow so dangerous a practice to exist, contrary to Rule 30(c). Unless a designated anchorage is provided for such vessels their presence in an ordinary anchorage through which vessels normally pass should be regarded as a breach of Rule 30(c) and their privilege as an anchored vessel accordingly compromised should a vessel under way collide with them.
That question was apparently not raised in the case of *Coral I*, but it is difficult to believe that any thinking seaman would do other than applaud the division of damages awarded by the Court, though this should not be taken as condoning the lack of vigilance shown by the other vessel.
10 *Ibid.*, p. 447.

11 Cf. Marsden, pp. 33–36.

12 *Ibid.*, p. 36.

13 *Ibid.*, p. 35. When *Corstar* anchored improperly across the channel with an indifferent watch at night she was held guilty of contributory negligence when *Eurymedon* struck her while proceeding up the River Thames. She failed to use her engines early on to keep from blocking the channel. Page 26.

Chapter Eighteen

Not Under Command — A Misconception

We saw in the case of *Frosta/Fotini Carras* how the display of not-under-command lights along with masthead lights was held a fault that could have altered the apportionment of blame had they been properly displayed. In the case considered here a similar fault was not considered causative, but the vessel displaying the signals was doing so improperly leading her to consider herself as a stand-on ship when she was not, and that was a fault that most decidedly contributed to the collision.

Djerada was a Moroccan vessel bound for Dunkirk from Casablanca carrying a full cargo of phosphate when on a clear but stormy night in the early hours of November 10, 1969 she collided some 7 miles north-west of Calais with the Polish ship *Ziemia Szezecinska*.* That the Moroccan vessel had experienced serious difficulties was not a point of dispute; that these entitled her to display not-under-command lights is another matter.

Djerada had been battered by heavy weather from November 6th onwards, which became so severe on the morning of the 9th that she could no longer hold her course. She was rolling violently and her decks were continually swept by green seas. At about 1030 one of these tore off the upper of the three tarpaulins on No. 3 hatch and dislodged the cross-battens. The vessel was hove-to to re-secure the hatch and two black balls were hoisted during the operation. An hour later the ship was able to resume her course but the signals were left aloft. That afternoon she received a message that the Dunkirk pilot service had been suspended and she put about on a westerly course to await abatement of the weather.

The wind continued to blow with great force from the south-west and she could only hold her course with difficulty. It was feared that if she broached to she might lose her tarps with disastrous consequences. At about 1600 the two black balls were replaced with two vertical red lights which stayed there until the collision. At some time prior to her being sighted by the Polish vessel her after range light went out and was not replaced so that at the time of collision she was only showing a single mast light in addition to her sidelights and not-under-command lights.[1]

Djerada held her westerly course until around 0130 on the 10th when the weather moderated somewhat allowing her to come around on an easterly heading. Having executed that operation it was quite obvious that she had not lost her powers of manoeuvre. She was making good a course of roughly 088° which meant she had to steer about 095° there being a north-easterly current set of about 1 knot; she was making close to 6½ knots over the ground at the time. Not long thereafter, in spite of the heavy traffic that is a regular feature of navigation in the Dover Strait, the master went below leaving the 2nd mate in charge. At 0240 course was altered to make good a course of 105°, which meant she had to steer between 115° and 120° in order to

---

* *Djerada* was 336′ long and 3,805 gross tons; *Ziemia Szezecinska* (hereinafter referred to as *Ziemia*) was 598′ in length and 16,451 gross tons.

counter the effect of current set and leeway. She had been under observation by the Polish ship for some ten minutes at this time.

Ziemia was on a course of 041° making a speed of about 15 knots over the ground. On first sighting *Djerada* she saw only a single white light some 30° on the port bow about 5 miles away. Not long thereafter the 2nd mate, who had a junior watch officer to assist him as well as a helmsman and a lookout, saw a red light below a white light and not unnaturally thought it was a small ship that would pass clear down his port side. That would have meant that her bearing would have opened, but had he watched her closely he would have found that it was steady or nearly so. A short time before the collision he made a course change of 4° to starboard only to discover not long thereafter a second red light under the first one and a green light below that. He was faced not with a small vessel passing safely down his port side as he had assumed but a much larger ship crossing from port to starboard and apparently not under command. She was by now very close and the 2nd mate ordered hard right helm and flashed the signal "U" (You are standing into danger) on his Aldis lamp. Moments later at 0259 the stem of *Djerada* struck *Ziemia* on her port side aft at an angle of 65–70 degrees leading aft.

Djerada, probably because she considered herself to be not under command, made no effort to avoid *Ziemia* though she may have hauled to starboard at the last minute in a desperate attempt to evade the Polish ship. What seems very obvious is that neither watch officer was paying much attention to the other until they were so close that one could no longer ignore the other. The 2nd mate of the Moroccan vessel was very much preoccupied with the task of fixing his vessel's position as he approached his port of destination. He was taking a set of bearings every ten minutes and that allowed him little time to watch *Ziemia* which he apparently assumed would keep out of his way. [2] At the time of the collision *Djerada* was less than 6 miles from the Dyck lightvessel that marks the entrance of the approach to Dunkirk. Why the master had not been called, let alone why he had left the bridge in the first place, is difficult to understand. The 2nd mate's absorption with the navigation of the vessel led him to neglect the lookout that good seamanship demands. He needed assistance and the master's absence proved disastrous.

Mr. Justice Brandon found the lookout of *Djerada* deplorable and that neglect a direct cause of the collision. He further found the exhibition of not-under-command lights as not justified, which fault was compounded by showing a masthead light causing *Ziemia* to conclude that she was other than the lights seen suggested. [3] That misconception of *Djerada* that she was not under command led her to the fatal assumption that she was in a privileged position in respect to other vessels and perhaps led her to believe that *Ziemia* would keep out of her way. It was lastly held that had she given the strict attention to the movements of *Ziemia* that duty required, and put her engines full astern when it became apparent that there was imminent risk of collision if she did not act, the action of the Polish ship taken *in extremis* could have been of such effect as to have avoided the collision.

With so much fault on the part of *Djerada* it might seem there was little left for *Ziemia*, but the Court did not take such a simplistic view. Her lookout was deemed as poor as that kept on *Djerada*. Had the Polish 2nd mate looked closely at the vessel on his port bow with the binoculars he should have seen that she was not what she at first appeared. Had he done so he would have been obliged in spite of the confusion engendered by the masthead light to have taken action to prevent *Djerada*'s close approach, and for that he was held to blame. Furthermore, had he taken the elementary precaution of checking her bearing he would have been alerted to the fact that she must be crossing in spite of what he had initially though she was doing. No mention was made of the fact that her master was not on the bridge, and though the 2nd mate had the assistance of a junior watch officer the experience and judgment that the master might have brought to this situation were missing, and his presence might have prevented the faults that led his vessel to share in a portion of the blame.

After considering this plethora of fault Mr. Justice Brandon concluded that *Djerada* must bear the major portion of the blame and so attributed three-fifths of the fault to her with the balance to *Ziemia*. When the case came to appeal Lord Justice Cairns saw no reason to disturb the judgment and denied the appeal against it.

Notes

1 *L.L.R.*, 1976, Vol. 1, p. 53.
2 *Ibid.*
3 Cf. Marsden, p. 7.

Chapter Nineteen

Keeping a Proper Lookout

If any single fault predominates in the cases described her it is clearly the failure to keep a proper lookout. In some of them we have seen evidence that the conning officer did not see, or at least ignored, the other vessel until it was too late to evaluate her situation adequately and react accordingly. In others the approaching ship had been seen for some time but failure to observe her closely through binoculars led to a faulty appreciation of her aspect leading to misconceptions as to her heading and approach. Neglect to pay heed to the aural lookout led other vessels into difficulties, but perhaps the most common fault in recent years is the disregard by mariners of the information available from radar.

While the watch officer has other duties and responsibilities besides seeing that a proper lookout is kept at no time can any other duty take precedence. At certain times the task of fixing the vessel's position can assume an equal urgency, and normally in such a situation the master and perhaps another officer will be present to assist so that the primary duty of keeping a proper lookout is not neglected. If for any reason the watch officer feels he is unable to maintain a proper lookout and discharge his other navigational duties as well he must immediately inform the master of his need for assistance (see the IMO Recommendation on Navigational Watch-keeping under "Lookout").

The watch officer will also have unlicensed personnel to assist him in this duty. At night time, when in congested waters, or when the visibility is restricted, an unlicensed seaman must be posted as a lookout and he should have no other duties. He should preferably be an able seaman, but if an ordinary seaman (or other rating) is used for this purpose he must be thoroughly instructed in the duties of a lookout and an entry made in the logbook to that effect.

When the vessel is being steered by auto pilot the helmsman, when he is not occupied elsewhere, will usually assist with the lookout in addition to keeping a close check on the gyro and magnetic compasses. It is a custom of long standing with many officers to rely heavily on the man at the wheel to keep a lookout while he is busy with the navigation of the vessel or other tasks. Many seamen take considerable pride in the diligence with which they carry out this duty, so much so that they may resent a watch officer who may appear to place less than complete reliance on them.

An experienced and competent watch officer will quite naturally place more reliance on some seamen than others, depending upon his assessment of their capability and reliability. Nevertheless, the watch officer must on no account assume that the duty of keeping a proper lookout can be left in the hands of a seaman alone. The writer recalls an incident many years ago when a ship on which he was serving was approaching Nantucket lightship from some hundred miles to the east. It was shortly after the 2nd mate had assumed the watch in the afternoon. The visibility was good and the ship was being steered by auto pilot. The able seaman standing by the wheel was a man of long experience, trustworthy, and a reliable lookout. The 2nd mate was also an officer of very considerable experience, highly competent, and very diligent in the performance of his duties. In passing through the chartroom the writer found him busily engaged in some task at the chart table (he had been there by later estimate about fifteen minutes). On entering the wheelhouse a large Russian factory (fishing) vessel was seen about a point on the starboard bow on a relative course of about 215° around a mile and a half off. We were of course the "burdened" vessel and the Russian was obviously adhering to her "privilege". The reason the able seaman failed to see her was that she was behind an obstruction and he was *standing still* next to the gyro repeater, and as the vessel was on a collision course he could not have seen her until she either altered course or it was too late.

Here was a thoroughly competent and reliable seaman keeping the lookout for a thoroughly reliable and competent 2nd mate who learned a valuable lesson that day without the trauma of having it literally "rammed" home.

In another incident that took place in 1948 the steamer *American Veteran* was steaming up Boston Harbour with a pilot at the con on a bright and clear summer afternoon. The master was a man of great experience and competence who enjoyed the respect of both his employers and his peers. The chief officer and the carpenter were on the bow standing by the anchors, but no seaman had been posted as a lookout. A small charter fishing boat was returning to her berth and was being overtaken by the *American Veteran* and the pilot, master and watch officer were all well aware of her presence. The same was not the case on the charter boat.

The ship was light and as she neared the boat the latter became obscured from view under the bows. The captain of the boat then altered course sharply to port unaware of the ship overtaking close on its port quarter, was struck, overturned, and sank almost immediately. A woman passenger was drowned but all the others were saved.

In spite of an unblemished record the master was subsequently charged with inattention to duty for failure to have a lookout on the bow and to blow a passing signal. His license was suspended for thirty days and he only narrowly escaped prosecution on a civil charge of manslaughter.

The question of who may constitute a competent lookout is one that needs more satisfactory definition in light of recent changes and attitudes. It would be unreasonable and unrealistic to insist that only an able seaman is qualified, especially today when the distinction between able and ordinary seaman may have no practical significance other than the certificate held. Nor did the courts so hold when the great bulk of able seamen could be expected to be more able than the ordinary variety.

In a case that would be considered ancient by modern seafaring standards (Chamberlain v. Ward, [1859]) it was held that lookouts "must be persons of suitable experience, properly stationed on the vessel, and actually and vigilantly employed in the performance of that duty." And that is a definition that by-and-large is adequate in today's circumstances.

The relevant question is what constitutes "suitable experience?" It would seem patently absurd to assume that an individual who joins a ship with no previous experience aboard a vessel and literally cannot distinguish the bow from the stern has "suitable experience". Yet this is not uncommon today, and such an individual may be posted as a lookout leaving a busy harbour under conditions of less than ideal visibility.

In an attempt to resolve this dilemma between insufficient experience and operating necessity some vessel operators in consultation with their legal staffs have taken a position that an ordinary seaman properly instructed in the duties of a lookout can thereby overcome this lack of "suitable experience". There can be no quarrel with the necessity to properly instruct the lookout in the manner and method in which he should carry out his duties.[1] Indeed, many otherwise competent and able seamen could profit from more instruction in this respect, and when the vessel enters an area where the duties and information required from a lookout materially changes, as from an open sea passage to coastal conditions, or when entering a harbour or leaving it, the lookout, regardless of his experience and competence should be instructed as to what is expected of him.

But to return to the problem of the inexperienced seaman. It would be difficult to justify, should a casualty occur, the employment of a totally inexperienced man as a lookout even if he had previously been thoroughly instructed in the duties of a lookout. Having no experience the question of "suitable experience" would almost inevitably arise, and unless it could be shown that the experience of this man could in no way have contributed to the result there would follow an almost equally inevitable attribution of fault for his employment in that critical capacity.

But if such would be the case we are faced with an equally compelling question of where and how is such "suitable experience" acquired? The obvious answer is that it should not be acquired under the more demanding conditions found in inland waters. A man, totally unfamiliar with strange surroundings (a ship) is almost certain to experience a considerable degree of bewilderment when placed in such an environment, and to thrust upon him the duty of lookout with only brief and very likely incomplete instruction may well, at the time, only add to his confusion.

But while some shipboard experience would seem essential before an ordinary seaman can be considered to be a fully qualified lookout a part of the requisite "suitable experience" can and should be acquired through instruction. While it is difficult if not impossible to gain that blend of knowledge and experience that we recognise as "seamanship" other than through "on-the-job" exposure, some of its skills can, nonetheless, be successfully taught in schools. Marlinspike seamanship is a clear example, and training for certified lifeboatman is another. Instruction in the duties of a lookout can without doubt be taught in a similar way, and it is probably *best* taught in such manner since the training a new ordinary may receive on-the-job will not unlikely be not only incomplete but inadequate. What would be most helpful here is a comprehensive training film.

Such training could go far if not all the way towards qualifying most entrants to a career as seaman as a qualified lookout. Indeed, a young eager ordinary seaman can quickly become a superior lookout if given encouragement and training. Too often he soon comes to regard it as a boring and unpleasant chore, and once that impression takes hold his performance as a lookout is bound to suffer.

Unfortunately in these days of rapid turnarounds and turnovers the job of sorting out the ordinary is one that will appear to be of very low initial priority, and as it is customary for ordinary seamen to stand much if not most of the lookout watches it not infrequently happens that an ordinary of questionably "suitable experience", if not completely devoid of any experience or instruction, will be found entrusted with that duty in a busy waterway or channel. The reasons for that are several, and they are by no means all easily identified, but one that seems easy to discern though is not necessarily obvious, is the devaluation of the lookout as a means of information with the advent of radar.

It is a common practice aboard ship today, though perhaps not as common as it should be, to use radar constantly during hours of darkness regardless of the state of visibility. By so doing vessels are usually revealed before their lights become visible, and especially dimly lit craft such as sailboats that might not otherwise be discovered until close aboard. Admittedly some of these may escape detection due to the poor reflecting qualities of the materials of their construction, but more often than not this failure is due to faulty adjustment of the set.

It is hence rather rare, or at least relatively so, for a lookout to report any floating object, ship or otherwise, that an alert watch officer has not already had under observation for some time; and the same holds true even more so with the discovery of land. The reports of lookouts have accordingly become somewhat redundant, and are too often openly regarded as such by watch officers. Their acknowledgment of the reports of the lookout is sometimes one of ill-concealed annoyance so it is natural that the lookout may feel that if the watch officer regards his reports as a waste of time, as his attitude indicates, then his activity is meaningless, which is hardly conducive to the pursuit of vigilance on his part.

If he accordingly neglects the lookout and is not called to account for such neglect his suspicions of the insignificance of his activity will be confirmed and strengthened. It is incontestably true from a point of practical experience that the assistance required of the lookout today is less (assuming an alert watch on the bridge) than it was in pre-radar days, and that has created a problem of motivation that while not altogether non-existent before was of considerably less relative significance. The lookout's relationship to the watch officer has undergone a subtle transformation that is only imperfectly realised if at all.

While radar is the preponderant influence in this transformation it is not the only one. The means whereby the lookout passes on the information has become less efficient and can in fact become dangerously distracting. Before the advent of radar the typical vessel's bridge was usually close enough to the bow so that the information could be passed directly. A signal on the ship's bell, followed by a shout of "Where away?" if there was any doubt on the part of the mate, which in turn was answered by a shout of "Two points on the port bow sir," or whatever, was a much superior method of passing information than we have today on many ships.

The bow telephone was a response to larger ships and bridges farther aft, but it created problems that were unforseen at the time and have been largely ignored since. A most glaring exposure of the problem came during the hearings into the collision between *Andrea Doria* and *Stockholm* where it was found that at the crucial moment of discovery of *Doria's* lights the 3rd officer's attention was momentarily distracted by the ringing of the telephone by the lookout in the crow's nest. Except for that momentary distraction a different result might have ensued.

Although that caused a brief flurry of comment and speculation at the time the rectification of the problem, and it is a real one, or rather the recognition of its potential importance, has been understandably avoided.

To this day the bow telephone has remained a source of annoyance and distraction for the watch officer. He can ignore it at his peril since there is always the remote possibility that the information the bow lookout is trying to pass on may be crucial; but more often than not he will merely be reporting a light that has already been seen, and not infrequently it will come at a time when the mate has his attention directed towards a more pressing matter. Hence the annoyance with which he is liable to greet a report of no material significance.

But how does this effect the relationship of the lookout to the watch officer? Before radar there was an almost open rivalry between the lookout and the mate as to who could see a light or ship first. He was engaged in a contest he had a good chance of winning. Today the cards are stacked against him. The mate has the radar to tell him where to look and he has binoculars with which to look so that the information passed on to the bridge by the lookout is almost invariably stale, and he may be told as much. There is no longer much fun in the game, it is a pure chore, or at least has come to be so regarded by many.

Before the lookout was in competition for the same information as the mate. That is no longer the case. Though he must still report lights seen at a distance on the off chance that the mate has not seen them his real function is to discover those things that the mate may be unable to discover as readily. His "normal" function now is in reality that of a short-range lookout.

On the high seas he will report every light he sees on the horizon if only to alleviate boredom, but his primary job is to discover the small wooden or fibreglass yacht burning a feeble light, or a growler when nearing the limits of ice drift.

As the vessel nears coastal waters he will endeavour to report only those lights that are material to the vessel's navigation, but to succeed in that he should be given some guidance by the watch officer in the matter of what to ignore, and that is a delicate affair that needs close examination and a new approach. The safe thing it might seem would be to issue no instructions and trust to the discretion of the lookout. If he is given definite but general instructions, as they must be, there is the danger that he may fail to report a light that could in retrospect (in a court) be considered material.

The next question to be answered is where should the lookout be stationed? Again we have an old answer that has lost none of its validity either from a practical or legal standpoint. Shortly after the turn of the century Mr. Justice Wadill delivered an opinion that, "while it is true that no specific location on a vessel is prescribed for the lookout, it goes without saying that such location should be at that point best suited for the purpose alike of hearing and observing the approach of objects likely to be brought into collision with the vessel upon which the lookout is located."[2]

That location has normally been taken to mean as far forward and as far down as possible, i.e., in the eyes of the vessel, and in 1917 Mr. Justice Hough delivering an opinion in the case of the *Manchioneal* stated unequivocally that, "By the overwhelming weight of authority it is settled that the proper place for a lookout is, under ordinary circumstances on the bow."[3]

157

More recently (1951) Mr. Justice Willmer pointed out a further reason for posting the lookout forward:

> This case [*The British Confidence*] well illustrates the soundness of the principle that the lookout should be posted forward, or at any rate in a position where he is by himself and does not have his attention distracted by hearing conversations between the master and the officer of the watch, or between the master and the helmsman, or between the officer of the watch and the helmsman. . . .[4]

If the lookout is stationed on the bridge for whatever reason he should most definitely not be in the wheelhouse where he may be subject to such distractions.

In assessing the need for posting a lookout it boils down to the question of: can a lookout if posted aid the conning officer in his duties, and if posted where can he best acquire the information that may be of help to the conning officer?

It is well established that both from long accepted practice and common sense that there is normally no necessity to have a lookout, i.e., a seaman whose only duty is to assist the watch officer in that imperative duty of keeping a proper lookout, on the open sea during daylight in clear weather. The watch officer himself can normally see all that is needed. The fact that he might on occasion neglect the lookout duty in attending to another task is another matter.

During such conditions of unimpaired visibility the lookout can be best kept on the bridge because of its height and normally unrestricted view. If something is to be seen it will first be seen from there (assuming equality of eyesight and attention). The watch officer also has binoculars at his disposal, and more often than not he will be using radar even under the best conditions of visibility. Hence should for any reason another lookout be deemed necessary under *these* conditions his station should usually also be on the bridge.

When the conditions of visibility alter with the onset of darkness or atmospheric restrictions (fog, rain, mist etc.) so that the bridge is no longer the most favourably situated location in all respects the lookout should be so placed where he can compensate for the handicaps that the altered conditions of visibility impose upon a lookout from the bridge. Where the vessel is on the high seas and the conditions of visibility have only been diminished by darkness the only advantage of stationing the lookout forward on the bow is that he might see small dimly lighted craft or unlit floating hazards to navigation slightly sooner than they could be seen from the bridge.

Though such craft are unlikely to be encountered far from land the number of yachtsmen venturing offshore in the wooden or fibreglass hulled boats so difficult to detect on radar has increased dramatically in recent years. The loss of containers as well as other deck cargoes in the middle of the ocean is also by no means rare, and in the northern trans-Atlantic trades the presence of ice during the season must be considered. The lookout's duty as we have already suggested is basically concerned with the discovery of objects at medium to close range that may not be readily discernible from the bridge. Under such circumstances the lookout can best assist the watch officer by being stationed on the bow. From that position he can better detect those things that can be seen less easily from the bridge while at the same time having a clear though somewhat less advantageous view of objects at a distance. But when under these conditions the weather starts to make up so that spray begins to be taken over the bow the slight but not insignificant advantages of his station on the bow begin to be counter-balanced by other considerations.

The most immediate consideration is the discomfort of the lookout (assuming there is yet no danger of shipping green water). Though many licensed seamen, and particularly the older ones, may scoff at and ridicule such a suggestion it is not something that can be brushed aside as an effeminate excuse. While an occasional dash of salt spray cannot be adequate justification from a legal standpoint for removing a lookout from his normal station on the bow a lookout who is concerned with seeking shelter from the elements can hardly be an effective lookout. If he is hidden from view from the bridge, as he is on many container ships, he may in fact abandon the lookout entirely in his search for shelter, and while that may be deplorable it cannot be ignored entirely in deciding where a lookout will provide the most effective assistance.

While, as already noted, it has long been accepted that the proper station of the lookout is on the bow, we have seen in previous chapters that the most usual station for him now appears to be on the bridge. The fact that a practice is common does not, of course, mean it is correct, and many of the vessels involved in these collisions hardly recommend themselves as examples to be followed. Nonetheless, the practice of keeping the lookout on the bridge has become an accepted practice for a variety of reasons of varying validity.

On ships where two seamen are assigned to each watch they ordinarily alternate as helmsman and lookout. Where the bow may be a tenth of a mile or more forward of the bridge the practicality of the shift from the duties of lookout to helmsman recommend the bridge wing as the station. A lookout on the wing is also more conveniently located for reporting what he sees and hears. He can also point out what it is he sees thereby eliminating the worrying erroneous report of a "light dead ahead" that is in fact a point on the bow. The watch officer can also monitor and supervise a lookout on the wing. On the bow his attention can only be assumed.

While most of the time the bridge wing may be a perfectly acceptable station for the lookout it should not be presumed that it always is. It would not be a proper station on a large vessel with the bridge aft and diesel engines or a container vessel with "reefers" on deck, if the vessel is in fog. Nor would it be the most advantageous station for a night time passage of the Dover Strait where encounters with small craft can be expected. The question is simply one of where can the lookout best acquire and pass on information for the safe navigation of the vessel.

In a number of cases analysed in previous chapters we have seen where lookouts were allowed to vacate their posts to call their reliefs, help rig the pilot ladder, or simply take a coffee break with no thought seemingly given to the exigencies of the situation. No court would condone the abandonment of the lookout for any of these reasons, but practical operating necessity — particularly where only two seamen are assigned to a watch — will often make it expedient to use the lookout temporarily for a duty other than of lookout. Where such questionable practices are indulged in it is imperative that the watch officer himself give such undivided attention to the lookout that another is not needed. In most circumstances that can be done, but where conditions are such (fog with traffic, approaching a busy pilot station) that the watch officer cannot safely dispense momentarily with the lookout he must make other arrangements.

No vessel can run smoothly without a well-organised routine. It allows the automatic performance of ordinary duties and tasks without the watch officer having to become directly involved. The danger of routine is in allowing it to continue to operate when circumstances dictate its suspension. The 2nd mate of *Transhawaii* obtaining a routine fix with *Republica de Colombia* close on his starboard bow; the seaman and cadet on *Horta Barbosa* both leaving the bridge to call their reliefs while the 2nd mate was busy plotting the position in the chart room, leaving the bridge and lookout abandoned with *Sea Star* approaching on the starboard bow; the able seaman rigging the pilot ladder as *Atlantic Trader* entered a fog bank. Blindly carrying out these routine tasks led all these vessels to grief. Assigning priorities is a crucial aspect of the watch officer's job, and when circumstances require more than normal attention be devoted to the lookout routine duties must await a more convenient time.

Regardless of what degree of importance is attached to the role of the unlicensed lookout his function in the final analysis is to act as the surrogate eyes of the watch officer. His role is to draw the attention of the mate on watch to such information as may have relevance to the navigation of the vessel. It is the watch officer's job to evaluate that information and use it as needed. Once the lookout has discovered and reported a vessel, aid, or hazard he may be said to have discharged his duty. This simple and straightforward philosophy evidently led the lookout on *Stockholm* to ignore a change in the lights shown by *Andrea Doria* as that vessel turned across *Stockholm*'s bow. From a practical standpoint discovery is all a watch officer can reasonably expect, but he can increase the potential of his lookout by judicious training and encouragement. Nonetheless, he can expect no more, and it is his responsibility for the continued observation of whatever the lookout discovers, which of course includes his own discoveries.

He must make a careful inspection of whatever comes to his attention, which includes observation with binoculars. We have seen in several cases in these pages where neglect of this routine precaution led to an innacurate assessment that contributed directly to the collision. Mere observation, however, will not suffice as numerous examples here so graphically prove. Observation of the compass bearing of a vessel closing is the traditional method of determining risk of collision, but that should be supplemented by radar observation and plotting if there is any question of risk of collision.

There is an unfortunate notion abroad that plotting is an activity only required in restricted visibility.* In some trades that might mean that a watch officer might go for weeks without plotting. Skills are developed and maintained by practice, and simple as this skill may be one stands in danger of becoming "rusty" in its practice if it is not used habitually. That means plotting in fair weather and foul.

Aside from practice, plotting gives the watch officer valuable information mere observation — no matter how acute — cannot provide. From it one can tell how close the other vessel will pass and whether she is maintaining her course. A close approximation of the direction of her movement and its rate can also be determined, all of which can be of great aid in assessing the degree of risk. To fail to determine this readily available information is imprudent and negligent, and both of these are classed as grave faults when judged in court.

Possibly the most serious fault in the practice of keeping a lookout is that of assuming that a vessel seen to be on a safe course will keep it. It is a safe assumption in such a vast majority of cases that some watch officers seem to lose sight of the fact that it is only an assumption and not a fixed fact. Chapters Six and Twelve give examples of the hazard of that assumption and Chapter Five delineates the specifics of that hazard.

The watch officer has no more important responsibility than that of seeing that a proper lookout is maintained at *all* times. Unfortunately the task is usually as boring as it is essential, which is probably the chief reason for its neglect. One of the main challenges facing the watch stander is learning to cope intelligently with the problem of boredom. That may often lead him to become absorbed in other aspects of his job to the detriment of the lookout, and that is a danger he must guard against constantly. The radar is a great aid and boon in carrying out this primary duty, but it too has its hazards. Officers tend to sometimes become mesmerised by the radar, operating as if they were in a perpetual fog never raising their eyes to the horizon. While radar can tell you many things your eyes cannot, your eyes can also tell you things radar cannot. As vessels begin to close the most important thing about them is their aspect. Change of aspect is the first and most immediate warning of a change in course and no radar or ARPA can reveal aspect. As a vessel nears a position from which any deviation from course might bring her into close quarters an occasional glance at the radar scope to see how far off she is may be desirable, but during the final stages of a clear weather approach the rule is "eyes only", and when she is in that position where she can "reach you" your surveillance of her progress must be constant until she is past and clear.

While the importance of an aural lookout has been substantially diminished since radar came into use that device has by no means made the need for a listening watch redundant. Vessels underway in narrow channels or other restricted waterways would almost certainly be held at fault should they collide with another vessel, particularly one at anchor, with no lookout on the bow in restricted visibility. In circumstances where the lookout must be posted forward to acquire information — such as hearing a ship's bell — that is best and most quickly obtained from that position he should not be forced to rely on a telephone for the transmission of such information. He should be equipped with a "walkie-talkie" or some similar means of communication since a matter of seconds under such circumstances may mean all the difference.

A very recent development, and one that is bound to assume increasing recognition, within the scope of aural lookout is the necessity to listen on VHF radio under certain circumstances. In American waters this is not a matter of choice or inclination but is required by law, and there have been some tentative attempts to extend this need for listening on VHF to a wider purview. While such efforts are probably premature it seems quite likely that in the not too distant future a vessel's failure to respond to a VHF call in unambiguous circumstances might be seen

---

* Availability of an ARPA does not render proficiency in manual plotting redundant. The relationship is the same as that of SATNAV to a sextant.

to be a fault. Where its use is required consideration should be given to the positioning of the receiver in relationship to the user so as to eliminate as far as possible interference with its use.

While VHF radio can be a great boon in a manoeuvring context it is by no means an unmixed blessing. In intership communication it can be a dangerous distraction if the attempt to establish contact with the vessel one wishes to speak with is not done well before the need to use VHF for exchange of manoeuvring information. Another problem that is well known to its users but has received insufficient attention is the noise level occasionally encountered on the bridge where more than one channel is being monitored.

The remarks made herein regarding assigning lookouts occasional tasks or routine duties to be carried out during their period of duty as lookout should not be taken as condoning such practices. They are meant simply as observations on practices that are widespread and often customary, and as they will undoubtedly continue to be both widespread and customary, particularly in vessels with reduced manning scales, they should be seen for what they are: calculated risks and treated accordingly. That is not to suggest that a court would condone them because they seem to have some claim to be included among the "ordinary practices of seamen", but by recognising the risk their practice entails these risks may be minimised where operating "necessity" seems to require them.

* * * * * * * *

Notes

1 See Griffin, p. 271; also cf. Cockcroft & Lameijer, pp. 33–40.
2 Griffin, *ibid.*; also cf. Marsden, pp. 606–07, and Farwell, pp. 423–25.
3 Page 276; cf. Marsden, pp. 605–06.
4 Marsden, p. 606.

Chapter Twenty

Conclusion

The practice of keeping a proper watch at sea is in essence a question of avoiding collision with other vessels or the sea-bed and obstructions arising from it. While the latter aspect of this problem will yield to a greater or lesser degree to a certain amount of logical analysis and deductive reasoning the problem of keeping out of collision with other ships is a much less clear cut affair. This is demonstrated by the fact that while lengthy tomes have been written on the art and practice of navigation no one has quite succeeded in pinning down with precision the principles of the practice of collision avoidance.

There are of course substantial and valuable books on the Rules of the Road, or COLREGS as they are less romantically known today. Yet no one has succeeded, to spell out in clear and specific detail how one should keep out of collision.[1] It might seem that a well-developed intuitive sense, about which almost nothing can be written, is, if not an essential, certainly a very valuable asset in practicing the art of collision avoidance, or as it is prosaically known, "handling a vessel in traffic". We have tried, nonetheless, to offer some observations on this quasi-arcane skill.

The body of law or regulations known today as COLREGS would, if understood and followed by *all* seafarers, almost undoubtedly succeed in its purpose in eliminating the blunders that are the prelude to the vast majority of collisions and leave us with a slim residue of accidents that little short of divine intervention can prevent.[2] The *Lloyd's List* casualty pages, however, proclaims ceaselessly and emphatically that luck plays a much greater part in keeping vessels from colliding than the Collision Avoidance Regulations.

It is a somewhat ironic fact that up until very recently it was almost unknown for a seafarer to be charged with a violation of the Rules unless he came to the attention of the authorities via the road to an admiralty court. One could flout, ignore, or stand in a state of supreme ignorance of the Rules with only the slightest chance of being brought to task unless one was caught up, or out, in a collision.[3] The only difference today is that in certain areas of the world "traffic tickets" are handed out to those who violate the provisions of the Rules pertaining to Traffic Separation Schemes, though the violator may or may not be prosecuted depending upon the policies of the country whose flag flies on the stern.

Most competent men who have spent their life following the sea have a good handful of stories concerning experiences with the "rules", and the haphazard grasp that the bulk of mariners encountered on the high seas have of them. Some years ago the Scots master of a vessel of Hong Kong registry who the author encountered in the Philippine port of San Fernando recounted an incident he had been a party to when called in to act as an extempore surveyor in a collision south of Singapore. The casualty occurred on a clear night on the open sea and the master of the burdened ship complained plaintively to the Scots master that "Here I was going along on the course I always steer and this ship just came along and ran into me." The fact that the other vessel was showing a broad red light at the time seemed of no particular relevance. We have seen a number of similar though perhaps not so extreme misconceptions in the previous chapters.

In a rather droll incident several years ago when steaming up the Bay of Biscay the author encountered a rather smart vessel of Scandinavian registry on a somewhat erratic reciprocal course. The ship had a large bone in her teeth and was making close to twenty knots but was curiously showing two black balls at the yardarm. In response to a query on the VHF if they were "not under command", the reply that they "were not commanding very well" was quite obvious, yet that did not prevent them from proceeding at full sea-speed in an area of quite heavy traffic.

There would hence seem to be some reason to suspect that the grasp of the Rules of the average watchstander is less than complete, and even when there is understanding there is often a lag between understanding and compliance. If the picture is indeed as grim as is suggested here, and it is in fact suggested that this is the case, then mere knowledge of and adherence to the Rules may not prevent one from being victimised by a less knowledgeable mariner.

If there is any one principle that can be enunciated as the key to collision avoidance it is "Treat all vessels encountered with extreme distrust and suspicion." To begin with, there is a distinct possibility that there is no one on the bridge of the other vessel if the encounter is far from land. Even if the bridge is manned there is an even greater possibility that the person at the con has at best a very rudimentary appreciation of the Rules. To add to these daunting prospects there is the mariner who may have more knowledge of the Rules but due to the bottle of wine he had with his meal is suffering from some temporary confusion. Though this may sound a bit tongue-in-cheek it is in essence a deadly serious assessment of the situation obtaining on the high seas today.

To add to the grimness of this bleak nautical vista is the fact that the percentage of *professional* seafarers employed in a licensed capacity today is steadily diminishing if the flag flying on the stern has any significance. While it is undoubtedly true that a considerable number of extremely professional seamen may be found on the bridges of vessels flying flags of dubious maritime distinction it is equally true that the shift of the balance away from traditional maritime flags has gone hand-in-hand with a deterioration of maritime watch-keeping standards.

There is a disturbing common thread running through many of the cases investigated in this book, except perhaps in those collisions due entirely to blind negligence or ineptness, of pressure stemming from economic "necessity" to shave corners and shade considerations of safety. Even where negligence and ineptitude predominate, the pressure of economic "necessity" can be found to operate where it results in trusting the navigation of a vessel to "seamen" whose slender qualifications are available for equally slender salaries.

Yet it is by no means the dominant factor in these collisions. The most common, one might say the almost inevitable, causative element is clearly the failure of one or both of the parties involved to maintain a proper lookout visually or otherwise. The reasons for, and consequences of, this neglect we have examined in the previous chapter and will not repeat here the conclusions drawn there. It cannot be stressed too strongly, however, the necessity for masters to impress upon their watchstanders the vital importance of this primary duty and instruct them in the elementary procedures to be adopted in its performance.

As was pointed out in the previous chapter the greatest aid in keeping a proper lookout in weather both foul and fair is the radar. The misuse of this marvel unfortunately can produce "side-effects" as deadly as any caused by some modern drugs. The misinterpretation of the information supplied by radar and the "radar assisted collisions" resulting from such misuse led to the development of ARPAs (Automatic Radar Plotting Aids) as a means of dealing with this problem and the attendant difficulty of coping with plotting in heavy traffic. No master with any knowledge of his job would treat this development with disdain, and should he be so fortunate as to have it installed aboard his vessel familiarisation with its use — and seeing to his officers' training — should become an immediate priority. It is quite likely that many of the collisions described in the preceding pages would not have happened if one of the vessels involved had been ARPA equipped *and* it was being used properly.

But the same could be said of the use of radar. Had they used it effectively they would not have been led to the erroneous conclusions that brought them into close quarters and collision. ARPAs moreover are not proof against poor judgment, and there is the added danger that this equipment might lead some to use it in the same injudicious manner as they previously used their radars. It has, of course, been recognised that training must go hand-in-hand with installation, but training cannot provide the judgment without which the use of this equipment can become as hazard fraught as is the comparable use of radar. ARPAs may quite possibly benefit most those who need it least: the compotent professional mariner.

A less well-recognised threat to safety is the confusion frequently found as to which Rule or Rules apply in a particular instance. The case described in the penultimate chapter is a dramatic instance of such confusion leading to a collision. While an undeniably vivid illustration, it was, however, not a typical one. It was based upon misconception and inadequate knowledge of the Rules rather than ambiguity of their application. A more characteristic example would be those described in Chapter Eleven where vessels on converging courses confused overtaking courses with crossing ones and vice-versa. Nor were these the only instances. Such confusion seems to be more common than is widely recognised.

It might be replied that this confusion can be largely if not entirely avoided through study and understanding of the Rules, but that by itself will not protect one from the confusion in the mind of the conning officer of an approaching ship who thinks he is in a stand-on position when he is in fact a give-way vessel. That problem will not yield readily to anything short of direct communication between the two ships.

There have been a number of direct and indirect references to the use of VHF as a means of direct communication in such circumstances, and in some cases it has been used — or rather misused — with unfortunate effect (the *Ore Chief/Olympic Torch* collision is an example). That has led some critics of the use of this equipment to conclude that it is more a hazard than a help, and should be used only sparingly if at all. It is unfortunate that those who deal with the legal consequences of infractions of the Rules see only mistakes and not the much more numerous examples of success.

While the use of VHF in pilotage waters is widely accepted as a proven and indeed essential aid in collision avoidance in such places its use for the same purpose in international waters is still suspect if not directly opposed in some influential maritime circles. Those who actually use the equipment, i.e., practicing seafarers, are coming to recognise it as a means of dispelling the uncertainty that underlies every collision not due entirely to mechanical failure or the unpredictable acts of God. Their experience also tells them that there are problems associated with the use of this equipment, as there is with radar, and awareness of these problems must be constantly kept in mind if they are to be avoided.

It is not suggested here that the use of VHF is the final answer to the resolution of uncertainty in marine encounters, but the equipment is widely available and can solve the problem in many cases. What is incontestable is that without discovery of the intentions of an approaching vessel there is no practical means for "solving" the collision problem.

A final solution of the problem will perhaps involve a visual display of decoded information from an interrogated[4] vessel that can bypass the problems of both language and ambiguity of its use. Such a solution would also avoid the distraction that is one of the more intractable difficulties associated with intership communication via VHF. But until that time failure to avail oneself of VHF, with a full appreciation of its limitations, as a means to discover the intentions of an approaching vessel and monitor the execution and modification of those intentions may come to be regarded as an unseamanlike neglect to use available navigation equipment in the same way as it is now regarded in those waters where its use is required by law.

* * * * * * * *

Notes

1 There have been a host of articles, often based on manoeuvring diagrams, over the past decade or so (notably in the *Journal* of the Royal Institute of Navigation) dealing with approaches to this problem. While they may be sound in theory none have inspired such enthusiasm as to have been widely accepted in practice. The most notable contributors in this area have been B. J. Calvert and Rear-Admiral J. Garcia-Frias (see Kemp, pp. 59–63, 94–104). A manoeuvring diagram for restricted visibility is given in Cockcroft, p. 225. Also cf. Cockcroft, "Manoeuvres to Avoid Collision", *Safety at Sea International*, May 1972.

2 See Marsden, pp. 7–12 on "inevitable accident"; also Griffin, pp. 537–50, and Gilmore & Black, pp. 397–98.

3 There are, of course, the rare cases such as *American Aquarius/Atlantic Hope* and *Miraflores/Abadesa* collisions where a third vessel was involved in the circumstances but not the fact of the collision.

4 Assuming that interrogator/transponder systems are then in use.

References

Books

A. N. Cockcroft and J. Lameijer, *A Guide to the Collision Avoidance Rules*, Stanford Maritime Press, London, 1982, 3rd edn.

J. W. Griffin, *The American Law of Collision*, Ann Arbor, Mich., 1949.

Grant Gilmore and Chas. L. Black, *The Law of Admiralty*, The Foundation Press, Brooklyn, N.Y., 1957.

Kenneth C. McGuffie, *Marsden: The Law of Collision at Sea*, Stevens & Sons Ltd., London, 1961, 11th edn, with 3rd Cumulative Supplement up to February 15, 1973.

Peter Padfield, *An Agony of Collisions*, Routledge & Kegan Paul, 1966.

Farwell's Rules of the Nautical Road, prepared by F. E. Bassett and R. A. Smith, Naval Institute Press, Annapolis, Md., 1977, 5th edn.

Mathematical Aspects of Marine Traffic, Academic Press, London, 1979.

J. F. Kemp, "Factors in the Prevention of Collisions at Sea", unpublished doctoral thesis, 1973, library, School of Navigation, London Polytechnic.

R. G. Curtis, "An Analysis of Dangers of Ships Overtaking", 1977, Academic Press.

Journals

Lloyd's Law Reports, cited as *L.L.R.*

American Maritime Cases, cited as *A.M.C.*

Reports

Report of the Marine Board of Investigation and Decision of the Commissioner for Maritime Affairs, April 25, 1973, *Royston Grange/Tien Chee*.

Report of the Marine Board of Investigation Pacific Glory/Allegro Collision, April 25, 1973, Monrovia, Liberia.

Articles

Journal of the Royal Institute of Navigation:

  Bell, F. C., "The Mystery of Andrea Doria", April 1971.

  Curtis, R. G., "Determination of Mariner's Reaction Times", September 1978.

  ———, "The Probability of Close Overtaking in Fog", September 1980.

  Cortlett, E. C. B., "Studies on Interaction at Sea", May 1979.

  Dand, I. W. and P. J. V. Paget, "Interaction at Sea", September 1979.

  Hooft, J. P., "Manoeuvring Large Ships in Shallow Water I & II", April and July 1973.

Proceedings of the U.S. Naval Institute:

  Cahill, R. A., "The Burden of Being Privileged", January 1965.

Safety at Sea International:

  Cockcroft, A. N., "*Fotini Carras/Frosta* Collision", August 1974.

  ———, "Manoeuvres to Avoid Collision", May 1972.

Mathematical Aspects of Marine Traffic:

Index